Range Research:

Basic Problems and Techniques

edited by C. Wayne Cook
and James Stubbendieck

Published by the
Society for Range Management
2760 West Fifth Avenue
Denver, Colorado 80204

Revised edition, first printing

ISBN 0-9603692-3-6

Library of Congress Catalog   85-063270

Bob Patton

Printed in the United States of America
Jostens, Broomfield, Colorado

Contents

Chapter 3. Methods of Studying Vegetation

Chapter 4. Studies of Root Habits and Development

Chapter 5. Methods of Measuring Herbage and Browse Utilization

Chapter 6. Livestock Selection and Management in Range Research

Chapter 7. Methods for Studying Rangeland Hydrology

Chapter 8. Economic Research in Range Management

Chapter 9. Sampling Methods with Special Reference to Range Management

Chapter 10. Experimental Designs

Chapter 11. Problems Involved in the Application of Research Techniques in Range Management

Foreword

Range management concerns the synthesis and use of information relating to the structure and function of rangeland ecosystems. A complete understanding of biological systems is indeed a challenge to all range scientists and, as a result, new and eventful research ideas will continue to exist for many years to come. Even the most comprehensive review of research methods about a single compartment of rangeland ecosystems fails to identify all of the unknown facts about the ecological component operating within even that one compartment of the total system.

Monitoring intricate interactions of various components within compartments of ecosystems as they are affected by other components within other compartments seldom lends itself to one satisfactory method. Most research methods, for whatever purpose, will display both limitations and suitabilities and will require modification for the refinement and statistical reliability desired. New methods will evolve because no known technique is available to measure flawlessly a particular natural biological function or the consequences of a treatment or manipulation.

Complete standardization of methods, even if possible, is not suggested herein. This would presume that fully satisfactory techniques were available to meet each objective. Nevertheless, improvement and unification of methods is a goal to be sought if the various range research programs are to yield comparable and consistent results.

The objectives of this book are to discuss the problems inherent to range research; to assemble the various methods used for different phases of range research; and to describe their use, limitations and suitabilities. It is hoped that this book will serve as a reference guide for range research methodology and as a textbook for advanced students who anticipate careers in this increasingly important field.

The first edition of this book was a product of many years of effort on the part of the Society for Range Management and the National Academy of Science—National Research Council. Through the cooperative efforts of the Society and the Council, a joint research methods committee was established and assigned the task of preparing the textbook *Range Research—Basic Problems and Techniques*. This task was completed in 1962 and was accomplished by means of assigning various phases of the subject matter to recognized specialists in the field. Each member of the joint committee was assigned one or more chapters to organize, compile, and edit material produced.

Joint Committee Members of the first edition were:

C. Wayne Cook, *Chairman*	E.H. Reid
Harold H. Biswell	L.A. Stoddart
R.T. Clark	M.L. Upchurch

The specialists contributing to the first edition were:

F.W. Albertson	E.H. McIllvain
A.L. Baker	L.B. Merrill
C.B. Baker	Meredith J. Morris
J.R. Bentley	Ben. O. Osborn
D.W. Bohmont	James G. Osborne
John T. Cassady	Bernard Ostle
D.D. Caton	Kenneth W. Parker
Roy A. Champan	G.F. Payne
S.V. Ciriacy-Wantrup	Joseph F. Pechanec
David F. Costel	C.V. Plath
Bliss Crandall	Rex D. Rehnberg
Robert A. Darrow	H.G. Reynolds
William P. Dasmann	Laurence E. Riordan
R.E. Davis	Joseph H. Robertson
Don A. Duncan	C.B. Roubicek
E.G. Donford	C.E. Shelby
Robert A. Gardner	Arnold M. Shultz
Herbert C. Hanson	W.O. Sheperd
H.J. Hargrave	Clair E. Terrill
Robert W. Harris	F.L. Timmons
W.R. Harvey	G.W. Tomanek
Austin A. Hasel	R.D. Turk
H.F. Heady	K.A. Valentine
John A. Hopkin	C.H. Wasser
A.L. Hormay	R.R. Woodward
Selar S. Hutchings	E.J. Woolfolk
W.M. Johnson	John C. Wright

This second edition is intended to be an updating of the original text. Range management is a relatively new science, originating sometime during the 1930's as a discipline offering university degrees. As a result, many range research methods and techniques have been developed at a rapid rate from 1930 to 1985. It was, therefore, recognized that the first edition published in 1962 was rather seriously out of date and needed revision in order to serve the current researcher in the manner for which it was intended.

A knowledge and understanding of the historical development of methods and techniques of range research is important. In addition, a reference is not necessarily out of date just because it is old. Therefore, many of the references cited in the first edition have been carried forward to the second edition.

Since the Society has a series of sciential committees that endeavor to keep abreast of changes in areas of range science and fields related to range science, it was suggested that the SRM carry out the task of updating this text. The Board of Directors of the Society, working through their Publications Committee, arranged for editors, contributors, and release of publication rights of the original text from the National Research Council. Drs. C. Wayne Cook and James Stubbendieck were appointed as coeditors. Later, Dr. John E. Mitchell became Chairman of the Publications Committee and supervised the completion of the project. Again, specialists in various phases to be updated were selected. These individuals were:

Contributors
Second Edition

E. Tom Bartlett
Department of Range Science
Colorado State University
Fort Collins, Colorado 80523

D.D. Briske
Department of Range Science
Texas A&M University
College Station, Texas 77843

C.M. Britton
Department of Range and Wildlife Management
Texas Tech University
Lubbock, Texas 79049

M.A. Brown
Delta Branch Experiment Station (USDA)
Stoneville, Mississippi 38776

John Buckhouse
Department of Rangeland Resources
Oregon State University
Corvallis, Oregon 97331

John L. Capinera
Department of Zoology and Entomology
Colorado State University
Fort Collins, Colorado 80523

Donald C. Clanton
West Central Research and Extension Center
University of Nebraska
North Platte, Nebraska 69101

* C. Wayne Cook
Department of Range Science
Colorado State University
Fort Collins, Colorado 80523

Gary Donart
Department of Animal and Range Sciences
New Mexico State University
Las Cruces, New Mexico 88003

D. Lynn Drawe
Rob & Bessie Welder Wildlife Foundation
Sinton, Texas 78387

Don D. Dwyer
Department of Range Science
Utah State University
Logan, Utah 84322

Norman R. French
Las Vegas, Nevada 89124

Roger Gates
Department of Agronomy
University of Nebraska
Lincoln, Nebraska 68583

Gerald F. Gifford
Department of Range, Wildlife, and Forestry
University of Nevada
Reno, Nevada 89512

E. Bruce Godfrey
Department of Economics and Agricultural Economics
Utah State University
Logan, Utah 84322

* M.M. Kothmann
Department of Range Science
Texas A&M University
College Station, Texas 77843

William C. Krueger
Department of Rangeland Resources
Oregon State University
Corvallis, Oregon 97731

Lowell E. Moser
Department of Agronomy
University of Nebraska
Lincoln, Nebraska 68583

* John E. Mitchell
Rocky Mountain Forest and Range Experiment Sta. (USDA)
Fort Collins, Colorado 80526

Mark L. Nelson
Department of Animal Sciences
University of Nebraska
Lincoln, Nebraska 68583

James T. Nichols
West Central Research and
Extension Center
University of Nebraska
North Platte, Nebraska 69101

* Phil Ogden
Range Management Program
University of Arizona
Tucson, Arizona 85721

George Pfeiffer
Department of Agricultural
Economics
University of Nebraska
Lincoln, Nebraska 68583

* Rex Pieper
Department of Animal and
Range Sciences
New Mexico State University
Las Cruces, New Mexico 88003

Elbert H. Reid
Forest Service (USDA)
624 S. Shields
Fort Collins, Colorado 80521

Lee Sharp
Department of Range Resources
University of Idaho
Moscow, Idaho 83843

Phillip L. Sims
Southern Plains Research Station
Woodward, Oklahoma 73801

Ronald E. Sosebee
Department of Range and
Wildlife Management
Texas Tech University
Lubbock, Texas 79409

* Freeman M. Smith
Department of Earth Resources
Colorado State University
Fort Collins, Colorado 80523

Stuart D. Smith
Department of Agronomy
University of Nebraska
Lincoln, Nebraska 68583

Dale E. Snyder
Soil Conservation Service
(USDA)
Redmond, Washington 98052

E. John Stevens
Department of Agronomy
University of Nebraska
Lincoln, Nebraska 68583

Walter Stroup
Department of Biometrics
University of Nebraska
Lincoln, Nebraska 68583

* James Stubbendieck
Department of Agronomy
University of Nebraska
Lincoln, Nebraska 68583

Toloumbaye Tadingar
Department of Agronomy
University of Nebraska
Lincoln, Nebraska 68583

James G. Teer
Rob & Bessie Welder
Wildlife Foundation
Sinton, Texas 78387

M. Joe Trlica
Department of Range Science
Colorado State University
Fort Collins, Colorado 80523

Kenneth P. Vogel
Department of Agronomy (USDA)
University of Nebraska
Lincoln, Nebraska 68583

Joe D. Wallace
Department of Animal and
Range Sciences
New Mexico State University
Las Cruces, New Mexico 88003

* S.S. Waller
Department of Agronomy
University of Nebraska
Lincoln, Nebraska 68583

David Wester
Department of Range and
Wildlife Management
Texas Tech University
Lubbock, Texas 79409

* John Workman
Department of Range Science
Utah State University
Logan, Utah 84322

Henry A. Wright
Department of Range and
Wildlife Management
Texas Tech University
Lubbock, Texas 79409

* Designates chapter chairmen

Chapter 1
The Range Research Problem

Introduction

Rangeland is a kind of land characterized by native vegetation (climax or natural potential) which is predominantly grasses, grasslike plants, forbs, or shrubs suitable for grazing and/or browsing. It includes lands revegetated naturally or artificially to provide a forage cover that is managed like native vegetation (Range Term Glossary Committee 1974). Rangeland includes natural grasslands, savannahs, shrublands, most deserts, tundra, alpine communities, coastal marshes, and wet meadows. It is the single largest land category in the world (43%), exceeding forestland (18%), derived cropland (10%), industrial-residential (4%), and non-productive areas such as glaciers and mountain peaks (15%) (Lewis 1969). Rangeland provides a variety of products including domestic livestock grazing, wildlife habitat, recreation, mineral production, as well as having watershed, scientific and aesthetic values. Rangelands are as diverse and complex as are the products and benefits they provide. Consequently, range management is the management of a renewable resource composed of several range ecosystems for the optimum combination and sustained yield of products and values.

Range science is the organized body of knowledge upon which the practice of range management is based (Lewis 1969). Successful range management, and the quantity and quality of products and values derived from rangeland, are dependent upon the degree of resource understanding that managers possess. Basic knowledge, which provides the foundation of range management principles, has been derived from two sources: historical and scientific. Historically, range management principles were developed from experience and observation. However, application of these principles was often restricted to unique situations, locations, or years, and their refinement was based on trial and error. Capabilities of the rangeland resource were often limited, and extensive land availability minimized the apparent economic liability of mismanagement, encouraging poor resource management. As was true with many fields of study, the development of the scientific approach resulted in initial research examining effects which were generally easily and reliably observed. Observation of more subtle differences and the need for more definite conclusions about such observations led to the use of statistics, by scientists, as a tool to examine results within the framework of natural biological variability. As this need for more reliable information arose, range science developed as a discipline to provide information from more formal and controlled research.

Contemporary multiple-use demands on the limited rangeland resource resulted in greater penalities associated with erroneous conclusions from observational data. Range scientists must take every precaution to develop reliable, repeatable data. Proper statistical considerations are one tool to minimize the risk associated with management recommendations derived from range research. The purpose of natural resources research is to develop new alternatives for the resource manager or to answer questions of fact that arise during management (Stoltenberg et al. 1970).

Range Research

Kinds of Research

Research may be classified as descriptive or comparative at either the basic or applied level. Problems may be addressed and data collected through a survey of existing conditions or with controlled, planned experiments (Fig. 1-1). Research is a continuous process as new findings often require evaluation or description of new attributes of the resource, or as conditions are

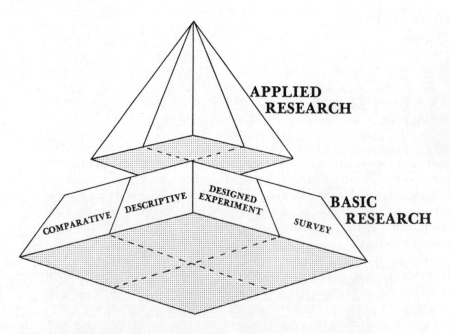

Figure 1-1. Kinds of research.

modified by changes in economics or public values. All biological research is conducted in an environment of inherent variability. Information generated is only as valuable as the care which goes into defining the hypotheses, planning, and implementing the data collections. Perhaps the most familiar type of descriptive research is that which generates "survey" data or generates basic information such as morphological development of grazed plants. Some attribute of the range resource is measured and described for an uncontrolled, but defined set of conditions.

Most other research efforts can be classified as comparative. In general, one or more variables are controlled to evaluate the impact on some response. In familiar terms, treatments applied in a designed experiment are purposefully structured so that some response variable may be measured under varied, but known, conditions. Comparative research may be subdivided into basic and applied investigations. Basic research is designed to quantitate natural phenomena, thereby developing basic factual knowledge regarding biological processes. Applied research develops principles of biological-environmental interactions which provide alternatives to current resource management. The goal of both descriptive and comparative range research is not the documentation of facts or principles for a specific experimental condition; rather, it is to provide inference about the expected occurrence or response under similar conditions. Inductive reasoning (specific to general) is the tool of logic which allows the extrapolation from the results of well-designed experiments to general conclusions or principles (Little and Hills 1978).

Inferential Theory

A population is defined as a set of individuals with similar attributes. Precise definition of the individual is not trivial and may be easily overlooked. Individuals may be pastures in a grazing study, range sites in a vegetation survey, or single grass plants in a study of carbon allocation. Care must be used in stating hypotheses and defining individuals which are compatible. Generally, the range researcher is unable to collect data from all individuals in a population. This restriction is imposed by the size of the population, time required to adequately measure variables of interest, costs of data collection, and the destructive nature of some measurements (Avery 1975). Additionally, the accessibility of all individuals is restricted when management alternatives are being developed for private and public land management. It then becomes necessary to "sample" the population for which inferences are to be made. Identification of the "population of inference" is a critical decision in the research process.

At this point there are several implications which are crucial to this "sample" mode of research. The uncertainty principle, a basic tenet of contemporary philosophy of science, states that no observation is made with complete certainty; there is always some uncertainty included. A possibility that sample data may misrepresent the population is ever-present. Therefore, conscientious use of statistical design and inferences based solidly on probability theory are not an adornment to the research process, but an integral and crucial part (see Chapter 10).

Constraints of Inherent Variability

If the range resource identified as the population of inference was entirely uniform and identical within location, across locations, and within and across years, then a single sample would accurately represent the expected occurrence or response for all individuals within the population. Assuming such uniformity, there would be no uncertainty associated with using sample measurements to define population means. However, all fields of research have at least one feature in common, i.e., the variability of experimental material (Federer 1955). Since no sample can accurately measure in every aspect the population from which it is drawn, it follows that an estimate derived from a sample is subject to error (Jolly 1954). This degree of uncertainty results in a risk associated with inferences developed from sampling. Useful research attempts to provide inferences in which the risk of being in error has been defined and, if possible, minimized.

Properties of Estimates Based on Samples

Two major criteria influencing the reliability of inferences exist in research projects. Precision is the attribute which describes the extent to which observations are dispersed or scattered about their mean value. Experimental error is a measure of the inherent variability of the population and subsequent variation in response of individuals within the population treated alike. Experimental error also reflects errors in experimental procedure and data collection and must be considered in the selection of experimental design and analysis. The magnitude of experimental error, and therefore the sensitivity of the experiment, partially determines the precision of the experiment (see Chapter 9).

Accuracy defines the ability of sample estimates, such as the mean, to reflect the true value (population parameter) regardless of their precision. Bias, a lack of accuracy, is associated with the manner in which samples are selected or responses measured. A sample is free of bias if the average estimate of the parameter resulting from repeating the sample a number of times is equal to the parameter itself. If a bias is incorporated into sampling, unknown deviation from the population mean may occur. The bias will result in a higher degree of inference risk as the sample estimates become atypical compared to those sampled without bias. Many experiments have inherent bias in some estimates (e.g., means) but are unbiased in other estimates (e.g., differences among means). The tolerance of bias in an experiment applies only to bias in estimates of parameters not directly used in inference.

The two most important principles in research design are randomization and replication (see Chapters 9 and 10). Proper randomization provides certainty that the principles of probability theory may be employed in analyzing results. Without this assurance, meaningful conclusions are impossible. Randomization also assures an unbiased selection of samples from the population. This will provide an equal opportunity for all individuals within the population to occur in a sample. Estimates derived from samples selected in this way have a higher probability of accurately reflecting population parameters than those with some bias in the selection. The inherent variability of individuals treated alike implies that multiple samples must be used to insure that data are not an artifact of a one-time sampling accident.

Replication, the observation of more than one experimental unit treated alike, provides evidence of repeatability and is the only way to provide an estimate of experimental error. This estimate must be present if any scientific inference is to be made. Determination of experimental error (degree of variability among individuals treated alike from the same population) allows the reliability of inference to be quantified.

Studies in which there is no replication within the population of inference and no replication of treatments within the study area are classified as general observations or demonstrations. Such "unreplicated" studies (individuals of the population of inference are not randomly sampled) are often used in range research. The validity of an unreplicated study, which depends on a restricted sample arbitrarily assumed to be "representative", is dependent upon the researcher's accumulated experience and intuition about variation and, therefore, applies only to the limited population observed. It has no formalized degree of risk associated with it. Moreover, the quality of the data are dependent upon the quality of the researcher's assumptions about the demonstration. Since demonstrations permit no test of these assumptions, there is no assurance that the researcher's experience and intuition applies to the new demonstration area. Often a concept of "most representative" is employed by range researchers to indicate that sample individuals are typical of the population. Replication of treatments is the only way to adequately characterize the variability within the inference population. Demonstrations provide information about the study area only. Their applicability to the population is severely limited, since there is no defined probability relating measurements made to those that would occur for all individuals within the population. Information gained from demonstrations may provide limited documentation about a previously established response under new conditions and can be useful in future research planning. However, replication which provides a quantitative estimate of the experimental error, is essential to the transfer of knowledge regarding a population and removes the human error associated with estimating experimental error and identifying a "typical" individual within the population. The number of replications required is also an important issue and relates to the precision of the experiment. The number of replications should be sufficient to insure an adequate representation of the population inference.

The research process follows an orderly progression regardless of the discipline. Procedures are outlined in Figs. 1-2 to 1-4. The research problem must first be clearly defined. A thorough plan must be developed to address the problem and answer the questions posed. Research is conducted and results are then evaluated. The conclusions drawn and interpretations made are most useful when they address findings related to the problem and are publicly reported.

Defining the Research Problem

Developing a meaningful research project depends upon the researcher's ability to identify and prioritize areas of research need (Fig. 1-2). Careful examination of existing knowledge in the selected field is critical. Suitable problems for comparative research can be either basic or applied. The acceptability of proposed research problems is often determined by the mission of

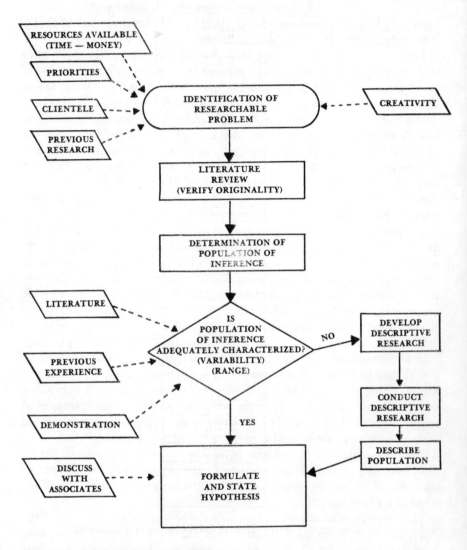

Figure 1-2. Defining the research problem.

the granting agency and the relevance of the findings to the clientele served. This generally has resulted in an emphasis on applied rather than basic range research. However, the importance of basic research should not be overlooked. The findings resulting from basic research provide the understanding of fundamental relationships and responses that can guide the development of practical range management plans and strategies. Developing a research proposal which is complete and feasible is critical. The researcher is in a position to evaluate the problems to be addressed, particularly with reference to available resources. An excessively ambitious proposal with little chance of being adequately completed because of insufficient funding or support is no

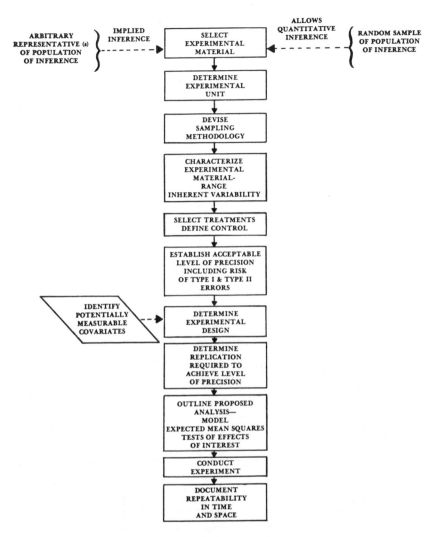

Figure 1-3. Planning the research approach and conducting the experiment.

more useful than a proposal which ignores the important problems. Moreover, research which is inadequately planned will inevitably become ensnarled at some point before the end of the project. An all too frequent example is that of the researcher who resists communicating with the statistician until the data are collected, only to find that an ornately complex set of data has been created for which no adequate procedure of statistical analysis has yet been devised, or worse yet, there is a conceptual flaw in the design obvious to the statistician but unnoticed by the researcher. The lesson this teaches is that "Lone Ranger" research is generally a poor idea. Experts from all relevant subject matter disciplines must be included as members of the research team. If they are included as afterthoughts (e.g., including a statistician after the fact or a chemist only if chemistry becomes an issue), the feasibility of utilizing the full extent of the cooperator's expertise, and therefore the quality of the final result, is inevitably compromised.

A carefully conducted review of the literature is important in defining precisely the proposed investigation. Reports of completed research frequently contain information which will guide the researcher in his/her selection of treatments, sampling methodology, and often identify areas in which further investigation appears important. It is also important to clearly identify the originality of the proposed research effort. Advances in the understanding of a resource are expedited by the creativity expressed in defining research problems. Research can attempt to refine current understanding, or it can, through synthesis and innovative interpretation of current knowledge, provide unique insight.

A major challenge to any range researcher is the tremendous diversity and variability of the rangeland resource. A second characteristic of rangeland is the variety of potential uses and the possibility for conflicting priorities among users. These attributes demand that most research dealing with rangeland be approached in a multi-disciplinary framework. The variablity of rangeland precludes any static description of an appropriate research group, however, the team is likely to include scientists with expertise in dealing with the vegetation, soils, animals, statistics, and economics in the area under study. Other potential disciplines should be represented as well.

Defining the Population of Inference

A significant component of the research proposal is the definition of the population to which findings of the research will apply. A clear statement of intended application of the results of the research will be helpful both in correct selection of experimental material and interpretation of findings. The population of inference must be characterized. Inherent variability and range of values likely to be encountered for parameters of interest are probably the most important characteristics to be considered. Previous experience with the resource in the researcher's locale and previously published reports relating to the resource will be useful in characterizing the population of inference. The use of demonstrations as valuable sources of information regarding the population should be considered at this time.

Statement of Objectives

Objectives must be clearly identified prior to the formalization of the experiment. They should include the hypotheses to be tested, the population of inference and variables to be measured. The hypotheses should be stated both biologically and statistically. Thus, a one-to-one correspondence is defined at the initiation of the research which will result in unambiguous analysis.

Planning the Research Approach

A formal research proposal can be an extremely useful tool, both before the research is begun as well as while the experiment is being conducted. A thorough research plan for comparative research will address and resolve two "opposing forces" which operate in experimental work. The first of these involves Type I and Type II errors. A Type I error occurs when there is no true difference between subsets of the population treated differently, but the null hypothesis of no difference is rejected. The probability or risk of a Type I error is established by the probability level (α) at which the experimenter chooses to declare differences significant, as well as the extent to which the analytical methods used are consistent with the design and characteristics of the response variable. Thus, the risk of a Type I error may be determined directly. A Type II error occurs when the null hypothesis is in fact false, (i.e., real differences do exist), but they are not detected. The risk of a Type II error depends on the extent to which the experimental design is consistent with biological reality. For example, use of a block design when a completely random design is warranted may increase the likelihood of a Type II error. Similarly, inadequate replication, when the magnitude of the experimental error is high or the difference considered biologically important is small, will result in increased risk of Type II error. Risk of Type II error is often characterized by its inverse, power. Power is defined as the likelihood of a real difference being declared significant. The power of the test is related to the magnitude of the real difference, the size of the error variance of mean or differences among means (which may be decreased by providing more replications), and the level of probability selected to declare significant differences. Since the magnitude of the true difference is unknown and the error variance can only be approximated in advance, power can only be approximated prior to conducting the experiment. As the risk of a Type I error is decreased, so is the power of the test unless the sample size is increased. The researcher must be guided in his/her planning by the importance of detecting a difference, if it exists, and the magnitude that is of practical importance. Very often, this decision should be based upon the cost of the treatment examined and the expected value of return if the treatment is successful.

The second dichotomy which must be rectified is controlling experimental error through the use of homogeneous experimental material (to improve sensitivity) and the concomitant restriction this places on the population of inference. This may be overcome to some degree by the use of experimental designs which group heterogeneous experimental material into somewhat homogeneous subunits (e.g. block designs or stratification).

Selection of Experimental Material

Selecting the experimental material is dependent on the population of inference (Fig. 1-3). However, in range research it is often realistically dependent upon the availability of all experimental material within the population of inference. Availability often becomes the limiting factor in defining the theoretical population of inference. This constraint may not be unique to range research; however, it often compromises the inferences that are made. Additionally, it is incumbent upon the researcher to select experimental material which is truly representative and of suitable size for adequate replication, so that inferences can be made for a much larger population. A nonrandom choice restricts the population of inference. This emphasizes the responsibility of the researcher to accurately characterize the population and the importance of biological interpretation rather than strict statistical evaluation. For example, results from an experiment investigating revegetation techniques would be intended to apply to all similar pastures in a geographical region. However, the researcher would not have access to all pastures in the region from which he/she might make a random selection, statistically restricting the inference. The researcher must then select representative pastures which are available and use his/her previous knowledge to extrapolate findings for probable users.

Repeatability is realized from a random sample of the population of inference. Consequently, it becomes extremely important for range researchers to provide evidence of repeatability in time and/or space if sampling of the population is restricted. Multiple locations are necessary to evaluate repeatability in space. Additionally, climatic variation requires that repeatability over years receive as much attention as repeatability over location. Repeatability can be supported if treatments are applied in more than one year at multiple locations.

Determining the Nature of Experimental Error

The experimental unit corresponds to the smallest subset of the experimental material such that any two units may be independently assigned different treatments in the actual experiment (Cox 1958). Definition of the experimental unit follows directly from the population of inference chosen and variability between experimental units provides estimates of experimental error.

It is extremely important that researchers properly identify treatments when designating experimental units. As an example, transects within a pasture are not experimental units if treatments such as stocking rates are applied to pastures. The transects within a pasture did not have an equal opportunity to receive each of the treatments. They are merely subsamples within a single experimental unit. Animals within a pasture are not appropriate experimental units to evaluate vegetative response through animal performance if treatments are applied to pastures. If steers are individually implanted with a growth stimulant and placed on pasture, they are the experimental units for the implant treatment, assuming no potential pasture by treatment interaction.

The appropriate experimental unit is not only a function of the experimental material but also the design of the experiment. For example, in a randomized complete block design there are two levels of experimental unit: the replicate and the plots within each replicate. Moreover, multifactor experiments are commonly conducted so that the experimental unit with respect to one factor is a subset of the experimental unit with respect to another factor. Consider an experiment involving different irrigation levels applied to large areas of land, and different grass varieties applied to subdivisions within these areas. The large areas are experimental units with respect to irrigation and experimental error relevant to inferences on irrigation levels is determined by variability among these areas. However, the smaller plots are the experimental units for the varieties. Thus, it is crucial that experimental units be precisely defined in conducting and reporting research.

Developing Sampling Metholodgy

Sampling plans must be developed which are simple, cost effective, and efficient to quantify the parameters of interest. It is frequently useful to collect pretreatment data in order to improve the understanding of the experimental material, evaluate sampling techniques, and provide "baseline" data about the experimental material before treatments are imposed. It also can be useful in providing an estimate of experimental error which can indicate the number of replications necessary for a desired level of confidence.

Selection of Treatments

Success of a comparative experiment rests on the careful selection of treatments. Treatments must be biologically sound and sufficiently different to provide a reasonable chance of demonstrating a response in the population. The number of treatments should be evaluated, particularly when quantitative levels are employed. With limited resources, too many treatments sacrifice precision and provide little additional information. Selection of appropriate control treatments must receive attention. Controls should represent the response accurately without treatment. For example, untreated "controls" within grazing exclosures are often not representative of an untreated pasture; rather, they represent a grazing rest treatment within the exclosure.

Establishing Level of Precision

Level of precision depends upon the biological variability of the experimental material in both descriptive and comparative research. Precision is reflected in the confidence interval about any effect estimated. In descriptive research, the precision achieved affects the certainty with which a parameter is estimated and can be established prior to the research. Similarly, comparative research involves description of more than one treatment. As such, comparative research must first be concerned with the precision of variable measurements. Secondly, decisions about acceptable degree of precision in comparative research depend upon the penalty associated with committing Type I or Type II errors.

In most research, the choice of an alpha level is not well considered; usually it is the result of a mixture of tradition and arbitrary rigidity. Statistical folklore states that $\alpha = 0.05$ was embodied with mystical powers. However, the story of its development casts doubt on its universal application. R.A. Fisher, the father of the analysis of variance, was confronted by a graduate student who wanted to know what the "right alpha level" would be. Fisher was busy, somewhat annoyed, and in an effort to terminate the conversation, simply suggested that 1 in 20 would be "good". From this inauspicious beginning, many researchers apparently regarded $\alpha = 0.05$ as the only choice. A somewhat more flexible, but equally mystical, approach for setting the alpha level is to use $\alpha = 0.05$ if the consequence of a Type I error is of "normal seriousness", $\alpha = 0.10$ if the consequence is "less serious", and $\alpha = 0.01$ if the consequence is "more serious". A variation of this approach is to set $\alpha = 0.10$ because the power of the test is so tenuous that the researcher cannot afford to set alpha any lower and peers will not allow it to be any higher. None of these approaches are particularly satisfying criteria for setting alpha levels.

A rational approach to the problem is suggested by decision theory. This is a branch of statistics concerned with strategies for making decisions which maximize the likelihood of an advantageous outcome. Strategies are based upon the knowledge of the probability of the various outcomes and associated relative gains or losses. For example, suppose in a given experiment the economic consequence of a Type I error is 10 times that of a Type II error. A simple decision theory approach would be to solve for α and β (the probabilities of a Type I and Type II error, respectively) so that $10\alpha=\beta$. For a given number of replications and magnitude of treatment differences considered economically important, one can easily determine a critical region for which $10\alpha=\beta$. This can also be used as a check on the advisability of the experiment. If the solution in the example above suggests $\alpha = 0.09$ at $\beta = 0.90$, the probability of a Type I error (0.09) is adequate; however, the probability of finding no difference when a real difference exists is too great (0.90). This indicates that either the number of planned replications is inadequate or that attempting to detect such small treatment differences is unrealistic. In cases where the consequence of Type I and II errors cannot be easily translated into economic terms, the decision theory approach is more abstract. However, even at its worst, it is no more arbitrary than using $\alpha = 0.05$ on the basis of tradition. At its best, decision theory provides a logical method to determine an appropriate alpha level.

If treatment differences are detected, the transfer of information to potential users is seriously impaired when effects have not been precisely estimated. This is particularly evident when economic returns are calculated for a proposed management strategy. For example, where a small cost of applying a treatment which does not work exists, a probability level of 0.2 may be adequate to declare significant differences. The "practical" difference becomes the product of expected response and price/unit versus the cost of producing the expected response. If the economics are generally fixed, then the critical item in the decision making process becomes the precision of the estimate. Given fluctuating economic conditions, a researcher would provide more service by interpreting significance based on his/her current evaluation of benefit while providing probabilities for further evaluation under different conditions.

The Design Process

The design process may be considered as two sequential phases. The selection of the treatment levels to be included in the experiment is called the treatment design. The assignment of treatment levels to experimental units is called the experiment design. Initially a treatment design is selected. This evolves from the biological questions to be answered. It involves a thorough statement of the treatments which will be used to address the hypotheses.

Experiment design is dependent on the variability of the experimental material and the objectives of the experiment. Several experiment designs may be acceptable for a specific treatment design; however, one will generally be the most appropriate for the experimental material (see Chapter 10). Consider a fertilizer trial on subirrigated meadows conducted at two locations. Location I is very uniform, while Location II has a distinct pattern in vegetation associated with previous management. The treatment design might be 0, 100, and 200 kg/ha of nitrogen. The experiment design at Location I could be a completely random design with 3 replications. The experiment design for Location II might be a randomized complete block design with 4 replications.

While most researchers are conversant with the principles of experiment design, it is advisable, and generally most useful, to consult a statistician familiar with biological field data at this stage in the planning process. The design selected should be as simple and cost effective as possible, while still allowing valid and sensitive tests of the hypotheses and a sufficient range of inference. It is at this point that the compromises between error control (homogeneous experimental material) and broad inference (heterogeneous material) must be evaluated and resolved to meet the objectives of the research. Measurement of variables related to those of primary interest is a useful consideration which is frequently overlooked in selecting experimental designs. The use of covariates and certain designs provides tools for error control strategies.

Determining Necessary Replications

The number of replications is dependent on two major factors: (1) the practicality and expense associated with sampling each replication and (2) the statistical sensitivity desired. Statistically, an estimate of the number of replicates required depends on:

1. An estimate of population variance.
2. The magnitude of the difference to be detected.
3. The likelihood of failing to detect a real difference considered acceptable (Type II error).
4. The level of significance to be used in the actual experiment (Type I error).
5. Whether a one- or two-tailed test is required (Steel and Torrie 1980).

The number of replications needed for the statistical verification must be compatible with the feasbility of data collection. If the number of replications required is beyond the researcher's ability to sample, reconsideration of the research problem is imperative. A first consideration should be simplification of the treatment design (see Chapter 10).

Outlining Proposed Analysis

A major frustration occurs when the researcher discovers upon completion of the experiment that the tests important to the evaluation cannot be made in a straightforward fashion. This can be easily avoided by outlining the analysis at the planning stage. The advice of a statistician provides confirmation that the design is appropriate and the desired tests can be performed. The research plan should include the format of data summary tables, an outline of the linear or nonlinear models assumed in the design process, and, if appropriate, an analysis of variance table including expected mean squares and designated "F test" ratios that identify the proper error terms. Contingency plans should be outlined for potential problems in execution of the experiment.

In comparative research, testing hypotheses is the culmination of the analysis. Often range research is composed of more than two treatments; consequently, multiple comparison procedures are sometimes desirable. Comparisons should be determined prior to the experiment. Appropriate mean comparisons become extremely critical in evaluating treatment response in an unambiguous manner. Unfortunately, there are no standard multiple comparison procedures that can be universally applied. Comparison techniques must be selected which are compatible with the experiment design and consistent with the objectives. Unusual events which may have occurred during the experiment must also be considered. Several excellent references available on selecting multiple comparison procedures include Chew (1976, 1977, 1980), Petersen (1977), Little (1978), Carmer and Walker (1982), and Nelson and Rawlings (1983).

Conducting the Research

The value of a clearly written research proposal and thoroughly planned experimental design becomes most evident as the research is conducted. The proposal should serve as a complete set of instructions describing what needs to be done and how it is to be completed. Scientists must be alert observers while conducting the experiment. Valuable insight may be gained from intuition about responses or phenomena affecting the biological system which are not being directly measured. These observations may then lead to new hypotheses and new research.

Application of Treatments

Treatments are, in general, the effects of primary interest in comparative research. They must be applied to the experimental units with appropriate care to ensure that they represent the effects described in the hypotheses to be tested. For example this may require frequent calibration of any mechanical device used in treatment application. Consideration should also be given to find methods which allow application of a treatment to replicates as consistently as possible.

Collection of Data

Data collection, when a complete research plan has been written, becomes a matter of measuring the required variables. Good record keeping is the product of good planning. Anticipating the data that needs to be recorded, the order measurements should be taken (calendar of sampling), and the potential problems that could occur will save time and effort in the field.

Records should be accurate, complete, legible, and permanent. A daily log, which supplements data records, describing what measurements and other observations were made, can be of considerable assistance in reconstructing any deficiencies in the data discovered later. Care should also be exercised in being certain that measurements are accurate. This may require calibration of scales or other measuring devices on a frequent schedule.

Evaluating Research Results

Evaluating the research should not be considered as the culmination of data collection. It should be an on-going process through which the researcher modifies and refines his research effort. Flexibility should be an integral component of the research program to allow the scientist the opportunity to adjust methodology and parameters of interest based on the data. However, method or procedure must not be confounded with treatment or years.

Data Verification

The quality of the research project is dependent, in part, on the care exhibited in data collection (Fig. 1-3). Every effort must be made to provide accurate and complete records and to minimize the occurrence of any missing information in the data set. During each data collection period, research notes should be maintained with verification that all data or samples have been collected. Initiating the analysis portion of the research program requires a complete data set. If values are missing from the data set, further analysis may be jeopardized. However, it is common for computerized statistical "packages" to compensate for missing values which may influence the sensitivity of the analysis. The importance of understanding any statistical package is emphasized in the handling of missing values. It must be decided whether zeroes or blanks are the appropriate characterization of a value, since the results generated will have different mathematical solutions.

Once the data set is complete, it is commonly entered into a computer. The more times data are transferred, the more likely transcription errors will occur. Consequently, strong consideration should be given to computerization of the data collection process. Many kinds of data can be recorded directly in the field or laboratory on magnetic media and transferred directly to a computer. When data are not directly computer compatible, it generally must be transferred from data sheets to computer sheets and then entered into the computer. If this is the case, it would be beneficial to adapt computer sheets to field data sheets. Whenever data must be transferred prior to entry into the computer, the first step in data summarization must be the verification of the data set with the original data sheets. This can be a time consuming process, but it guarantees the validity of future analysis and interpretation. The verified print-out of the "raw" data is the first component of the analysis process. It is then necessary to provide any conversion factors (e.g., lbs/A to kg/ha, etc.) and create any new variables.

Creation of an appropriate data set of means is the next step in analysis where subsampling of experimental units has been employed. This generally requires means by treatment-replication, averaging over any subsample values. At this point it is very useful to examine a graphical representation of the data. It is also important to characterize the nature of the distribution and the variance. A "box and whisker" graph is one technique which provides clear information about the distribution of observations (Tukey 1977). It may become apparent at this stage that the data set has true outliers which can be mathematically verified. True outliers should be deleted, if they can be correctly identified, and further analysis is not restricted by their absence. However, the experimenter should also be aware of the principle of the "golden observation." The explanation for the behavior of these outliers may be the key to rich new areas of knowledge or inquiry.

Data Analysis

Any analysis which has been proposed for a data set has inherent assumptions in its development. Researchers must first evaluate their data set with regard to its compliance with the assumptions. If there is a deviation from the basic assumptions, its magnitude and potential effect on inference should be determined. As an example (Steel and Torrie 1980) the assumptions underlying the analysis of variance are:

1. Treatment and environmental effects are additive.
2. Experimental errors are random, independent, and normally distributed about a mean of zero and with a common variance.

Routine tests are available to evaluate deviations from the assumptions of the analysis. Use of these tests should precede further analysis. Often transformations of the data can be utilized if treatment and environmental effects are nonadditive. Transformations can also be used to correct data having a distribution of experimental errors which is decidedly skewed. Effects that do not have a common variance can provide a more serious problem requiring an alternative analysis. In certain instances, non-parametric analysis may be useful in overcoming data which are not normally distributed.

Interpretation of Experimental Outcomes

Interpreting the results of an experiment provides the researcher with the opportunity to identify biological responses. The relevance of the biological interpretation and the practicality of further application take precedence over an arbitrary level of statistical significance. Statistics are a tool with which the likelihood for similar biological responses is quantitated. This provides an understandable means of reporting the credibility of the biological interpretation. The statistical principles employed in developing the experimental procedure are used to quantify and minimize the risk that an observed biological response was a random occurrence rather than a treatment effect. The interpretation of results must benefit from discussion with associates to further verify the correctness. The importance of the human interpretation with regards to the population of inference is especially conspicuous in range research since the statistical theory of selection of experimental material is often violated, placing a greater burden on the researcher and less importance on the finality of statistical tests of significance.

Communication of Results

Reporting conclusions is the culmination of the research project. It is also the means by which current knowledge is expanded. This communication process requires the synthesis of all of the findings based on the statistical reliability and the intuition and previous experience of the researcher. It is a

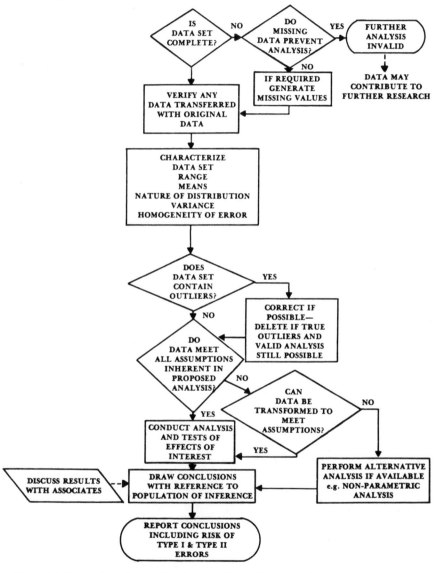

Figure 1-4. Evaluation of research outcome and reporting conclusions.

characterization of the results by the researcher who is in a position to interpret the importance of his work beyond the statistical evaluation. The accurate reporting of results must include the necessary information to allow a reader to make an informed and critical evaluation of the results and their interpretation. The report must include some evaluation of the problem and objectives of the research. It must adequately relate the work to previous literature. It becomes extremely important in the transfer of information from scientist to scientist that the population of inference, experimental unit, experimental design, treatment comparisons, and data collection methodology be accurately described in detail. If the research were descriptive, then some measure of precision must be included in the presentation of the data. Results must be synthesized and discussed. Conclusions should be made within the limits of extrapolation with care given to identify unique occurrences within the data which might influence the final interpretation. "Negative" results (experiments in which treatment differences are not detected) have often been considered unsuitable for formal publication. However, the potential use of negative results in further research development or resource management decisions can never be considered any less important than that of positive results. The goal of research is to add to the existing knowledge.

References

Avery, T.E. 1975. Natural resources measurements. McGraw-Hill, New York, New York.

Carmer, S.G., and W.M. Walker. 1982. Baby bear's dilemma: a statistical tale. Agron. J. 74:122-124.

Chew, V. 1976. Comparing treatment means: a compendium. HortScience. 11:348-357.

Chew, V. 1977. Comparisons among treatment means in analysis of variance. Tech. Bull. ARS-H-6. USDA, Washington, D.C.

Chew, V. 1980. Testing differences among means: correct interpretation and some alternatives. HortScience. 15:467-470.

Cox, D.R. 1958. Planning of experiments. John Wiley and Sons, New York, New York.

Federer, W.T. 1955. Experimental design: theory and application. Oxford and IBH Publ. Co., Calcutta, India.

Jolly, G.M. 1954. Theory of sampling, p. 8-18. *In:* D. Brown (ed), Methods of surveying and measuring vegetation. Bull. 42. Commonwealth Bur. Pastures and Field Crops, Hurley, Berkshire, England.

Lewis, J.K. 1969. Range management viewed in the ecosystem frame. p. 97-187. *In:* G.M. VanDyne (ed), The ecosystem concept in natural resource management. Acad. Press, New York, New York.

Little, T.M. 1978. If Galileo published in HortScience. HortScience. 13:504-506.

Little, T.M., and F.J. Hills. 1978. Agricultural experimentation. John Wiley and Sons, New York, New York.

Nelson, L.A., and J.O. Rawlings. 1983. Ten common misuses of statistics in agronomic research and reporting. J. Agron. Educ. 12:100-105.

Petersen, R.G. 1977. Use and misuse of multiple comparison procedures. Agron. J. 69:205-208.

Range Term Glossary Committee. 1974. A glossary of terms used in range management. Soc. Range Manage, Denver, Colorado.

Steel, R.G.D., and J.H. Torrie. 1980. Principles and procedures of statistics. McGraw-Hill, New York, New York.

Stoltenberg, C.H., K.D. Ware, R.J. Marty, R.D. Wray, and J.D. Wellons. 1970. Planning research for resource decisions. Iowa State Univ. Press, Ames, Iowa.

Tukey, J.W. 1977. Exploratory data analysis. Addison-Wesley Publ. Co., Reading, Massachusetts.

Chapter 2
Assessment of Habitat Factors

Introduction

Natural ecosystems vary both in time and space. They are complex, multifaceted mosaics of landscapes, affected by soil, water, climatic, fire, and biotic factors. In range research, it often is necessary to control or isolate habitat factors, especially when hypotheses involve the testing of ecological principles. This chapter examines concepts for classifying, evaluating, and controlling habitat factors that will help to design experiments and interpret and apply results.

Ecosystem Classification

Land must be classified to provide an effective basis for management and land use planning. Consequently, range science and related disciplines have developed many classification schemes, based primarily on vegetation and soils (West 1982). However, range scientists have not always considered site classification when designing or conducting field research, particularly on studies encompassing larger land areas. Inclusion of ecosystem classification in the research design can increase the usefulness of research results.

Hierarchical classifications based on vegetation date from the early work of Clements (Weaver and Clements 1929). The classification system developed by Daubenmire (1968), with the habitat type as its lowest level, has been widely used by forest and range ecologists. The habitat type categorizes land units on the basis of their climax vegetation (Daubenmire and Daubenmire 1968).

A classification system similar to that of the habitat type has been adopted by the SCS. The SCS classification is built around the range site concept (Dyksterhuis 1949, Shiflet 1973). Criteria for differentiating range sites are similar to those for habitat types, except that the former also considers differences in potential production. With the introduction of phase levels of habitat types, the two systems have become more alike. The SCS approach has the added advantage of correlating soils with range sites so that soils information can be used to help identify disturbed range sites. Hironaka et al. (1983), however, incorporated soils information into sagebrush-grass habitat types of southern Idaho. Therefore, the concepts of habitat type and range site appear to be converging, at least when considering rangeland.

As West (1982) has pointed out, the complexities associated with current natural resource management have led federal agencies to use more integrated approaches to land classification instead of those based solely on vegetation. In the United States, an example of a multiple component classification system is the hierarchical ecoregion concept proposed by Bailey (1976).

Hierarchical, multiple component classification systems have focused primarily on large areas using physiographic algorithms, and have tended to be incompatible with the finer grained systems based on vegetation (Bailey et al. 1978). Most range field research takes place near the lower end of the classification hierarchy. For such work, habitat type/range site descriptions should serve adequately for some years to come.

Ecological Factors Influencing Range Research

Climatic Factors

Climate is the primary factor determining range forage production. Field studies of forage production and use by grazing animals must recognize and evaluate climate, which may vary widely with geographic area and season. An appraisal of the microclimate is essential to an understanding of the ecological life history of individual range plants and animals and of the character and function of biotic communities.

Characterization of Regional or Areal Climate

Macroclimate variables associated with rangeland include precipitation, temperature, and evapotranspiration. These variables are generally embodied in any hierarchical classification system used to stratify the range sites being studied. However, it is often useful to provide summary statistics of climatic variables if this information is not available in the literature.

Climatic variables are not independent of each other. For example, temperature and solar radiation often are positively correlated. This covariance element can cause problems when specifying climatic variability in synecological research. Paterson et al. (1978) combined several climatic variables in southwestern Australia, using principal component analysis, in a manner allowing the transformed variables to account for climatic variation independently.

Climatic fluctuations can have a profound effect on structure and function of rangeland ecosystems. Their influence has been shown to be the greatest in semiarid environments, which are characterized by widely varying rainfall (Thornthwaite 1941). Climatic fluctuations affect both species composition and productivity of plant communities (Miles 1979). Productivity has been shown to respond to climatic factors both between and within seasons (Uresk et al. 1975).

Climatic fluctuations create difficulties in the description of climatic variables. Average annual values can be meaningless, or even misleading. For example, it has been known for at least 25 years that herbage production of some ecosystems responds almost completely to short-term seasonal precipitation patterns (Blaisdell 1958). Unfortunately, little research has been conducted on quantitative approaches towards dealing with fluctuations. Ford and Milne (1980) used time series analysis to evaluate plant responses to environmental fluctuations. However, this research area needs further development.

Microclimate

Microclimatology and instrumentation have advanced greatly since Geiger's (1965) classic book. Much of the impetus behind such progress has resulted from the development of physiological ecology as a discipline in range research (Sosebee 1977). A comprehensive review of the literature in microclimatology is beyond the scope of this chapter; however, a brief general overview can be useful to those interested in autecological studies of range plants. The four primary parameters measured at the boundary layer are temperature, radiation, humidity, and wind (Unwin 1980).

Temperature. Temperature is a familiar property in a qualitative way, but is not easy to define quantitatively. Temperature is basically a measure of heat intensity in a system, but not its quantity. It is measured using a thermometer. Thermometers fall into several categories according to their method of operation; however, the most common ones used in range research are based on electrical principles.

Electric thermometers have the advantages of being accurate and well suited for automatic recording. This category includes thermocouples (self-generating current) and thermisters and silicone diodes (require outside source of current). Thermocouples have the advantages of being reliable, reasonably accurate over wide temperature ranges, inexpensive, and easy to install.

Thermistors are semiconductors of ceramic materials made from sintering mixtures of metallic oxides. The resistance of a current sent through a thermistor varies inversely with temperature, which allows the latter to be determined by a voltage output. The advantages of thermistors over thermocouples include greater accuracy within a narrower temperature range and a circuit permitting longer lead wires. A disadvantage is that the relationship between thermistor resistance and temperature follows a nonlinear curve, but this problem can be mitigated by using parallel thermistors with series resistors (Fritschen and Gay 1979).

Silicone diodes have been shown to have a constant sensitivity to temperature over wide temperature ranges. Nonetheless, they have not been employed widely in range research.

Solar radiation. Solar radiation is a term encompassing all radiant energy emitted by the sun. Solar radiation varies from cosmic and gamma radiation (very short wavelengths) through ultraviolet, the visible spectrum and infrared ranges (short wavelengths) to radiowaves (very long wavelengths). At the earth's surface, however, solar radiation refers to shortwave radiation from just below to just above the visible spectrum.

Radiant energy is primarily measured in micrometeorology using radiometers. Radiometers work by producing an electric signal from the differential absorption of radiant energy on two different-colored surfaces. Several kinds of radiometers are available, depending on what form of radiant energy needs to be measured. For example, pyroheliometers are instruments designed to measure direct solar radiation, while net radiometers measure the radiation balance between incoming solar radiation and that energy reflected by the earth's surface.

Humidity. Humidity refers to the amount of water vapor in the air. Atmospheric water can be expressed in terms of absolute humidity (mass of water per unit volume of air), relative humidity (proportion of atmospheric water in relation to amount of water the air is capable of holding), or directly as vapor pressure. There are two general approaches towards measuring atmospheric water, using psychrometers or using hygrometers. In microclimatology, the latter is most commonly selected because it is suited for automated recording procedures and it can easily make measurements in the boundary layer. For example, a dew-point hygrometer, in which vapor pressure is determined by cooling a small mirrored surface to the dew point and measuring the temperature change, is well adapted to microclimatological work.

Wind. Wind speed and direction measurements have been made by mechanical anemometers and wind vanes in standard weather stations. These instruments, unfortunately, are not adapted to boundary layer meteorology because of their physical size and the relatively high threshold wind speeds required to start mechanical devices. Electrical anemometers circumvent both of these problems, and, hence, have found increasing use. Although the principle of electrical (or thermal) anemometry has been available for many years, recent advances in electrical engineering have only in the past 20 years provided the equipment now available. For thorough discussions on microclimatology and its measurements, see Platt and Griffiths (1964), Oke (1978), and Fritschen and Gay (1979), and Unwin (1980).

Measuring the Soil Environment

Within a given soil, two climatic variables are commonly required by range researchers, soil temperature and soil water. The former is measured at the soil surface by fire ecologists and throughout the profile by others.

Soil Temperature

Soil temperature can be of greater ecological significance to plant life than air temperature, especially in areas of contrasting slope and aspect (Chang 1968). Ambient soil temperature measurements are taken with the same instruments that are used to record air temperature, but often have added structural adaptations for inserting them into the soil. Thermocouples have been used more in recent years because of their small size, accuracy, and suitability for automated data recording systems.

Soil temperature recording at the soil surface requires more careful instrumentation than that below ground for two reasons. First, unless the thermometer is shielded, direct solar radiation can give elevated readings. Second, daily soil temperature ranges commonly exceed corresponding boundary-layer air temperature ranges significantly; consequently, recording equipment must be capable of monitoring large changes over short periods of time.

Range fires can elevate soil surface temperatures beyond the operating range of liquid and some electrical thermometers. Iron-constanan thermocouples attached to a double glass-wrapped silicone-impregnated wire, however, have been shown to be suitable for obtaining most field temperature data (Stinson and Wright 1969). Pyrometers, asbesto cards containing commercial temperature pellets that melt at specific temperatures, can be used as an inexpensive alternative to thermocouples (Bailey and Anderson 1980). The disadvantage of pyrometers rests in their inability to record temperature in relation to time. Wright and Bailey (1982) briefly discussed measurement techniques in their review of fire ecology.

Soil Water

Soil water measurement techniques have advanced rapidly in the past 25 years. However, methods available before this period are still used in range research. For example, the gravimetric method, which consists of obtaining a soil sample, weighing it both before and after oven-drying (24 hours at 105° C), and expressing soil water as a percentage of the dry weight, has great utility in situations where more sophisticated equipment is unavailable and where destructive sampling does not invalidate the experimental design.

The use of electrical resistance units, commonly called "Bouyoucos blocks" (Bouyoucos and Mick 1940), has apparently declined somewhat in recent years. Their operation is based on the relationship between soil water potential and the electrical resistance between two electrodes embedded in the blocks. In addition to soil water potential, electrical resistance units are strongly affected by varying soil salt concentrations. Where this problem occurs, gypsum blocks are preferred because of their buffering capacity. Electrical blocks are most accurate in drier soils, especially when following a drying curve. When soil water potential increases along a wetting curve, however, hysteresis effects can be substantial (Platt and Griffiths 1964).

In the 1950's, a neutron scattering technique was developed which measured actual soil water content (Gardner and Kirkham 1952). The method is based on the principle that "fast" neutrons are more effectively scattered and slowed by hydrogen than by any other element; moreover, hydrogen atoms are most commonly found in soil as part of water molecules. Soil water is measured by inserting a neutron probe, consisting of a source of fast neutrons and a detector of scattered "slowed" neutrons, into a tube placed in the soil. The detector consists of a metal foil which becomes radioactive when capturing slowed neutrons.

The neutron probe cannot be used where precise estimates of soil water are needed at specific points within the profile. In ecological research, it has the further disadvantage of not directly measuring soil water availability to plants (i.e., potential). However, it is excellent where water dynamics in the overall soil profile require monitoring, and calibration curves with soil water potential have been developed.

In more recent years, a new technique, following upon advances in thermocouple psychrometry, has become increasingly popular for measuring water potential in soil-plant systems. Thermocouple psychrometry makes use of a phenomenon called the Peltier effect which deals with the exchange of heat energy between thermocouple junctions and its immediate environment (Spanner 1951).

By passing an electrical current through a thermocouple in one direction, its sensing junction can be cooled sufficiently to condense water upon it. The amount of water condensed is a function of soil water vapor pressure. When the current is terminated, the condensed water immediately starts to evaporate, thereby depressing the junction temperature in relation to the evaporation rate. Hence, soil vapor pressure can be determined from the temperature depression caused by this evaporative cooling.

Recent developments in electronics and thermocouple design have made thermocouple psychrometers much more practical for field use (Brown and Van Haveren 1972). Their application to plant-soil water studies involving xeric ecosystems has provided new knowledge on the water relations of semi desert and desert range plants, particularly at water potentials well below the standard wilting point of -15 atmospheres (Moore and Caldwell 1972, Frank 1983).

Soil Characteristics and Qualities

Soil science is a complex field, closely allied with plant science, and an integral part of ecology. For this reason, the range scientist should consult with a soil scientist when carrying out research involving the recognition of soils and measurement of their properties. No attempt is made here to discuss the details of techniques or procedures for determining the various soil features significant to the characterization, research, and management of rangeland soils. The significance of the feature is mentioned, but standard texts, manuals, and handbooks should be consulted for specific analytical procedures.

Factors of Soil Formation

Rangelands are characterized by a great diversity of soils, which is to be expected because of the wide differences in the natural factors of soil formation (i.e., climate, living matter, parent material, relief, and time) (Jenny 1941, Soil Survey Staff 1975). Natural characteristics of a soil at any one place are the result of the integrated effect of climate and living matter as conditioned by relief acting on soil parent material over a period of time.

Rangeland, in general, cannot be characterized by any one of the factors of soil formation. The many combinations of factors produce a wide variety of soils. For example, soils formed with the climate and living matter of the hot deserts of the Southwest vary from those characteristic of meadows in the high Rocky Mountains, or the grasslands of the Great Plains.

Soil parent material is highly variable in physical features and chemical composition as well as mode of deposition. Relief varies from level plains to nearly vertical cliffs. The time factor in the formation of soils varies from almost zero, as for soils forming in recent alluvium, to many thousands of years for soils formed with material weathering from bedrock or ancient sediments.

Soils of range areas can be differentiated only broadly on the basis of soil formation factors alone; not enough is known about the effect of the multitude of combinations and interactions of soil materials with soil-forming factors to permit precise statements about soils at a given site. Nevertheless, these factors should be appreciated. This is particularly true in making appraisals of areas for experimental work, because the more that natural factors and processes of soil formation are uniform, the more uniform are the natural characteristics of soil.

In addition to natural factors and processes, human activity also must be considered as a significant modifying factor. Soil changes brought about by human-induced erosion; compaction from livestock trampling or equipment; soil water changes from gullying, drainage, or irrigation; and plant-nutrient changes through fertilization may be of great significance in relation to the kind and amount of forage produced.

Classification of Soils

Soils may be classified in several ways, depending on objectives. Three commonly used ways, actually interconnected, are: (1) soils classed according to differences in one property, such as texture, color, or reaction; (2) soils classed according to their qualities or attributes as manifested in behavior or performance, such as erodibility, water retentivity, permeability or productivity; and (3) soils classed as existing natural units of the landscape according to distinctive combinations of a number of soil characteristics. An example of the last method is the hierarchical classification system generally used in the United States (Soil Survey Staff 1975). Categories defined in *Soil Taxonomy* can provide information that is useful in range research and management. Information is general in classes of the upper categories and becomes progressively more specific in classes of the lower categories.

Common Differentiating Characteristics

Most behavior and performance characteristics of soils can be related to, or identified with, soils at all taxonomic levels on the basis of combinations of the following characteristics:

Thickness of horizons and soil depth. Thickness of horizons is usually measured perpendicularly to the soil surface. Thickness of soil is the summation of the thicknesses of horizons regardless of ease or suitability for root growth and penetration. The term "soil depth" commonly refers to that portion of the soil from the surface downward to underlying bedrock, hardpan, unconsolidated substratum, or other material that would greatly affect root distribution, soil, water, or nutrient supply.

Arrangement and number of horizons. The number and relative positions of the horizons in the profile, as well as the degree of gradation from one horizon to the next, are all important characteristics.

Structure. Soil structure refers to the aggregation of primary soil particles. Soil structure classes are based on shape (e.g., granular, blocky, prismatic, or platy), size, and distinctness of visible aggregates. Structure is an extremely important characteristic of soils because of its influence on permeability, erodibility, and therefore, productivity. The maintenance, restoration, or improvement of horizon structure at the soil surface can be one of the more important management concerns pertaining to rangeland soils.

Color. Color is one of the most obvious characteristics of soils. It may have little to do with vegetation response, but can be indicative of important quality differences. Dark-colored soils generally are higher in organic matter than light-colored soils; uniformly colored soils, particularly those of reddish hues, are usually well-drained and well-aerated; and soils with low chroma mottles, where color differences are not simply a result of differences in decomposing rock fragments, are usually indicative of restricted drainage.

Soil color is measured according to the Munsell system (hue, value, and chroma) by comparing dry and moist soil samples with standardized color chips. Soil color names, such as grayish brown or reddish brown, are based on limits within the Munsell system.

Texture. Soil texture refers to the relative proportions of various size groups of individual soil grains: clay, silt, and sand. In the absence of erosion, texture is a constant characteristic of any soil. Differences in water and nutrient retention, permeability, erodibility, and workability are affected by texture, so it, nonetheless, has an important influence on soil behavior.

Textural classes, such as sandy loam and clay loam, are based on proportions of the soil grains in each size group. Experience permits one to make close estimates by feeling soil between the fingers. Rock fragments (larger than 2 mm) are important to recognize, as to amount, predominant size, and shape, because of their influence on soil water retention and soil workability. Terms, such as "gravelly" and "cobbly", for rock fragments are used to modify textural class names.

Consistence. Soil consistence refers to the degree of cohesion and adhesion, or resistance to deformation or rupture. Consistence varies with soil water, kind and amount of clay, and amount of organic matter. Consistence of the surface horizon has an important influence on soil behavior and management.

Soil consistence is usually expressed qualitatively (e.g., hard, soft, friable, plastic) rather than quantitatively. Classes are not rigidly defined, and yet, they are described in sufficient detail to be expressive of soil differences (USDA Soil Conservation Service 1983).

Reaction and base status of horizons. Soil reaction refers to the degree of active acidity or alkalinity. It is probably the most commonly used single chemical test made on soils because of its general connection with plant growth. It is measured according to pH values, usually by colorimetric method in the field and by electrometric method in the laboratory. Reaction classes are commonly used, such as slightly acid or moderately alkaline. Soil reaction classes and corresponding ranges in pH values are used by the USDA Soil Survey Staff (USDA Soil Conservation Service).

The pH value of a soil can give an indication of its base status (determined in laboratory or with field kit); that is, the relative amount of exchangeable cations. In general, soil acidity varies inversely with base status. Alkaline reactions generally indicate a high base status or a saturation of the exchange complex with calcium, magnesium, sodium, and potassium. Soils with pH values of about 7.8 or above are commonly, but not always, calcareous, and soils above pH 8.5 normally are high in exchangeable sodium; however, the reverse of this does not necessarily hold. Calcareous soils can be identified by effervescence with dilute (0.1 N) hydrochloric acid.

Although pH is related to base status, it does not indicate the proportions of the various cations. A soil with a pH of 7.5, well within the optimum range for the growth of many forage plants, may be exceedingly low in calcium and high in magnesium; or it may be high in sodium relative to other bases. In both cases a nutritional imbalance exists that would affect plant growth.

Those working in plant-soils relationships must be aware that a positive relationship between pH and base status has validity only in the limited universe in which the relationship was established. In some places, the general relationship between pH and base status does not hold.

The following features (soluble salts, organic matter, and mineralogy) require laboratory analysis but are discussed because of their importance to the characterization, use, and management of rangeland soils.

Soluble salts. Excesses of soluble salts, which characterize saline and alkali soils, influence the kind and amount of range vegetation. Content of soluble salts is usually determined by electrical methods. Definitions of and techniques for identifying saline and alkali soils are in "The Diagnosis and Improvement of Saline and Alkali Soils" (U.S. Salinity Laboratory 1954).

A saline soil contains sufficient soluble salts distributed in the profile to impair productivity of certain plants. It is not strongly alkaline nor otherwise an alkali soil. A saline soil sample has a conductivity of its saturation extract greater than 4 mmho cm^{-1} at 25 C, or a content of soluble salts greater than 1.15% (dry soil basis). An alkali soil has either such a high degree of alkalinity or so high a content of exchangeable sodium, or both, that it impairs productivity for most plants. An alkali soil has a pH of 8.5 or higher, or an exchangeable sodium of 15% or higher, or both. A saline-alkali soil fulfills the requirements of both a saline and an alkali soil.

The kinds and amounts of salts are also important in their influence on characteristics of the soil other than plant growth. For example, alkali soils tend to disperse on wetting and to compact and become hard on drying.

Organic matter. Organic matter is generally most abundant on the surface and in the upper horizons. It includes freshly fallen litter as well as decomposed material. Organic horizons contain 12% or more organic carbon. Quantities must be determined in the laboratory, but with experience field estimations can be made. Total nitrogen content of the soil is also commonly determined, because the carbon-nitrogen ratio of organic matter is an important characteristic of soils as well as an indicator of fertility.

Mineralogy. The mineralogical composition of soil horizons depends on the mineralogical composition of the soil parent material. It also depends, in part, on processes of soil formation and the length of time over which these processes have occurred. The kind of clay resulting from decomposition of clay-forming minerals, such as the feldspars, has an important influence on soil behavior. Expanding lattice-type clays (montmorillonitic) are much more "clayey" in the sense of stickiness and in expansion and contraction than soils with the same amount of non-expanding lattice-type clays (kaolinitic) or amorphous clays (allophane). The kind and amount of clay affects the nutrient and water holding capacities of soils. Kind of clay is usually determined by X-ray diffraction pattern, differential thermal analysis, cation exchange characteristics, or electron microscopy.

Character and geology of parent material. Certain soil qualities are more readily inferred from type of parent material than from any other soil-forming factor. For example, some soils contain sufficient selenium to produce toxic concentrations in certain forage plants (Hamilton and Beath 1963). The same can be said for molybdenum (Kubota 1977). Other differences, such as abnormally low or high base status and certain mineral nutritional deficiencies or toxicities in some soils, are traceable to the character of plant material or of underlying parent rock. The low calcium and high magnesium content and other differences of certain soils formed from the decomposition of serpentine are directly traceable to the characteristic chemical nature of this rock.

Some Important Soil Qualities

Soil qualities are behavioral traits inferred from the various differentiating characteristics and may be attributed to a particular kind of soil. Such qualities can be predicted only to the degree that soil behavior is known and related to the differentiating characteristics. These predictions are only as accurate as the established relationships. With such information, soils can be grouped into interpretive classes of direct value in research or use in management decisions (Gardner and Retzer 1949). Soil qualities of particular importance in range research include erodibility, water retention, and permeability.

Erodibility. Erodibility refers to the relative susceptibility of a soil to erosion. Soil properties, such as texture and organic matter, that affect cohesive stability, along with slope length and shape, and surface cover are among the factors that affect erodibility.

While erodibility is not easy to measure nor to express quantitatively, the Universal Soil Loss Equation (USLE) (Wishmeir and Smith 1978) provides a general means of estimating erosion losses by water. Attempts to identify the factors influencing erosion by wind and to quantify their effects have been made by L. Lyles and his associates (Lyles 1983), building on the earlier work of others (Woodruff and Siddoway 1965). Additional information and references to research about water and wind erosion are given by Branson et al. (1981).

Water retention. Water retention refers to the power of soil to hold water at specified levels of moisture tension. Three levels are commonly defined: saturation, field capacity, and permanent wilting point. Field capacity may be determined by the pressure plate method with tensions at 1/3 to 1/10 atmospheres (U.S. Salinity Laboratory 1954). Permanent wilting point is obtained by the pressure plate method with tension at 15 atmospheres. Available soil water ordinarily refers to the amount of water a soil can contain between its permanent wilting point and field capcity. Soil texture (as well as content of rock fragments), organic matter content, and kind of clay influence soil water retention. Other methods of determining the state of soil water have been discussed in an earlier section of this chapter. For a good overall review of the subject, see Rawlins (1976).

Permeability. This quality of soil relates to the readiness with which it conducts or transmits fluids. Ordinarily it refers to a quality of individual soil horizons, but for some purposes the permeability of the least permeable horizon of a soil (except for the immediate surface layer) is used to denote permeability of the whole soil. In the field, estimates of permeability are usually made by considering structure, texture, porosity, and density. For example, medium and fine textured alkaline soils tend to disperse on wetting and become nearly impermeable (measurement methods are presented in Chapter 7).

Infiltration rate is governed by characteristics of the surface horizon and the least permeable layer of the wet soil. Frequently, on rangeland the limiting layer is at the soil surface where infiltration can be greatly influenced by changes in structure and compaction (Branson et al. 1981).

Infiltration rates can be estimated using several different approaches. Parr and Bertrand (1960) reviewed available techniques several years ago; however, infiltration technology concerning water application has remained fairly constant since then.

Perhaps the most commonly used procedure has been with the use of ring infiltrometers (Rauzi et al. 1968). It is helpful for comparing similar areas, but provides a poor simulation of actual infiltration under natural rainfall events (Branson et al. 1981). Infiltration can be estimated by precisely measuring precipitation, runoff, and evapotranspiration using a weighing lysimeter (Parton et al. 1981). At some experimental stations with gauged small watersheds, infiltration has been estimated during natural rainfall events by monitoring runoff (Sharp et al. 1964) (see Chapter 7).

Physiographic Factors

Physiographic factors include slope, exposure, and elevation. They vitally affect the environment of plants and animals in rangeland ecosystems. Topography affects plant communities directly by modifying environmental factors and indirectly through its influence on soil formation. An excellent review of environmental factors in relation to vegetation is presented by Daubenmire (1974). These relationships clearly portray the degree of interaction among the abiotic/soil/plant/animal components of rangeland ecosystems (Lewis 1969).

Range managers are more than ecosystem managers; they make decisions within a hierarchy ranging from the socioeconomic level at the top to the organism level at the bottom (Allen and Starr 1982). Within this hierarchy, physiographic factors influence both structure and function. For example, topography can influence the kind of livestock operation a grazier has available (cow-calf vs. steer vs. sheep), or whether the animals have to be shipped following the first storm in the fall, by its control over forage availability and quality. At the organism level, topography affects plant size, phenology, and many other factors.

Physiographic variation can be eliminated on an experimental range only by careful selection of area (see Chapter 1). Selecting similar pastures or planting areas generally is not as difficult on level or rolling plains. However, in mountains where exposure, water drainage, wind prevalence, soil type, and vegetation characteristics occur in a multiplicity of variations and combinations, selecting experimental areas is difficult. Measurement of microclimate in many subareas and careful study of soil and vegetation are necessary in selection of study areas and in subsequent data interpretation.

Plant Competition

The concept of interspecific competition has recently sparked intense debate among animal ecologists. Schoener (1982) reviewed the arguments pertaining to this subject for those interested in its theory.

Competitive relationships among plants are much less complicated, because, unlike animals, their lack of mobility greatly limits the possible time-space interactions that can lead to competition. Historically, plant competition studies have examined the relationships among individuals of different species in an environment where one or more abiotic variables was limiting (Harris and Wilson 1970). At the plant population level, competition has been identified as affecting both density and biomass, especially in crop species (Hutchings and Budd 1981). Risser (1969) reviewed the literature on plant competition in grasslands.

Interspecific competition can measurably affect the outcome of actual and simulated grazing studies (Archer 1984). Forage removal often results in a modification of competitive interactions among forage species which, in turn, can lead to changes in species composition and/or production which are independent of the defoliation treatment itself (Alexander and Thompson 1982).

Bentley and Whittaker (1979) examined the interspecific competition between two species of *Rumex* which are often found in association with each other. They demonstrated that, when grazed by chrysomelid beetles, a strong interaction existed between the levels of grazing pressure and competition. Newberry and Newman (1978) also have provided evidence of the interaction effect between defoliation and competition.

The influence of interspecific competition requires that the development of clipping or grazing procedures be more carefully designed for research in mixed stands than for monocultures. Care must also be taken in interpreting and extrapolating any results obtained.

Habitat Studies on Big Game-Livestock Ranges

Big game animals can be an important factor in rangeland ecosystems. For example, they can modify the abundance and distribution of vegetation. Not only can heavy browsing result in maintaining shrubs and small trees in open stands which otherwise would form a closed canopy, but selective use by big game can affect plant reproduction, and, therefore, community succession. Excessive numbers of elephants in Tsavo National Park, east Africa, reduced savannas and forested areas to treeless plains and shrublands before elephant populations were controlled (Leuthold and Leuthold 1976).

In planning research on areas supporting dense big game populations, researchers must decide whether the objective is to study the range with or without impact of big game animals. For example, use of various elevational ranges by big game animals in the Intermountain region of the western United States is usually seasonal. Areas in which migrating animals are absent during one season may be subject to heavy grazing during another season. It may be necessary to experimentally separate big game influences, but researchers should remember that in the decision-making process the manager must deal with all influences on the ecosystem, including big game. Depending upon the type of research, results of studies on game-proof plots may not apply on ranges where big game are present. It is generally advisable to evaluate big game use, especially where controversies exist.

The approach to the study of the influence of big game animals on a habitat depends on the size of the area, the animal involved, and related costs. On smaller areas, fencing often is cost-effective. Larger animals, such as elk, eland, bison, and elephants, may partially or totally destroy game exclosures, especially if herds are large; therefore, fencing costs may escalate where these larger herbivores are involved. Chemical repellents, such as Thiram (Arasan), have been effective in preventing deer use on vegetation in the dormant season for up to 6 months (Hawthorne 1980). On larger areas, the removal of the big game influence may be impractical or impossible, although cages may sometimes be used to remove their influence on vegetation. Of particular importance is the removal of the big game influence in seedling establishment studies. Fencing is essential in these cases because game can destroy a new seeding.

In some areas, cages and fences can have a measurable effect on adjoining vegetation by their influence on snow patterns, etc. Exclosures, therefore, must be large enough to allow sampling at sufficient distance from the "fenceline effect". Utilization cages used in range analysis are routinely moved each season to minimize bias from environmental modification. In research, where wildlife effects can be more subtle, the requirement for eliminating such bias is even more important.

Effect on Utilization and Range Condition

Several approaches can be used to determine the effect of big game on forage utilization and range condition. Where utilization checks are desired on livestock-free ranges, surveys can be made by the same methods used to determine livestock utilization. Where livestock use a range one season and game another, two surveys may be used—one to determine livestock use, the other to determine game use (Young 1955). Research is most complex when game and livestock use the same area at the same time. Under such conditions, game and livestock utilization may be separated by comparison of either livestock-free or game-free areas with dual-use areas.

Separating effects of big game use. The effects of big game utilization are commonly separated from that of domestic livestock by the use of exclosures. On ranges where deer occur, exclosures are applicable because these animals usually jump over or crawl through a standard barbed or net wire livestock fence. By constructing two exclosures in a nested design, three conditions of use can be studied: (1) combined used by all animals (outside exclosures); (2) use by game and small animals such as rodents (inside standard livestock fence); and (3) no use (inside game-proof fence). These nested exclosures are often called three-way exclosures.

Consideration should be given to location and size of exclosures. The location should be representative of the study area, with care being taken not to block normal routes of travel with the exclosure, thereby concentrating excluded animals around its perimeter. Size of the total exclosure should be no smaller than 0.4 ha (Yoakum et al. 1980) and the partial exclosure no smaller than 2 ha. Fencing costs can be reduced by building the nested exclosure in one corner of the larger exclosure so that two sides of the fence serve both plots.

An innovative variation of the nested exclosure design was tested by Grumbles (1964), who used a 0.5-ha central game exclosure with four 0.5-ha paddocks around the outside. Semi-tame white-tailed deer and cattle were allowed to forage in the paddocks at various combinations of deer and cattle, deer alone, and cattle alone.

Amount of forage removed by big game. An approximation of the quantity of forage removed by big game from large areas can be calculated by combining animal census data, period of use, and known daily forage intake values (French et al. 1956, Ammann et al. 1973, Alldredge et al. 1974, Wheaton and Brown 1983).

Pellet group counting is an easily applied indirect method of determining game use by cervids. The defecation rate of mule deer on winter range is about 13 pellet groups per day (Rasmussen and Doman 1943). In dry cool climates, pellet group counts can serve to determine deer-days use and concentration areas. This method is less effective in wet warm climates because of rapid decomposition of pellets and difficulty of finding pellet groups in dense vegetation. This technique is also difficult to apply with bovids that mark their territories with dung piles.

Food Habits

In areas where big game and livestock occupy the same ranges, an understanding of the food habits of both is essential to management efforts and application of research results. Excellent reviews of food habits research techniques can be found in Schemnitz (1980).

Direct observation using tame or semi-tame animals can be an effective method of determining food habits of big game. However, the method may not be applicable for all species, because tame animals may not exhibit the same feeding habits as wild animals (Wallmo and Neff 1970). Also, it is difficult to apply using both sexes because of social interactions, especially during times of reproductive activity. Tame animals are either taken into the study area on a leash or, if tame enough, allowed to roam freely. An observer watches the animal and records bites or "animal minutes" of each species consumed (Currie et al. 1977). Unfortunately, it is difficult to accurately duplicate diets of grazing animals by observation alone. Studies have shown that diets selected by grazing animals are higher in quality than hand-plucked samples (Van Dyne and Torell 1964).

Cafeteria feeding is another direct method of determining big game food habits. Captive animals are fed known amounts of native plants cut by the researcher and brought to the feeding pen. Quantities consumed are determined by weighing the forage before and after it is presented to the animals (Smith and Hubbard 1954). This technique is valuable in determining diets where plant community composition is simple. For more complex plant communities, this technique may be useful in ranking a few species against each other. In applying the technique, it must be remembered that plants may change in palatability after cutting, and that captive animals may not behave the same as wild animals.

Stomach content analysis is one of the most versatile methods of directly determining big game food habits. Extensive reviews of the method are available in the literature (Korschgen 1980). This direct method requires the sacrificing of animals or use of stomach contents from road or hunter kills. It may not be possible to sacrifice animals solely for food habits studies because of limited animal populations, difficulty of obtaining collecting permits, or other constraints. Stomach contents from road and hunter kills may not provide reliable estimates of diet because of various deficiencies in the method of sample collection. For example, only a single season may be represented in the sample, particularly with hunter kills.

Fecal analysis has become a popular direct method of diet analysis with the increased use of microhistological techniques (Sparks and Malechek 1968). Epidermal characteristics of plants consumed remain intact through the digestion process, thereby making identification possible for the trained technician (Holechek et al. 1982).

Analysis of material from esophageally- or rumen-fistulated animal is another method of direct diet analysis. This method does not require sacrificing animals, but the cannulation of big game is a delicate and expensive procedure. It requires tame animals, a veterinarian who is intimately familiar with the cannulation procedure, and a crew of dedicated and experienced persons to provide daily care and medication to the cannulated animals. The advantage of this method is in having a pool of animals that can be used at any time on any research area. The procedure has been used with limited success on white-tailed deer in Texas (McCollum 1972). Holechek et al. (1982) have reviewed fistula techniques in general.

Diet items obtained from stomach contents of cannulated animals can be identified by the investigator, a trained technician, or through the services of a commercial laboratory. If the individual researcher or technican does the analyses, access to a complete herbarium is essential. If done by a commercial laboratory, the investigator should make certain that the laboratory has access to plant items from the specific research area, as many plant species have similar characteristics and can be misidentified by the lab technican trying to serve large regions (Chamrad and Box 1964).

Food habit studies are of little value unless correlated to availability of the food items on the range. Availability data are collected by standard vegetation sampling techniques. Food habits and availability data can be combined through use of a preference index or desirability coefficient. Medin (1970) and Krueger (1972) have reviewed techniques for estimating food preferences.

Determining Big Game Populations

Researchers often must know the approximate number of animals on the range at a given time. Therefore, they must have a fast, relatively accurate method of determining animal numbers. Big game animals are extremely difficult to count. They are constantly moving and can conceal themselves easily and effectively. The range researcher should review wildlife census techniques discussed in Davis and Winstead (1980). Methods of estimating the size of wildlife populations may be divided into direct counts and methods involving sampling.

Direct counts. Aerial counts using helicopters or fixed-wing aircraft are probably the most common method of obtaining direct counts of big game animals. Aerial counts can be accurate, time-efficient, and suitable for statistical analyses. They are applicable to most kinds of big game in open or semi-open rangelands. Major disadvantages include high costs, especially for helicopter time, and the availability of experienced pilots and aircraft on a timely basis.

Aerial helicopter counts of wildlife species have been used successfully for management purposes for years in the western United States (Kufeld et al. 1980). Although managers have used the technique in an attempt to make "total" counts, total counts are usually not considered to be possible. For research purposes, strip counts provide precise data that allows the researcher to make statistical estimates of actual population size. Recently, Teer et al. (1984) have shown that 50, 33 or even 25% coverage of an area can provide reliable data on animal numbers. However, Caughley (1974), reporting on accuracy of aerial surveys, stated that more animals are missed than many researchers would like to admit.

Fixed-wing aircraft have been used extensively to count a number of species of big game in east African savannas and bushlands (Kahurananga 1981). Airplane censuses have also been used successfully to count big game in the western United States. The New Mexico Department of Game and Fish has used airplane censuses to set bag limits on pronghorn antelope and exotics (Morrison 1984). Airplane counts are particularly valuable where large areas must be covered.

Driving animals for total counts is not uncommon. Drives may be used to count male deer where the terrain will allow. Usually, counters are posted at the end of canyons, and the deer are driven past them. This technique is also applicable in grassland and open or low brushland when the area counted can be kept relatively small (i.e., 100 to 200 ha). Otherwise, the number of drivers and counters needed becomes too large for the average research project.

Sample counts. It is generally not possible to count all individuals in a population. Therefore, small representations are taken from the population and estimates are based on samples. Samples are usually portions of the area on which individuals are counted, ratios of known portions of the population to unknown numbers, or counts made of "animal sign" (i.e., fecal groups or tracks).

Techniques based on ratios of known animals in the population to unknown animals are usually some modification of the Lincoln Index (Jolly 1965). All require a known number of marked animals. It is assumed that marked animals are evenly distributed throughout the population and the chance of seeing one is based only on this proportion. This technique can be used in many different ways. Animals may be released into a population, or animals of a known age class may be used as the marked animals. Even different species may be used to establish ratios. Many modifications have been made to the Lincoln Index. Some include cumulative totals from several samplings while others establish several ratios.

Spotlight counts have been used extensively to sample both mule and white-tailed deer (Progulske and Duerre 1964). Fafarman (1978) found that spotlight counts in south Texas were more precise than other ground survey methods. Counts are made one to two hours after sunset, generally along a transect of at least 24 km, and transects are counted three or more times.

Pellet group counts can be used to estimate the population of game animals. The procedure was described earlier in this chapter.

Track surveys are also useful in counting game animals. Often the animals using a given water hole are counted by destroying tracks daily and counting tracks of animals that have watered. This technique is often useful for counting migrating animals moving in one direction across a roadway.

Pen Studies of Big Game

In research studies of big game involving food habits, nutrition, interspecific competition, parasitology, or other factors, it is sometimes necessary to confine the animals for closer experimental control than is possible under field conditions. Confinement may be in small pens (Smith 1953), paddocks (Grumbles 1964), or large enclosures approaching normal range conditions (McMahan and Ramsey 1965).

In general, fences necessary to confine big game animals must be stronger and higher than livestock fences. They must be free of holes underneath, around gates, and in corners. Such fences are expensive, averaging three to five times the cost of livestock fencing for confined animal studies.

Many research facilities for confined big game studies have been constructed in a standard square-corner design. Commonly, wings are provided to drive animals into an alley and from there into a cental working area where the animals can be treated and/or research data collected. Experience has shown that a high mortality rate exists among penned animals using the standard pen design, especially when wild-caught animals must be used. A newer design uses a round pen with a central, covered working area. Individual pens or paddocks radiate from the central working facility. The confined animals become accustomed to approaching the work area, and can be more easily handled while there. Death losses can be appreciably reduced by darkening the central working area or by handling the animals at night. Moreover, if brush and trees are left in a natural pattern in paddocks or larger pens, the animals are more content, less excitable, and have a higher survival rate.

Capturing Big Game Animals

For pen studies and other wildlife research, experimental animals of a particular species must be obtained in adequate numbers at the proper time. Animals lost by attrition also must be occasionally replaced. This requires a safe and reliable method for capturing these animals.

Where only a few animals are required, it may be possible to obtain tame or semi-tame animals that have been raised in captivity. Frequently, the offspring of captive research herds may be available. Some scientists may wish to obtain research animals by hand-raising captured young, especially if sufficient lead time is available before the project begins (Reichert 1972). If such animals are to be used for food habit or nutrition studies, their diets should be kept as natural as possible.

Where greater numbers of individuals are needed for larger experiments, a method of live-trapping wild animals is required. For a detailed discussion of trapping methods see Day et al. (1980). Bighorn sheep and elk have been baited into corrals and captured using a remotely closed gate. Considerable success has been obtained in catching deer in individual box-type traps baited with fresh alfalfa hay, apples, yellow corn, or other choice deer feeds. Drop-nets have proven successful or white-tailed deer in Texas (Ramsey 1968). Baiting animals for capture is most successful when natural food supplies are short.

Wild animals may be driven into corrals, tangle-nets, and even stock tanks for capture. Aircraft are frequently used to herd animals to the capture area, but vehicles and "beaters" also have been successful (Day et al. 1980). The deer farming industry in New Zealand has brought a series of innovative and efficient deer-capturing techniques to the researcher (Yerex 1979). Most of these techniques utilize the helicopter and are designed to capture the individual animal. They include the electric dart gun (animal is stunned by electrical charge), the shoulder-fired rocket net, and the helicopter-mounted, rocket-fired net. The disadvantages of these methods include their high cost and potential danger to the researcher.

Drug capture is another method of procuring individual animals alive. Since its first use on deer in the 1950's (Hall et al. 1953), the use of drugs has become an increasingly sophisticated method for capturing big game. Several different drug delivery systems are available, including both CO_2 and powder-fired rifles or pistols, blowguns or blowpipes, pole syringes or jab-sticks, and crossbows or longbows (Yoakum et al. 1980). Likewise, several different drugs are available for use on big game, including etorphine hydrochloride (M-99), succinylcholine chloride (Sucostrin or Anectine), ketamine hydrochloride (Vetalar), tiletamine hydrochloride and CI-716 (Tilazol), and xylazine hydrochloride (Rompun) (Yoakum et al. 1980). The use of drugs to capture animals is a complex procedure and should not be attempted without proper training and authorization.

Small Mammals

Small mammals are common inhabitants on western grazing lands. They feed on many plants which are valued for livestock forage. In some cases, range investigations can be invalidated by small mammal feeding pressure. In other instances, this factor is inconsequential. Evaluation of the qualitative and quantitative significance of small mammals requires considerable knowledge of their ecology, particularly the relations of various species to soil and vegetation.

Species Variability

The importance of rodents in range ecosystems varies with the species which are present. For example, where a range is occupied primarily by grasshopper mice, the effect is indirect and probably minor, because these animals live largely on insects (Bailey and Sperry 1929). At the other extreme, a colony of prairie dogs sometimes can cause such devastation to range vegetation as to vitiate completely any grazing treatment with domestic livestock (Taylor and Loftfield 1924). Most effects are somewhere in between (O'Meilia et al. 1982).

Life habits of individual species have a fundamental bearing on how rodents should be treated in investigative work. Small mammal populations are affected by vegetation condition. Certain rodents, because of their preference for plants in earlier stages of succession, are held at low population levels when ranges are in good or excellent condition. This relation seems to hold for the California ground squirrel (Fitch 1948) and the Merriam kangaroo rat (Reynolds 1950). Other species prefer and attain greater numbers in the latter stages of plant succession. This group includes species such as the pocket mice of southern Arizona (Reynolds and Haskell 1949).

The effect which rodents have on vegetation also varies with range condition. Moore and Reid (1951) found that, where mountain meadows of Oregon were in poor condition, populations of the Dalles pocket gopher were sufficient to prevent range recovery. Rabbits and rodents of the mesquite-snakeweed (*Prosopis-Gutierrezia*) type also have exerted sufficient grazing pressure to prevent improvement of severely grazed sites (Norris 1950).

The kind of plant material consumed varies with locality and season. Both blacktailed and whitetailed jackrabbits in eastern Colorado utilized primarily western wheatgrass *(Agropyron smithii)*, but the former preferred more shrubby and weedy habitats while the latter was found primarily on grassy uplands (Flinders and Hansen 1972). In northern Utah, winter feeding trials indicated equal utilization of winterfat *(Ceratoides lanata)* and saltsage *(Atriplex muttallii)* with little use of shadscale *(Atriplex confertifolia)* by jackrabbits. However, in spring winterfat was highly preferred, and shadscale utilization was double that of saltsage (Currie and Goodwin 1966). In the Mojave Desert, jackrabbits fed largely on grasses in the spring and early summer but on woody plants in late summer through winter (Hayden 1966).

The kind of plant material consumed in relation to range condition has a bearing on what effect a rodent species may have upon rangelands. The Merriam kangaroo rat stores large quantities of seed in the surface soil, much of which is never reclaimed. The spread and abundance of large-seeded perennial grasses is thus encouraged during favorable climatic periods (Reynolds 1950). However, on rangelands infested by mesquite (*Prosopis* spp.) the same rodent is an important agency for the dissemination of this undesirable shrub (Reynolds 1954).

The effect of rodents, particularly burrowing species, upon the soil cannot be ignored (Taylor 1935). Burrowing brings sublayers of soil to the surface and can improve water infiltration and retention; however, pocket gopher activity at high elevations sometimes leads to soil displacement and erosion (Ellison 1946). Pocket gophers evidently can benefit plant nitrogen levels through vertical soil movement (Coppock et al. 1983), but they have also been shown to decrease forage availability, basal cover of desirable range plants, and rate of succession (Foster and Stubbendieck 1980).

Diet Analysis

The proportion of different plant species consumed by small herbivores can be examined by microscopic examination of stomach contents. Samples of fresh stomach material are preserved in formalin, from which the microscope slides are prepared. The actual microhistological technique was first developed by Sparks and Malechek (1968), and has been described by Holechek et al. (1982) in their review of techniques for determining diets of range herbivores.

In addition to stomach contents, fecal material of small mammals has been analyzed using microhistological techniques. This has been shown to be appropriate for major items; however, minor diet constituents may not be detected (Neal et al. 1973), because of the fragility of some plants in the preparation process (Samuel and Howard 1983).

Isolating the Small Mammal Effect

Rabbits and rodents can seriously affect reseeding studies and other research on small plots. Introduced forage species, fertilization, irrigation, and other range improvement treatments all have the potential for making an area more attractive to both large and small mammals than surrounding rangeland. As a result, treatment areas receive greater utilization and disturbance than control plots, thereby confounding many results pertaining to community structure and production. Grant et al. (1977), for example, found that, when applying supplemental water and nitrogen to shortgrass prairie, the population density of the prairie vole increased dramatically within 3 years from less than 5 individuals per hectare to about 100. They primarily attributed the increase to greatly enhanced herbage, litter, and standing crop, which provided more protective cover.

Exclosures can be used for either eliminating or measuring the effect of rodents. The main drawback is fence cost. Exclusion of a combination of climbing and burrowing rodents such as ground squirrels and gophers requires a 1.2-m wire mesh fence equipped with a horizontal top metal flange from the outer edge of which is hung a metal strip. To discourage burrowing, fences may need to be buried to 0.75 m underground (Fitch and Bentley 1949).

Fences constructed to provide differential exclusion have been used effectively for separating the influence of rodents and domestic livestock on range vegetation (Taylor 1935). Norris (1950) employed nested plots for studying the separate effects of rodents, rabbits, and cattle on semidesert rangelands. Each exclosure occupied about 1 ha and was constructed to exclude separately (1) cattle; (2) cattle and rabbits; and (3) cattle, rabbits and small rodents.

Poisoning or trapping sometimes is used to eliminate rabbits and rodents from research areas. Success varies with area size and the home range of the rodent. Trapping is useful primarily for small areas and small populations, where the biological effect of the animals may be small with control. Baiting with toxicants can have a broader application; however, this approach faces regulatory restrictions, both by government and funding agencies. Turner et al. (1977) and Crouch (1979) have discussed chemical control of pocket gophers, both directly and through reducing their food supply.

Measuring the Small Mammal Effect

The influence of rodents on some range studies can be determined from a knowledge of food habits and populations. For example, the effect of jackrabbits has been estimated by establishing plots for repeated examination of individual plants (Currie and Goodwin 1966). Records of plant height and diameter, as well as twig counts, were maintained as an approach to estimating forage intake by jackrabbits.

French et al. (1976) used a modeling approach to integrate energy requirements of small mammal populations and primary production of grasslands. The populations generally utilized less than 10% of the available forage, but during dry years utilization increased to 20%.

Indirect methods can be used for estimating forage removal in different vegetation types. The average defecation rate of jackrabbits is 531 pellets per day (Arnold and Reynolds 1943). By counting pellet accumulations during given time periods and applying the feeding requirements of rabbits, the amount of herbage removed by rabbits can be estimated.

Fitch and Bentley (1949) employed the enclosure technique for determining the effect of three rodent species on annual grass range in California. Nearby constant populations of rodents were confined to enclosures and the amount of vegetation consumed was measured. With these data and with known populations of pocket gophers, ground squirrels, and kangaroo rats, the annual herbage consumption by these animals was estimated.

Effects of pocket gophers in shortgrass prairie have been evaluated in terms of surface area covered by gopher mounds and the implications for infiltration of rainfall and evapotranspiration of soil water (Grant et al. 1980). Plant production was higher near the mounds, although increased infiltration evidently was not the cause. Mounds produced by burrowing animals provide sites for establishment of plants that otherwise may not persist in the prairie (Platt and Wiess 1977).

Remote sensing techniques can be applied to evaluating the effect of small mammals on ecosystems under conditions where they form large colonies. This is especially true in the case of prairie dogs which can form "towns" covering thousands of hectares (Dalsted et al. 1981).

Census Methods

All methods of determining indirectly the effect of rodents in range research require a census technique for ascertaining numbers. Counts of animals per unit area have been used successfully, particularly for diurnal species. Rabbit numbers can be estimated by making counts along sampling strips or roadways (Kline 1965).

Workings can be used satisfactorily in censusing some species. Nests of woodrats and mounds of bannertail kangaroo rats are conspicuous and easily counted. Mounds of pocket gophers, ground squirrels, and pocket mice can easily be counted, but conversion factors between animal numbers and workings are necessary for an actual rather than a relative census. A count of rabbit pellets can also be converted to number of individuals per unit area (Taylor and Williams 1956).

Small mammals which cannot be readily observed must be trapped to estimate their numbers. Usefulness of trapping techniques vary according to characteristics of the populations. Data from open populations (i.e., those that change during the study because of mortality, migration, or recruitment of young) require different statistical treatments than those from closed populations.

Densities of closed populations can be estimated by trapping animals in lines or areas, and estimating the area from which they were removed. Another method (Peterson Method) involves the release of marked animals in an area, or marking a subsection of the population, and estimating the density from the proportion of marked animals in subsequent resamples. An extension of this technique (Schnabel Method) requires repeated sampling, with animals in each sample being classified according to whether and when they had been previously captured. Catch-effort methods base animal number estimations on the effort (i.e., time or number of traps) required to capture them. Another method is based on constant effort, with the population density resulting from a projection of the numbers taken from successive samples when constant effort is devoted to obtaining each sample. For information on these census methods and others, see Seber (1973), Caughley

(1977), Hawthorne (1980), and Davis (1982).

Assessment of Insect Herbivory

Despite their small size, insects often compete effectively with livestock on western rangelands. Grasshoppers alone are believed to consume 21 to 23% of available forage annually in many places in the western United States (Hewitt and Onsager 1983). Forage consumption by insects is poorly understood because of the diverse feeding habits of this complex assemblage of phytophages (Fig. 2-1) and the dearth of research directed towards livestock-insect-host plant relationships. Nevertheless, some progress recently has been made in the overall assessment of insect consumption (Burger and Teer 1981).

On many rangelands, grasshoppers are the most significant insect pests. The species responsible vary considerably (Hewitt 1977), depending on geographic location, community structure, and time. Food habits of many important grasshoppers have been provided by Capinera and Sechrist (1982a) and Hardman and Smoliak (1982). Other insects known to be detrimental to forage production include the Mormon cricket, range caterpillar, black grass bugs, and white grubs. Many insects commonly associated with rangeland, such as harvester ants, termites, cutworms, leafhoppers, and seed-infesting insects, may well have significant effects on forage availability, but information on their impact is scarce (Watts et al. 1982). Quantitative assessment of insect impact is dependent upon proper insect identification, knowledge of food habits, adequate insect sampling procedures, and forage loss estimates.

Insect Identification

Expertise in systematic entomology often is difficult for not only range management specialists, but also entomologists. Without accurate identifications it may not be possible to differentiate, for example, between damaging grass-feeding and beneficial weed-feeding grasshoppers. Information about the following insects should be useful to range researchers, although insect identification specialists also may need to be consulted: Grasshoppers in Arizona (Ball et al. 1972), California (Strohecker et al. 1968), Colorado (Capinera and Sechrist 1982a), Idaho (Hewitt and Barr 1967), Oklahoma (Coppock 1962), Wyoming (Pfadt 1965); North American subfamilies of Gomphocerinae and Acridinae (Otte 1981); beetles (Arnett 1963); ants (Cole 1968); flies (Cole 1969); bugs (Slater and Baranowski 1978); cactus-feeding arthropods (Mann 1969); grass-feeding insects (Thomas and Werner 1981).

Food Habits

Insect food habits are determined by direct observation (Pfadt 1949, Anderson and Wright 1952), choice tests (Mitchell 1975, Capinera 1978, Capinera et al. 1983), habitat association (Beavis et al. 1982, Rottman and Capinera 1983), and crop analysis (Mulkern et al. 1969, Pfadt and Lavigne 1982). Rangeland insect feeding habits vary from very narrow (monophagy, or feeding on a single plant genus only) to very broad (polyphagy, feeding on plants from two or more families), with oligophagy (feeding on more than one genera of plants within a single family) being very common. Plant abundance

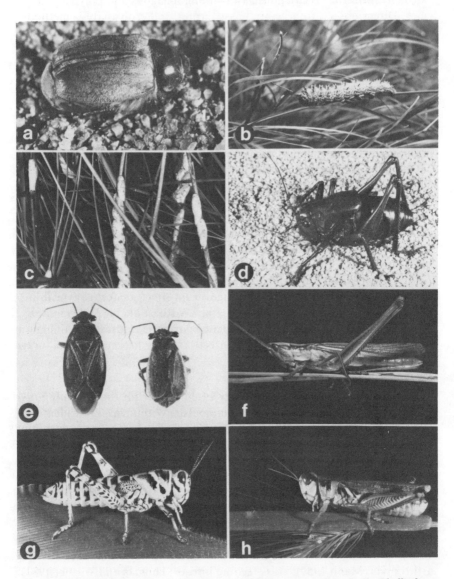

Fig. 2-1. Examples of rangeland insect pests: A, an adult white grub or June beetle, *Phyllophaga* sp.; B, range caterpillar larva, *Heileuca oliviae;* C, a grass-infesting scale insect, *Eriopeltus* sp.; D, Mormon cricket, *Anabrus simplex;* E, black grass bugs, *Irbisia brachycera* (left) and *Labops hesperius* (right; F, a grass-feeding grasshopper, *Mermiria bivittata;* G, a forb-feeding grasshopper, *Dactylotum bicolor;* H, a grass- and forb-feeding grasshopper, *Melanoplus sanguinipes.*

strongly influences feeding behavior of oligophagous and polyphagous species. Direct observation, habitat association, and crop analysis methods of food habitat determination will be influenced by host availability. In choice tests, host plant abundance can be carefully controlled. Environmental conditions (Lewis 1982) or forage availability (Mitchell 1975) may alter host preference. Gangwere (1961) presented a useful discussion of food preference by grasshoppers.

Sampling Procedures

A variety of insect sampling techniques have been used successfully on rangeland. The method utilized is determined by specific characteristics of the insect and habitat, precision desired, and time and monetary considerations. Southwood (1978) presented a comprehensive treatment of insect sampling methods, many of which are applicable to rangeland habitats.

Absolute methods commonly are used for grasshopper population estimates. For example, spring and autumn grasshopper surveys are conducted annually throughout the western United States. Population density is estimated by flushing grasshoppers from a series of plots; the margins of these plots are determined visually. Precision is improved by delineating margins of sample units, and a wand may be useful for flushing grasshoppers from dense foliage. Other absolute grasshopper sampling techniques include night cages, cage samplers, and net samplers. A vacuum is sometimes used in conjunction with the cages (Rottman and Capinera 1983). A comparison of several techniques is presented by Onsager (1977). Night cages or other sampling techniques which capture insects when they are inactive appear to be superior in terms of sampling precision, but visual flush estimates are more economical. The wandering quarter method is useful for estimating range caterpillar densities due to the gregarious and highly visible characteristics of larvae (Hansen et al. 1982). Absolute techniques, especially cage-vacuum techniques, are useful for a wide variety of rangeland insects.

The method most commonly used for estimating relative abundance of rangeland insects is the sweep net. It is an inexpensive method; however, capture efficiency varies in relation to vegetation and insect characteristics. While the sweep net sometimes is used for grasshopper sampling (Holmes et al. 1979), comparison of different vegetative types or levels should be avoided, as sweeping is less efficient in short vegetation. Also, grasshopper community structure varies, with plant community characteristics (Capinera and Sechrist 1982b), and some species (the banded-wing grasshoppers, in particular) are not sampled adequately by sweeping. The flush-capture technique (Capinera and Sechrist 1982b) gives a less biased estimate of grasshopper community composition.

Indices of insect abundance are sometimes used instead of direct insect sampling. Grasshopper feeding, for example, is correlated with abundance. Hewitt and Onsager (1980) placed potted barley seedlings on rangeland to estimate grasshopper abundance from levels of consumption. Assessment of grasshopper damage using remote sensing has been demonstrated in cropland, but would be more difficult in heterogeneous rangeland environments.

Indices also are used to assess populations of insects other than grasshoppers. Mormon crickets are exceedingly gregarious and tend to occur in highly visible bands which probably can be used as an index of cricket abundance. Similarly, harvester ant mound density is easily ascertained, while actual ant populations are difficult to determine (Rogers and Lavigne 1974). White grubs are most easily located by the irregular patches of dead grass sod resulting from their feeding activities (Wiener and Capinera 1980), and black grass bugs by stunted, discolored patches of grass, or speckled foliage (Todd and Kamm 1974).

Estimation of Forage Loss

Direct and indirect estimation of forage consumption by insects is possible. Direct methods utilize natural densities of insect herbivores (Todd and Kamm 1974), manipulations of density through insecticide application (Ansley and McKell 1982), or manipulations through caging of insects with known vegetation availability (Hewitt et al. 1976). Occasional problems with this approach are associated with insufficient data (i.e., not enough experimental insect densities to cover the wide range of naturally occurring densities), and use of improper statistical models depicting the relationship between insect abundance and forage loss. For example, forage reductions may be suggested at low pest densities, when, in fact, net production remains the same due to compensatory growth by the plant (Dyer and Dokhari 1976). Direct estimation of forage reduction may encompass measurement of plant biomass, quantity and quality of seed heads, plant height and phenology, litter production, and plant chemistry (protein and carbohydrate levels, digestibility, etc.).

Indirect estimation of forage reduction involves simulation of insect herbivory. In some studies, insect damage is simulated by mechanical clipping of above-ground or below-grund plant material (Detling et al. 1979, Painter and Detling 1981). Clipping studies do not simulate injury by insects with piercing-sucking mouthparts, and they may not accurately simulate injury by insects with chewing mouthparts (Capinera and Roltsch 1980). Also, most simulation studies use a single, instantaneous defoliation event, whereas actual insect defoliation may be protracted, or may consist of multiple events.

Modeling studies simulate insect consumption or densities, or both. Occasionally, plant growth and physical environment are also simulated. The principal insect-rangeland computer model studies involve range caterpillars (Bellows et al. 1983) and grasshoppers (Rodell 1977). Simulation models are gaining increasing acceptance for estimating insect impact, but further validation of their predictive abilities is necessary. Modeling often requires major assumptions (e.g., insect mortality rates) because of insufficient population biology research. Nonetheless, simulation modeling shows great potential for integrating the overall effects that arthropods have on rangeland ecosystems in order to test management-oriented hypotheses (Van Dyne 1978).

Literature Cited

Alexander, K.I., and K. Thompson. 1982. The effect of clipping frequency on the competitive interaction between two perennial grass species. Oecologia. 53:251-254.

Alldredge, A.W., J.F. Lipscomb, and F.W. Whicker. 1974. Forage intake rates of mule deer estimated with fallout cesium-137. J. Wildlife Manage. 38:508-516.

Allen, T.F.H., and T.B. Starr. 1982. Heirarchy, perspectives for ecological complexity. Univ. Chicago Press, Chicago, Illinois.

Ammann, A.P., R.L. Cowan, C.L. Mothershead, and B.R. Baumgardt. 1973. Dry matter and energy intake in relation to digestibility in white-tailed deer. J. Wildlife Manage. 37:195-201.

Anderson, N.L., and J.C. Wright. 1952. Grasshopper investigations on Montana range lands. Tech. Bull. 486. Montana Agr. Exp. Sta.

Ansley, R.J., and C.M. McKell. 1982. Crested wheatgrass vigor as affected by black grass bug and cattle grazing. J. Range Manage. 35:586-590.

Archer, S., and Detling, J.K. 1984. The effects of defoliation and competition on regrowth of tillers of two North American mixed-grass prairie graminoids. Oikos 43:351-357.

Arnett, R.H. 1963. The beetles of the United States. Catholic Univ. Press, Washington, D.C.

Arnold, J.F., and H.G. Reynolds. 1943. Droppings of the Arizona and antelope jackrabbits and the "pellet census". J. Wildlife Manage. 7:322-328.

Bailey, A.W., and M.L. Anderson. 1980. Fire temperatures in grass, shrub, and aspen forest communities of central Alberta. J. Range Manage. 33:37-40.

Bailey, O., and C.C. Sperry. 1929. Life history and habits of grasshopper mice, genus *Onychomys*. Tech. Bull. 145. USDA, Washington, D.C.

Bailey, R.G. 1976. Ecoregions of the United States (map). USDA Forest Service, Intermountain Region, Ogden, Utah.

Bailey, R.G., R.D. Pfister, and J.A. Henderson. 1978. Nature of land and resource classification—a review. J. Forest. 76:650-655.

Ball, E.D., E.R. Tinkham, R. Flock, and C.T. Vorhies. 1972. The grasshoppers and Orthoptera of Arizona. Tech. Bull. 93. Arizona Agr. Exp. Sta.

Beavis, W.E., J.C. Owens, J.A. Ludwig, and E.W. Huddleston. 1982. Grassland communities of east-central New Mexico and density of the range caterpillar, *Hemileuca oliviae* (Lepidoptera: Saturniidae). Southwestern Natur. 27:335-343.

Bellows, T.S., J.C. Owens, and E.W. Huddleston. 1983. Model for simulating consumption and economic injury level for the range caterpillar. J. Econ. Entomol. 76:1231-1238.

Bentley, S., and J.B. Whittaker. 1979. Effects of grazing by a chrysomelid beetle, *Gastrophysa viridula*, on competition between *Rumex obtusifolius* and *Rumex crispus*. J. Ecol. 67:79-90.

Blaisdell, J.P. 1958. Seasonal development and yield of native plants on the upper Snake River plains and their relation to certain climatic factors. Tech. Bull. 1190. USDA, Washington, D.C.

Bouyoucos, G.J., and A.H. Mick. 1940. An electrical method for the continuous measurement of soil moisture under field conditions. Tech. Bull. 173. Michigan Agr. Exp. Sta.

Branson, F.A., G.F. Gifford, K.G. Renard, and R.F. Hadley. 1981. Rangeland hydrology. 2nd ed. Kendall/Hunt Publ. Co., Dubuque, Iowa.

Brown, R.W., and B.P. Van Haveren (ed.). 1972. Psychrometry in water relations research. Proc., Symposium on thermocouple psychrometers. Utah Agr. Exp. Sta.

Burger, G.V., and J.G. Teer. 1981. Economic and socioeconomic issues influencing wildlife management on private land, p. 252-273. *In:* R.T. Dumke, G.V. Burger, and J.R. March (ed), Wildlife management on private lands. Wisconsin Chapter, The Wildlife Soc. Dep. Natur. Resources, Madison, Wisconsin.

Capinera, J.L. 1978. Studies of host plant preference and suitability exhibited by early-instar range caterpillar larvae. Environ. Entomol. 7:738-740.

Capinera, J.L., and W.J. Roltsch. 1980. Response of wheat seedlings to actual and simulated migratory grasshopper defoliation. J. Econ. Entomol. 73:258-261.

Capinera, J.L., and T.S. Sechrist. 1982a. Grasshoppers of Colorado: identification, biology, and management. Bull. 584S. Colorado Agr. Exp. Sta.

Capinera, J.L., and T.S. Sechrist. 1982b. Grasshoppers (Acrididae)-host plant associations: response of grasshopper populations to cattle grazing intensity. Can. Entomol. 114:1055-1062.

Capinera, J.L., A.R. Renaud, and N.E. Roehrig. 1983. Chemical basis for host selection by *Hemileuca oliviae:* role of tannins in preference of C_4 grasses. J. Chem. Ecol. 9:1425-1437.

Caughley, G. 1974. Bias in aerial survey. J. Wildlife Manage. 38:921-933.

Caughley, G. 1977. Analysis of vertibrate populations. John Wiley & Sons, New York, New York.

Chamrad, A.D., and T.W. Box. 1964. A point frame for sampling rumen contents. J. Wildlife Manage. 28:473-477.

Chang, J. 1968. Climate and agriculture, an ecological survey. Aldine Publ. Co., Chicago, Illinois.

Cole, A.C. 1968. *Pogonomyrmex* harvester ants. Univ. Tennessee Press, Knoxville, Tennessee.

Cole, F.R. 1969. The flies of western North America. Univ. California Press, Berkeley, California.

Coppock, D.L., J.K. Detling, J.E. Ellis, and M.I. Dyer. 1983. Plant-herbivore interactions in a North American mixed-grass prairie. I. Effects of black-tailed prairie dogs on intraseasonal aboveground plant biomass and nutrient dynamics and plant species diversity. Oecologia. 56:1-9.

Coppock, S. 1962. The grasshoppers of Oklahoma (Orthoptera: Acrididae). Proc. Ser. P-339. Oklahoma Agr. Exp. Sta.

Crouch, G.L. 1979. Atrazine improves survival and growth of ponderosa pine threatened by vegetative competition and pocket gophers. Forest Sci. 25:99-111.

Currie, P.O., and D.L. Goodwin. 1966. Consumption of forage by black-tailed jackrabbits on salt-desert ranges of Utah. J. Wildlife Manage. 30:304-311.

Currie, P.O., D.W. Reichert, J.C. Malechek, and O.C. Walmo. 1977. Forage selection comparisons for mule deer and cattle under managed ponderosa pine. J. Range Manage. 30:352-356.

Dalsted, K.J., S. Sather-Blair, B.K. Worcester, and R. Klukas. 1981. Application of remote sensing to prairie dog management. J. Range Manage. 34:218-223.

Daubenmire, R.F. 1968. Plant communities, a textbook of plant synecology. Harper and Row, New York, New York.

Daubenmire, R.F. 1974. Plants and environment, a textbook of autecology. 3rd ed. John Wiley & Sons, New York, New York.

Daubenmire, R.F., and J.B. Daubenmire. 1968. Forest vegetation of eastern Washington and northern Idaho. Tech. Bull. 60. Washington Agr. Exp. Sta.

Davis, D.E. 1982. CRC handbook of census methods for terrestrial vertibrates. CRC Press, Inc., Boca Raton, Florida.

Davis, D.E., and R.L. Winstead. 1980. Estimating the numbers of wildlife populations, p. 221-245. *In:* S.D. Schemnitz (ed), Wildlife management techniques manual. 4th ed. Wildlife Soc., Washington, D.C.

Day, G.I., S.D. Schemnitz, and R.D. Taber. 1980. Capturing and marking wild animals, p. 61-88. *In:* S.D. Schemnitz (ed), Wildlife management techniques manual. 4th ed. Wildlife Soc., Washington, D.C.

Detling, J.K., M.I. Dyer, and D.T. Winn. 1979. Net photosynthesis, root respiration, and regrowth of *Bouteloua gracilis* following simulated grazing. Oecologia. 41:127-134.

Dyer, M.I., and U.G. Bokhari. 1976. Plant animal interactions: studies of the effects of grasshopper grazing on blue grama grass. Ecology. 57:762-772.

Dyksterhuis, E.J. 1949. Condition and management of rangeland based on quantitative ecology. J. Range Manage. 2:104-115.

Ellison, L. 1946. The pocket gopher in relation to soil erosion on mountain ranges. Ecology. 27:101-114.

Fafarman, K.R. 1978. Spotlight counts of white-tailed deer on the Welder Wildlife Refuge, Texas. M.S. Thesis. Texas A&I Univ., Kingsville, Texas.

Fitch, H.S. 1948. Ecology of the California ground squirrel on grazing lands. Amer. Midland Natur. 39:513-597.

Fitch, H.S., and J.R. Bentley. 1949. Use of California annual plant forage by range rodents. Ecology. 30:306-321.

Flinders, J.R., and R.M. Hansen. 1972. Diets and habitats of jackrabbits in northeastern Colorado. Range Sci. Dep. Sci. Series No. 12. Colorado State Univ., Fort Collins.

Ford, E.D., and R. Milne. 1980. Assessing plant response to the weather, p. 333-362. *In:* J. Grace, E.D. Ford, and P.G. Jarvis (ed), Plants and their atmospheric environment. The 21st Symp. of British Ecol. Soc., Edinburgh, England. Blackwell Sci. Publ., Oxford, England.

Foster, M.A., and J. Stubbendieck. 1980. Effect of the plains pocket gopher *(Geomys busarius)* on rangeland. J. Range Manage. 33:74-78.

Frank, A.B. 1983. Plant-water relationships of crested, pubescent, slender, and western wheatgrasses, p. 399-401. *In:* J.A. Smith and V.W. Hays (ed), Proc. XIV International Grassland Congress, Lexington, Kentucky. Westview Press, Boulder, Colo.

French, C.E., L.C. McEwen, N.D. Magruder, R.H. Ingram, and R.W. Swift. 1956. Nutrient requirements for growth and antler development in the white-tailed deer. J. Wildlife. Manage. 20:221-232.

French, N.R., W.E. Grant, W. Grodzinski, and D.M. Swift. 1976. Small mammal energetics in grassland ecosystems. Ecol. Monogr. 46:201-220.

Fritschen, L.J., and L.W. Gay. 1979. Environmental instrumentation. Springer-Verlag, New York, New York.

Gangwere, S.K. 1961. A monograph on food selection in Orthoptera. Trans. Amer. Entomol. Soc. 87:67-230.

Gardner, R.A., and J.L. Retzer. 1949. Interpretive soil classification: timber, range, and watersheds. Soil Sci. 67:151-157.

Gardner, W., and D. Kirkham. 1952. Determination of soil moisture by neutron scattering. Soil Sci. 73:391-401.

Geiger, R. 1965. The climate near the ground. Trans. by Scripta Technical, Inc. from the 4th German edition. Harvard Univ. Press, Cambridge, Massachusetts.

Grant, W.E., N.R. French, and D.M. Swift. 1977. Response of a small mammal community to water and nitrogen treatments in a shortgrass prairie ecosystem. J. Mammal. 58:637-652.

Grant, W.E., N.R. French, and L.J. Folse, Jr. 1980. Effects of pocket gopher mounds on plant succession in shortgrass prairie ecosystems. Southwest. Natur. 25:215-224.

Grumbles, J.B. 1964. A technique for evaluating the grazing relationships between steers and white-tailed deer in the Coastal Bend area of Texas. Ph.D. Dissertation. Texas A&M Univ., College Station, Texas.

Hall, T.C., E.B. Taft, W.H. Baker, and J.C. Aub. 1953. A preliminary report on the use of flaxedil to produce paralysis in the white-tailed deer. J. Wildlife Manage. 17:516-520.

Hamilton, J.W., and O.A. Beath. 1963. Uptake of available selenium by certain range plants. J. Range Manage. 16:261-265.

Hansen, J.D., J.C. Owens, and E.W. Huddleston. 1982. Life tables of the range caterpillar, *Hemileuca oliviae* (Lepidoptera:Saturniidae). Environ. Entomol. 11:355-360.

Hardman, J.M., and S. Smoliak. 1982. The relative impact of various grasshopper species on *Stipa-Agropyron* mixed prairie and fescue prairie on southern Alberta. J. Range Manage. 35:161-176.

Harris, G.A., and A.M. Wilson. 1970. Competition for moisture among seedlings of annual and perennial grasses as influenced by root elongation at low temperatures. Ecology. 51:531-534.

Hawthorne, D.W. 1980. Wildlife damage and control techniques, p. 411-439. In: S.D. Schemnitz (ed), Wildlife management techniques manual. 4th ed. Wildlife Soc., Washington, D.C.

Hayden, P. 1966. Food habits of black-tailed jackrabbits in southern Nevada. J. Mammal. 47:42-46.

Hewitt, G.B. 1977. Review of forage losses caused by rangeland grasshoppers. Misc. Pub. 1348. USDA, Washington, D.C.

Hewitt, G.B., and W.F. Barr. 1967. The banded-wing grasshoppers of Idaho (Orthoptera:Oedipodinae). Bull. 72. Univ. Idaho Agr. Exp. Sta.

Hewitt, G.B., and J.A. Onsager. 1980. A comparison of two methods of estimating forage destruction by grasshoppers. J. Econ. Entomol. 73:657-659.

Hewitt, G.B., and J.A. Onsager. 1983. Control of grasshoppers on rangelands in the United States-a perspective. J. Range Manage. 36:202-207.

Hewitt, G.B., W.H. Burleson, and J.A. Onsager. 1976. Forage losses caused by the grasshopper *Aulocara elliotti* on shortgrass rangeland. J. Range Manage. 29:376-380.

Hironaka, M., M.A. Fosberg, and A.H. Winward. 1983. Sagebrush-grass habitat types of southern Idaho. Bull. 35. Idaho Forest, Wildlife, and Range Exp. Sta.

Holechek, J.L., M. Vavra, and R.D. Pieper. 1982. Botanical composition determination of range herbivore diets: a review. J. Range Manage. 35:309-315.

Holmes, N.D., D.S. Smith, and A. Johnston. 1979. Effect of grazing by cattle on the abundance of grasshoppers on fescue grassland. J. Range Manage. 32:310-311.

Hutchings, M.J., and C.S.J. Budd. 1981. Plant competition and its course through time. Bioscience. 31:640-645.

Jenny, H. 1941. Factors of soil formation. McGraw-Hill Book Co., New York, New York.

Jolly, G.M. 1965. Explicit estimates from capture-recapture data with both death and immigration-stochastic model. Biometrika. 52:225-247.

Kahurananga, J. 1981. Population estimates, densities, and biomass of large herbivores in Simanjiro Plains, northern Tanzania. Afr. J. Ecol. 19:225-238.

Kline, P.D. 1965. Factors influencing roadside counts of cottontails. J. Wildlife Manage. 29:665-671.

Korschgen, L.J. 1980. Procedures for food habits analysis. p. 113-127. S.D. Schemnitz (ed), Wildlife management techniques manual. 4th ed. Wildlife Soc., Washington, D.C.

Krueger, W.C. 1972. Evaluating animal forage preference. J. Range Manage. 25:471-475.

Kubota, J. 1977. Molybdenum status of United States soils and plants, p. 555-581. *In:* W.R. Chappell and K.K. Petterson (ed), Molybdenum in the environment. Vol. 2. Marcel Dekke, Inc., New York, New York.

Kufeld, R.C., J.H. Olterman, D.C. Bowden. 1980. A helicopter quadrat census for mule deer on Uncompahgre Plateau, Colorado. J. Wildlife Manage. 44:632-639.

Leuthold, W., and B.M. Leuthold. 1976. Density and biomass of ungulates in Tsavo East National Park, Kenya. E. Afr. Wildlife J. 14:49-58.

Lewis, A.C. 1982. Leaf wilting alters a plant species ranking by the grasshopper *Melanoplus differentialis.* Ecol. Entomol. 7:391-395.

Lewis, J.K. 1969. Range management viewed in the ecosystem framework. p. 97-187. *In:* G.M. Van Dyne (ed), The ecosystem concept in natural resource management. Academic Press, New York, New York.

Lyles, L. 1983. Erosive wind energy distributions and climatic factors for the West. J. Soil & Water Conserv. 38:106-109.

Mann, J. 1969. Cactus-feeding insects and mites. Bull. 256. U.S. Natu. Mus., Washington, D.C.

McCollum, J.M. 1972. Botanical composition of the diet of whitetailed deer. M.S. Thesis. Texas A&M Univ., College Station.

McMahan, C.A., and C.W. Ramsey. 1965. Response of deer and livestock to controlled grazing in Texas. J. Range Manage. 18:1-7.

Medin, D.E. 1970. Stomach content analyses: collections from wild herbivores and birds, p. 133-145. *In:* H.A. Paulsen, E.H. Reid and K.W. Parker (ed), Range and wildlife habitat evaluation—a research symposium. Misc. Pub. No. 1147. Forest Service, USDA, Washington, D.C.

Miles, J. 1979. Vegetation dynamics. Chapman and Hall, Ltd., London, England.

Mitchell, J.E. 1975. Variation in food preferences of three grasshopper species (Acrididae: Orthoptera) as a function of food availability. Amer. Midland Natur. 94:267-283.

Moore, A.W., and E.H. Reid. 1951. The Dalles pocket gopher and its influence on forage production of Oregon mountain meadows. Cir. 884. USDA, Washington, D.C.

Moore, R.T., and M.M. Caldwell. 1972. The field use of thermocouple psychrometers in desert soils, p. 165-169. *In:* R.W. Brown and B.P. Van Haveren (ed), Psychrometry in water relations research. Proc., Symposium on thermocouple psychrometers, Utah Agr. Exp. Sta.

Morrison, B.L. 1984. Utilization of aerial survey data to set pronghorn harvest quotas in New Mexico. Proc. Symp. Game Harvest Management, Caesar Kelberg Wild. Res. Inst., Texas A&I Univ., Kingsville, Texas.

Mulkern, G.B., K.P. Pruess, H. Knutson, A.F. Hagen, J.B. Campbell, and J.D. Lambley. 1969. Food habits and preferences of grassland grasshoppers of the north central Great Plains. Bull. 481. North Dakota Agr. Exp. Sta.

Neal, B.R., D.A. Pulkinen, and B.D. Owen. 1973. A comparison of fecal and stomach content analysis in the meadow vole *(Microtus pennsylvanicus).* Can. J. Zool. 51:715-721.

Newbery, D. McC., and E.I. Newman. 1978. Competition between grassland plants of different initial sizes. Oecologia. 33:361-380.

Norris, J.J. 1950. Effect of rodents, rabbits, and cattle on two vegetation types in semi-desert rangeland. Bull. 353. New Mexico Agr. Exp. Sta.

Oke, T.R. 1978. Boundary layer climates. Methuen & Co., Ltd., London, England.

O'Meilia, M.E., F.L. Knopf, and J.C. Lewis. 1982. Some consequences of competition between prairie dogs and beef cattle. J. Range Manage. 35:580-585.

Onsager, J.A. 1977. Comparison of five methods for estimating density of rangeland grasshoppers. J. Econ. Entomol. 70:187-190.

Otte, D. 1981. The North American grasshoppers. Vol. 1. Gomphocerinae and Acridinae. Harvard Univ. Press, Cambridge, Massachusetts.

Painter, E.L., and J.K. Detling. 1981. Effects of defoliation on net photosynthesis and regrowth of western wheatgrass. J. Range Manage. 34:68-71.

Parr, J.F., and A.R. Bertrand. 1960. Water infiltration into soils. Adv. Agron. 12:311-363.

Parton, W.J., W.K. Lauenroth, and F.M. Smith. 1981. Water loss from a shortgrass steppe. Agr. Meteorol. 24:97-109.

Paterson, J.G., N.A. Goodchild, and W.J.R. Boyd. 1978. Classifying environments for sampling purposes using a principal component analysis of climatic data. Agr. Meteorol. 19:349-362.

Pfadt, R.E. 1949. Range grasshoppers as an economic factor in the production of livestock. Wyoming Range Manage. 7. Wyoming Agr. Exp. Sta.

Pfadt, R.E. 1965. Key to the Wyoming grasshoppers; Acrididae and Tetrigidae. Circ. 210. Wyoming Agr. Exp. Sta. Mimeo.

Pfadt, R.E., and R.J. Lavigne. 1982. Food habits of grasshoppers inhabiting the Pawnee site. Sci. Monogr. 42. Wyoming Agr. Exp. Sta.

Platt, R.B., and J.F. Griffiths. 1964. Environmental measurement and interpretation. Reinhold Publ. Co., New York, New York.

Platt, W.J., and I.M. Weiss. 1977. Resource partitioning and competition within a guild of fugitive prairie plants. Amer. Natur. 111:479-513.

Progulske, D.R., and D.C. Duerre. 1964. Factors influencing spotlighting counts of deer. J. Wildlife Manage. 28:27-34.

Ramsey, C.W. 1968. A drop-net deer trap. J. Wildlife Manage. 32:187-190.

Rasmussen, D.I., and E.R. Doman. 1943. Census methods and their application in the management of mule deer. Trans. North Amer. Wildlife. Conf. 8:367-379.

Rauzi, F.C., C.L. Fly, and E.J. Dyksterhuis. 1968. Water intake on midcontinental rangelands as influenced by soil and plant cover. Tech Bull. 1390. USDA, Washington, D.C.

Rawlins, S.L. 1976. Measurement of soil water content and the state of water in soils, p. 1-55. *In:* T.T. Kozlowski (ed), Water deficits and plant growth. Vol. IV. Acad. Press, New York, New York.

Reichert, D.W. 1972. Rearing and training deer for food habits studies. Res. Note RM-208. USDA Forest Service, Fort Collins, Colorado.

Reynolds, H.G. 1950. Relation of Merriam kangaroo rats to range vegetation in southern Arizona. Ecology. 31:456-463.

Reynolds, H.G. 1954. Some interrelations of the Merriam kangaroo rat to velvet mesquite. J. Range Manage. 7:176-180.

Reynolds, H.G., and H.S. Haskell. 1949. Life history notes on Price and Bailey pocket mice of southern Arizona. J. Mammal. 30:150-156.

Risser, P.G. 1969. Competitive relationships among herbaceous grassland plants. Bot. Rev. 35:251-284.

Rodell, C.F. 1977. A grasshopper model for a grassland ecosystem. Ecology. 58:227-245.

Rogers, L.E., and R.J. Lavigne. 1974. Environmental effects of western harvester ants on the shortgrass prairie ecosystem. Environ. Entomol. 3:994-997.

Rottman, R.J., and J.L. Capinera. 1983. Effects of insect and cattle-induced perturbations on a shortgrass prairie arthropod community. J. Kansas Entomol. Soc. 56:241-252.

Samuel, M.J., and G.S. Howard. 1983. Disappearing forbs in microhistological analysis of diets. J. Range Manage. 36:132-133.

Schemnitz, S.D. (ed.). 1980. Wildlife management techniques manual. 4th ed. Wildlife Soc., Washington, D.C.

Schoener, T.W. 1982. The controversy over interspecific competition. Amer. Sci. 70:586-595.

Seber, G.A. 1973. The estimation of animal abundance. Hafner Press, New York, New York.

Sharp, A.L., J.J. Bond, J.W. Neuberger, A.R. Kuhlman, and J.K. Lewis. 1964. Runoff as affected by intensity of grazing on rangeland. J. Soil and Water Conserv. 19:103-106.

Shiflet, T.N. 1973. Range sites and soils in the United States, p. 26-33. *In:* D.N. Hyder (ed), Arid shrublands, proceedings of the third workshop of the United States/Australia rangelands panel. Soc. Range Manage., Denver, Colorado.

Slater, J.A., and R.M. Baranowski. 1978. How to know the true bugs (Hemiptera-Heteroptera). Wm. C. Brown, Dubuque, Iowa.

Smith, A.D. 1953. Consumption of native forage species by captive mule deer during summer. J. Range Manage. 6:30-37.

Smith, A.D., and R.L. Hubbard. 1954. Preference ratings for winter deer forage from northern Utah ranges based on browsing time and forage consumed. J. Range Manage. 7:262-265.

Soil Survey Staff. 1975. Soil taxonomy, a basic system of soil classification for making and interpreting soil surveys. Agr. Handbook No. 436. SCS, USDA, Washington, D.C.

Sosebee, R.E. (ed). 1977. Rangeland plant physiology. Range Science Ser. No. 4. Soc. Range Manage., Denver, Colorado.

Southwood, T.R.E. 1978. Ecological Methods. 2nd ed. Chapman and Hall, London, England.

Spanner, D.C. 1951. The Peltier effect and its use in the measurement of suction pressure. J. Exp. Bot. 2:145-168.

Sparks, D.R., and J.C. Malechek. 1968. Estimating percentage dry weight in diets using a microscopic technique. J. Range Manage. 21:264-265.

Stinson, K.J., and H.A. Wright. 1969. Temperatures of headfires in the southern mixed prairie of Texas. J. Range Manage. 22:169-174.

Strohecker, H.F., W.W. Middlekauff, and D.C. Rentz. 1968. The grasshoppers of California (Orthoptera: Acrididae). Bull. California Insect Surv. 10:1-177.

Taylor, R.H., and R.M. Williams. 1956. The use of pellet counts for estimating the density of populations of the wild rabbit, *Oryctolagus cuniculus* (L.). New Zea. J. Sci. and Technol. 38B:236-256.

Taylor, W.P. 1935. Some animal relations to soils. Ecology. 16:126-136.

Taylor, W.P., and J.V.G. Loftfield. 1924. Damage to range grasses by the Zuni prairie dog. Bull. 1227. USDA, Washington, D.C.

Teer, J.G., D.L. Drawe, and R.F. Urubeck. 1984. Sampling patterns and intensities for helicopter censuses of white-tailed deer. Proc., Symp. Game Harvest Manage., Caesar Kleberg Wild. Res. Inst., Texas A&I Univ., Kingsville, Texas.

Thomas, D.B., and F.G. Werner. 1981. Grass feeding insects of the western ranges: an annotated checklist. Tech Bull. 243. Arizona Agr. Exp. Sta.

Thornthwaite, C.W. 1941. Climate and settlement in the Great Plains, p. 177-187. *In:* Climate and man. Yearbook Agr. USDA, Washington, D.C.

Todd, J.G., and J.A. Kamm. 1974. Biology and impact of a grass bug *Labops hesperius* Uhler in Oregon rangeland. J. Range Manage. 27:453-458.

Turner, G.T., R.M. Hansen, E.H. Reid, H.P. Tietjen, and A.L. Ward. 1977. Pocket gophers and Colorado mountain rangeland. Bull. 554S. Colorado Agr. Exp. Sta.

Unwin, D.M. 1980. Microclimate measurement for ecologists. Academic Press, New York, New York.

Uresk, D.W., P.L. Sims, and D.A. Jameson. 1975. Dynamics of blue grama within a shortgrass ecosystem. J. Range Manage. 28:205-208.

USDA Soil Conservation Service. 1983. National soils handbook. USDA, SCS, Washington, D.C.

U.S. Salinity Laboratory. 1954. Diagnosis and improvement of saline and alkali soils. Handbook No. 60. USDA, Washington, D.C.

Van Dyne, G.M. 1978. Testing management-oriented hypotheses with simulation models. Ohio J. Sci. 78:190-203.

Van Dyne, G.M., and D.F. Torell. 1964. Development and use of esophageal fistula: a review. J. Range Manage. 17:7-19.

Wallmo, O.C., and D.J. Neff. 1970. Direct observations of tamed deer to measure their consumption of natural forage, p. 105-110. *In:* H.A. Paulson, E.H. Reid and K.W. Parker (ed), Range and wildlife habitat evaluation-a research symposium. Misc. Pub. No. 1147. USDA, Washington, D.C.

Watts, J.G., E.W. Huddleston, and J.G. Owens. 1982. Rangeland entomology. Ann. Rev. Entomol. 27:283-311.

Weaver, J.E., and F.E. Clements. 1929. Plant ecology. McGraw-Hill Book Co., New York, New York.

West, N.E. 1982. Approaches to synecological characterization of wildlands in the Intermountain West. p. 663-642. *In:* T.B. Thomas, L.O. House IV, and H.G. Lund (ed), In-place resource inventories: principles and practices. Soc. Amer. Forest., Washington, D.C.

Wheaton, C., and R.D. Brown. 1983. Feed intake and digestive efficiency of south Texas white-tailed deer. J. Wildlife Manage. 47:442-450.

Wiener, L.F., and J.L. Capinera. 1980. Preliminary study of the biology of the whitegrub *Phyllophaga fimbripes* (Le Conte) (Coleoptera: Scarabaeidae). J. Kansas Entomol. Soc. 53:701-710.

Wishmeir, W.H., and D.D. Smith. 1978. Predicting rainfall erosion losses-a guide to conservation planning. Handbook No. 537., USDA, Washington, D.C.

Woodruff, N.P., and F.H. Siddoway. 1965. A wind erosion equation. Soil Sci. Soc. Amer. Proc. 29:602-608.

Wright, H.A., and A.W. Bailey. 1982. Fire ecology-United States and southern Canada. John Wiley & Sons, New York, New York.

Yerex, D. 1979. Deer farming in New Zealand. Deer Farming Service, Div. Agr. Promotion Associates, Box 11-137, Wellington, New Zealand.

Yoakum, J., W.P. Dasmann, H.R. Sanderson, C.M. Nixon, and H.S. Crawford. 1980. Habitat improvement techniques, p. 329-403. *In:* S.D. Schemnitz (ed), Wildlife management techniques manual. 4th ed. Wildlife Soc., Washington, D.C.

Young, S. 1955. Big game exclosures in wildlife in Utah. Proc., Utah Acad. Sci. 32:65-69.

Chapter 3
Methods of Studying Vegetation

Introduction

Increased emphasis has been placed on quantitative evaluations in natural resource fields and ecology during the past 30 years. In some cases, new techniques have been developed, and in others, old techniques have been modified. However, much additional work is needed to develop measurement techniques with both high accuracy and precision.

The principal attributes of vegetation which can be measured or estimated are: (1) weight, (2) area (cover), (3) volume, (4) number (including frequency), (5) diversity (an attribute of species composition), (6) vigor, and (7) quality. Sometimes another dimension, plant height, is also measured and is a part of calculating volume.

Vegetational quality refers to nutritional adequacy for herbivores. Of interest to range workers may be (1) nutrient content, (2) digestibility, and (3) palatability and preference.

Weight

Weight of herbage or biomass is one of the most important characteristics of range vegetation and may be the best single measure of growth. Since moisture content varies among plants, weight is usually expressed as oven-dry (60–70 C) although sometimes air-dry or even green-weight is used.

Definitions

Confusion exists concerning terms used in conjunction with plant weight. With the rise of interest in production ecology and ecosystem analysis, the terms "biomass" and "standing crop" have been used nearly interchangeably. Odum (1959) defined biomass as "living weight, including stored food", while Billings (1964) defined it as "the total dry weight of organisms per unit area in an ecosystem." The Society for Range Management gives nearly identical definitions for the two terms (Range Term Glossary Committee 1974).

The terms herbage, forage, and browse, which are often used in the range literature, are not so clearcut. Herbage is "total aerial parts of herbs, individually and collectively" (Duvall and Blair 1962) or "herbs taken collectively" (Range Term Glossary Committee 1974). Forage is often used mistakenly for herbage, and definitions differ considerably. The following definitions have been given for forage:

"Unharvested plant material of any kind available for animal consumption" (Soc. Amer. Forest. 1950).

"All harvested and unharvested vegetation except mast and fruits of woody plants and harvested grains, that is available and acceptable to livestock or game animals" (Duvall and Blair 1962).

"That portion of the vegetation actually grazed by the animal or fed to the animal" (Van Dyne 1969).

Availability and acceptability should be included in the definition of forage. Forage should always be less than herbage.

Browse generally refers to parts of woody plants acceptable to animals (Dayton 1950, Duvall and Blair 1962, Range Term Glossary Committee 1974). With a few exceptions, availability is generally not considered even though shrubs and trees often grow out of the reach of animals (Rutherford 1979). Browse can be an overall inclusive list of woody plant species that are consumed by animals.

Quadrat Size and Shape

Since herbage weight is often determined from quadrats either by estimates or direct clipping, one is immediately faced with the choice of quadrat size and shape. Often a quadrat of standard size has been selected for ease of conversion to yield (Nat. Acad. Sci. 1962). Weight is multiplied by a given factor to obtain kg/ha or lb/A.

Perimeter-area ratios are of concern in selecting quadrat size and shape because of the borderline decisions which have to be made (Van Dyne et al. 1963, Pieper 1978, Risser 1984). A positive bias is likely to be associated with large perimeter-area ratios (Wiegert 1962, Van Dyne et al. 1963). Perimeter-area ratios decrease as quadrat size increases (Pieper 1978). Circles have smaller perimeter-area ratios than squares, which in turn, have smaller perimeter-area ratios than rectangles. Thus, based only on perimeter-area ratios, large circular plots would be most appropriate.

However, sampling and time efficiency must also be considered in determining quadrat size and shape. Rectangular quadrats may be useful in providing data with low variance (Oosting 1956, Soplin et al. 1975, Risser 1984). Studies on salt desert shrub vegetation (Wight 1967) and desert grassland vegetation (Pino 1954) showed that rectangular quadrats provided data with lowest variances. However, Papanastasis (1977) found that quadrat size was generally more critical than shape in lowering variances for bunchgrass vegetation in Greece. He recommended small quadrats when both time and statistical efficiency were considered. Since variance among quadrats is reduced as quadrat size increases, one must balance the increased precision in using large quadrats (Wiegert 1962) with larger sample size for smaller quadrats, given equal sampling time. In addition, using many small quadrats allows one to have better distribution of sampling units over the experimental area than with fewer larger quadrats.

Vegetational characteristics should also be considered when selecting quadrat size and shape. Plant pattern and density are two characteristics of prime importance (Pieper 1978, Risser 1984). For sparse vegetation with plants occurring in clumps, a rectangular quadrat may be most appropriate. If the plants have a more regular or random distribution, then quadrat size may be more important than shape.

Techniques to Determine Yield
Clipping
Clipping is probably the most common method for determining herbage

weight for research projects (Milner and Hughes 1968). Although the method is time consuming, it yields a direct and objective measure of herbage weight. Consistency is needed in terms of clipping heights and separation into live and dead components (Culley et al. 1933).

Hand clippers are often used and are especially useful if clipping is to be done by individual species. However, some difficulty may be encountered with coarse plants. Several types of powered shears have been described (Alder and Richard 1962), as well as those equipped with vacuum collectors (Becker 1959, Matches 1963, Van Dyne 1966). Others have used rotary lawn mowers (McGinnies 1959) and flail-type harvesters (Stubbendieck and Fenster 1981).

Often corrections have to be made to adjust for litter and soil particles in samples collected mechanically (Van Dyne 1966). Other problems using mechanical equipment to determine herbage weight include separating individual species and separating current growth from old, dead material. To analyze species from such samples, it may be necessary to use a point method similar to that described by Heady and Van Dyne (1965) or the dry-weight rank method (T'Mannetje and Haydock 1963).

Estimation and Double Sampling

Pechanec and Pickford (1937) described the weight estimate method to determine herbage weight using quadrats. They recommended extensive training with actual clipping to adjust estimates to improve accuracy. The authors suggested mentally establishing 10-, 20-, 50-, or 100-g units of vegetation, and the number of these units in each quadrat are added together. The method is fast, reasonably accurate, largely non-destructive, and results are easily checked by clipping (Goebel 1955, Shoop and McIlvain 1963). Disadvantages include the need to develop estimation skills, a high degree of concentration needed by the estimator, lack of accuracy with rank vegetation, and variation among observers, (Shoop and McIlvain 1963). These authors also stated that variances for estimates were lower than those for clipped quadrats. Estimators tend to underestimate quadrats with high herbage weights and overestimate those with low herbage weights.

Many papers have dealt with double sampling procedures to adjust herbage weight estimates (Wilm et al. 1944, Hilmon 1959 Tadmor et al. 1975, Cook and Bonham 1977, Ahmed and Bonham 1982). The method involves estimating herbage weight (by individual species if desired) of every quadrat and clipping a certain percentage of the quadrats. Regression analysis is applied to the data, with estimated weights as the dependent variable and clipped weights as the independent variable. All estimated values are then adjusted by the regression equation. Various procedures have been developed to determine the ratio of clipped to estimated quadrats (Hilmon 1959, Ahmed and Bonham 1982, Ahmed et al. 1983). For shortgrass vegetation, the optimum ratio was 1 to 6.8, clipped to estimated (Ahmed and Bonham 1982) and 1 to 11 for southern pine range in Florida (Hilmon 1959).

The major advantage of the weight estimate method is the increased size of sample which may be realized. For example, a 4-fold increase in sample size was realized in sampling mountain vegetation in northern Utah (Reese et al. 1980).

Indirect Methods

Since clipping is such a time-consuming method of determining herbage weight, researchers have looked for other variables which might be related to herbage weight. If some factors were relatively easy to measure and highly related to herbage weight, then they might be used to predict herbage weight.

Precipitation. Several studies have shown a high correlation between herbage weight and precipitation (Hutchings and Stewart 1953, Smoliak 1956, Sneva and Hyder 1962, Currie and Peterson 1966, Sneva and Britton 1983). In some cases, annual precipitation works well as the independent variable (Hutchings and Stewart 1953), while in other situations seasonal precipitation is more effective (Smoliak 1956, Pieper et al. 1971, Shiflet and Dietz 1974, Pumphrey 1980). Other studies have shown rather "poor" relationships (Murphy 1970, Cable 1975, Duncan and Woodmansee 1975). In the Southwest, the situation is apparently more complex. Parker (1963) found that differences in basal cover often obscured precipitation-herbage weight relations. An index of basal area by growing season precipitation could be used in southern New Mexico. In southern Arizona, precipitation of the previous growing season plus August precipitation of the current year yielded highest r^2 values (Cable 1975).

Using precipitation as an index to herbage production requires careful application. Several years of data are needed with a wide spread in precipitation totals. Several combinations of months may be tested to develop those with the strongest relationship. Data from one site may not be applicable to other sites (Pieper et al. 1971).

Cover. Cover is generally related to herbage weight. Payne (1974) reported that the correlation coefficient between canopy cover and plant weight was above 0.90 for 15 species while 34 species exhibited lower, but significant, correlations. Only 12 species did not show significant correlation between cover and weight.

In some cases, the addition of other factors may enhance the prediction of weight. Blankenship and Smith (1966) improved prediction of standing crop of several species in the Medicine Bow Mountains of southern Wyoming by including other attributes such as density, average maximum leaf length, average maximum stem length, number of stems, and number of pedicels. Often it is easier to estimate cover of compact plants with regular outlines than those with irregular outlines (Goebel et al. 1958, Reppert et al. 1962).

Use of cover to predict herbage weight is predicated on the idea that cover is easier to measure and can be done accurately. However, a variance is associated with cover measurements, and also one is associated with the regression equation developed for the prediction. These should be taken into consideration when judging the reliability of the procedure.

Twig Length and Diameter. Shrubs pose some special problems in determining browse weight. They are often large, have indeterminant growth, and are difficult to harvest. Several studies have been conducted to estimate individual twig weight for different species. Shafer (1963) simply determined the average weight of twigs of several eastern hardwood species and then counted the number of twigs on each plant. Several other workers have developed regression equations expressing the relationship between twig length and/or diameter and twig weight (Basile and Hutchings 1966, Lyon 1970, Halls and Harlow 1971, Ferguson and Marsden 1977, Dean et al. 1981, Provenza and Urness 1981, Bartolome and Kosco 1982). Most of these studies show a relatively strong relationship between twig length and diameter and twig weight. Once the relationship has been established, the researcher need only measure twig lengths or diameters to be able to predict twig weight. In some cases, additional measurements such as main stem diameter and number of twigs improves the relationship (Schuster 1965).

While these methods provide a means of estimating twig weight, they do not provide an estimate of standing crop per unit area. It is still necessary to extrapolate these data to an individual plant and to an area basis. Also, one needs to be sure that the equations hold from year to year and from site to site when growing conditions might be different (Ruyle et al. 1983).

Dimension Analysis. Another approach for woody species has been to measure one or more dimensions of the canopy and to relate these measurements to canopy biomass. In some cases simple measurements, such as canopy diameter, are sufficent as in the case of true mountain mahogany *(Cercocarpus montanus)* (Medin 1960). In other cases, additional measurements may be needed (Hutchings and Mason 1970). Ludwig et al. (1975) devised formulas for the volumes of several southwestern shrubs and related shrub canopy volume to weight. In many cases, higher coefficients of determination can be obtained if data are transformed to logarithms (Harniss and Murray 1976, Rittenhouse and Sneva 1977, Uresk et al. 1977, Whisenant and Burzlaff 1978, Bryant and Kothmann 1979).

These methods appear promising. However, density also has to be determined to calculate biomass per unit area. In addition, the equations apply only to shrubs with similar growth patterns and care must be used in extrapolating results to other populations (Bobek and Bergstrom 1978, Nadabo et al. 1980).

Capacitance Meter. Fletcher and Robinson (1956) described the use of an instrument to measure the capacitance of the air-vegetation mixture. Capacitance is directly related to the amount of moisture and salts in the vegetation. Therefore, it is indirectly related to the amount of vegetation present. A series of articles have described various instruments which have been developed (Campbell et al. 1962, Alcock 1964, Dowling et al. 1965, Johns et al. 1965, Neal and Neal 1965, Alcock and Lovett 1967, Carpenter et al. 1973, Neal and Neal 1973, Neal et al. 1976, Terry et al. 1981). Care must be exercised since moisture content of the vegetation, standing dead material, and woody stems can cause variations in use of the instrument.

Determining Herbage Weight When an Area Is Being Grazed

In many cases, it is desirable to determine herbage weight on ranges which are being grazed. Basically, there are two approaches to this problem: the use of movable exclosures and the use of small movable cages. Both approaches have disadvantages, but cages have been used more often then exclosures. Daubenmire (1940) and Hinnant and Kothmann (1982) discussed the uses of exclosures for vegetation sampling. Many types of cages have been developed, and each probably has its own advantages (Klingman et al. 1943, Cowlishaw 1951, Robertson 1954, Campbell and Lodge 1955, Stelfox 1957, Myers 1960, Wilbert 1961, Frischknecht and Conrad 1965, Frischknecht et al. 1970). Concern has been expressed over possible effects of these cages on the microenvironment inside the cage (Cowlishaw 1951, Heady 1957a, Owensby 1969). Heady (1957b) found differences in herbage weight inside and outside exclosures in the California annual type early in the growing season but not later. However, substantial differences were attributed to cages in tall grass vegetation in eastern Kansas (Owensby 1969). Greater production inside the cage may have been due to changes in the following factors: insolation, humidity, temperature, precipitation intensity, support, and wind movement. Use of either cages or movable exclosures removes the grazing effect during the year measurements are taken. Major differences in growth rate exist between grazed and protected plants (Cook and Stoddart 1953). Small cages have the advantage over movable exclosures. Since each sample unit can be located randomly, a more complete distribution of sample units can generally be obtained. The result should be an improved estimate of the mean and variance.

Area

The area occupied, or cover, has often been used as a primary attribute of vegetation in ecological or range studies. Cover can be used as a basis for comparison among plants of differing life forms and is a non-destructive measurement. Permanent sampling units can be established and repeated measurements taken. Basal cover has often been used to evaluate grasses while canopy or aerial cover has commonly been used for woody plants. Aerial cover was defined by Brown (1954) as the area covered by a vertical projection of the crown on the ground.

Estimation Techniques

Estimation techniques are perhaps the simplest of the techniques developed to determine cover. Cover can be estimated directly in percentage, but more often it is estimated according to cover classes. Many systems of cover classes have been used by American and European workers (Brown 1954, Mueller-Dombois and Ellenberg 1974). However, the system devised by Daubenmire (1959) has often been used in the United States. In this system, six cover classes were used:

Class	Range	Midpoint
	%	
1	0– 5	2.5
2	5– 25	15.0
3	25– 50	37.5
4	50– 75	62.5
5	75– 95	85.0
6	95–100	97.5

Unequal subclasses 1 and 6 were used to prevent skewed data for extremely sparse or dense vegetation. For each quadrat, the observer simply records the cover class. Data are summarized using the class midpoints.

Cover estimates may be refined by using grids or other devices. Goebel et al. (1958) and Cook and Bonham (1977) described a frame divided into small grids for sampling salt-desert shrub vegetation. Each grid equalled 5 cm by 5 cm cells or 0.25% cover when used on 1 m^2 quadrats. The observer counted the number of cell grids directly over the plants which summed into actual cm^2 of cover or relative percentage cover of the whole. Culley (1938) described a densimeter to aid in the estimation of basal cover for bunchgrasses. The instrument consisted of a calibrated tape which could be slipped over grass plants, pulled snugly around the base, and readings made directly on the tape. Poulton and Tisdale (1961) described small circles of different sizes to aid estimation of basal cover in sagebrush-grass vegetation.

One drawback with cover estimations is that training and adjustments of estimates are difficult. No direct determination of cover is possible, and estimates are subject to personal bias. Smith (1944) found that individuals varied considerably in estimates using an observation plot method that was used and described by Stewart and Hutchings (1936). Repeated experience on the same area tended to reduce the sampling error over time.

Line Intercept

The line intercept method was first described by Canfield (1941). It consists of stretching a tape or line between two points or stakes. Linear measurements are taken of all plants intercepted by a vertical plane running through the line. Therefore, the line has only one dimension, length. Basal or aerial intercept measurements can be made (Fig. 3-1). The length of the transect can vary according to the vegetation, but Canfield (1941) recommended a 15 m line for vegetation with cover between 5 and 15% and a 30 m line for cover below 5%. Similar procedures were described by Parker and Savage (1944) and Roe (1947). The line intercept method is often considered one of the most reliable methods for determining cover and is often used for comparing other methods (Hormay 1949, Whitman and Siggeirsson 1954, Johnston 1957, Kinsinger et al. 1960, Brun and Box 1963, Hanley 1978). The method was evaluated on an artificial population and found to have a comparatively small sampling error (Schultz et al. 1961).

The main drawback to the line intercept method is the time required to conduct the sampling. Field time was 52% greater for line intercept sampling than for line point sampling in the California chaparral (Heady et al. 1959).

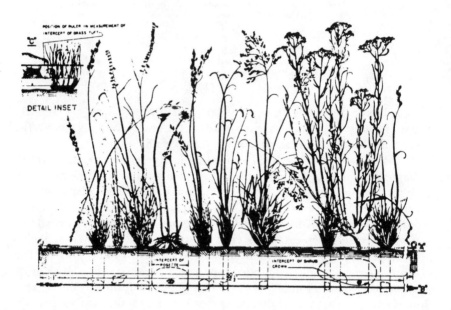

Fig. 3-1. A segment of a line transect showing the manner in which vegetation is measured. A. How the transect appears to the observer in the field. B. A diagrammatic projection of the intercepted portions of plants. C. Detail of measuring a plant at ground level (from Canfield 1942).

Time to summarize field data was about 92% greater for the line intercept method than for line-point sampling. A line is also difficult to stretch between two points in tall, dense vegetation.

Point Sampling

The point method of sampling was first mentioned by Levy (1927) and Levy and Madden (1933) in New Zealand. The method represents the reduction of a quadrat down to a dimensionless point (Drew 1944). If enough points are distributed over an area, then the percentage of points directly over plants should represent both actual and relative percentage cover. Several methods of point sampling have been developed. The point frame usually contains ten pins spaced 5 cm apart (Fig. 3-2). The pins pass through two holes in the frame and are sharpened to a point. Each pin is lowered and the species which the pin touches is recorded. Basal and/ or aerial cover can be sampled. After all ten pins have been lowered and data recorded, the point frame is moved to a new location. Thus, each frame of ten pins can be located randomly, but the pins are located systematically with respect to each other. Most frames are constructed with the pins positioned vertically, but some workers have recommended inclined pins to determine leaf area of certain species such as forbs (Tinney et al. 1937, Arny and Schmid 1942, Arny 1944, Winkworth 1955, Warren Wilson 1959, 1960, 1963a, 1963b).

Several modifications of the point frame have been suggested. Some of

Fig. 3-2. Modified ten-point frame (University of Nebraska photo).

these involved leather brakes to prevent the pins from digging into the ground (Heady and Rader 1958), magnetic brakes (Conrad 1969, Neal et al. 1969), spring brakes (Smith 1959), hinged frame (Sharrow and Tober 1979), and a wheel attachment for ease of movement (Nerney 1960).

In other cases, a transect has been used with point readings taken at intervals along a tape (Heady et al. 1959). The length of the transect and spacing between points can vary. Fisser and Van Dyne (1966) found that having 25 points per 1.5 m transect was as reliable as having 100 points on foothill grasslands of southwest Montana.

For rapid survey purposes, Evans and Love (1957) described the point-step method. A notch or mark on the tip of the boot could be used as the point as the observer paced across the study area. Where variation was statified into vegetation types such as herbaceous and woody 100 to 300 points within each stratum were recommended. Owensby (1973) described a tripod, single point frame to avoid bias in point placement when using the step-point method.

Earlier studies indicated that single points were more efficient than groups of pins (Blackman 1935, Greig-Smith 1964). Goodall (1952) showed that sample sizes were much smaller for single pins than groups of pins for comparable variances. A loss of statistical efficiency occurs when there is more than one point. Each frame, not each point, must be considered as independent. Goodall (1952) found that it took 2000 points with a ten point frame to achieve the accuracy of only 568 single points. Fewer random locations were required (200 vs. 568). Therefore, it is possible that the use of a 10-point frame may be more rapid.

Field studies have shown that point sampling often results in a positive bias (Goodall 1952, Whitman and Siggeirsson 1954, Johnston 1957, Warren

Wilson 1963a). These overestimations were largely attributed to bluntness of the point. Several pieces of equipment have been described to minimize the size of the point. A sighting tube (Winkworth and Goodall 1962) and a telescope attached to a disc mounted on a tripod (Burzlaff 1966) are two approaches used to minimize point size.

Loop Procedure

This method was developed by Parker (1951) to determine trend and condition on United States Forest Service land and was further refined and described by Driscoll (1958), and Parker and Harris (1959). Since the 2 cm loop is in reality a small plot, frequency is actually determined rather than hits of a blunt point (Hutchings and Holmgren 1959).

The method was evaluated to determine effectiveness in measuring differences in species cover changes and was found to be reliable (Smith 1962). Sharp (1954) found good agreement among observers, providing care was taken in relocating transect lines and plumbing the loop (Short 1953).

Most field studies show a positive bias in cover as determined by the loop procedure (Johnston 1957, Hutchings and Holmgren 1959). Degree of overestimation appears to be greatest for single-stemmed plants or those with small basal area (Hutchings and Holmgren 1959). Johnston (1957) found that loop sampling overestimated actual cover by 1.6 to 8.0 times depending on species and location. Hutchings and Holmgren (1959) found that the loop cover index depended on plant size and number, plant shape, variability of plant size, and plant pattern. They indicated that some of these sources of variation could be corrected by appropriate formulas, but others could not.

Later United States Forest Service studies also reported that loop readings showed only poor relationships with plant cover, herbage weight, and plant density (Francis et al. 1972). These studies present some of the problems associated with loop sampling.

Variable Plot Sampling

Variable plot sampling is based on a method developed by Bitterlich (1948). It was developed for sampling forests (Grosenbaugh 1958). It has been adapted for use on shrubs and bunchgrasses (Cooper 1957 and 1963, Hyder and Sneva 1960, Kinsinger et al. 1960, Fisser 1961). Calibrated prisms are most commonly used on forests. For use on shrubland, the instrument described by Cooper (1957) consisted of a small wooden base with a crossarm on one end and an eyehole on the other. All the shrubs surrounding the sampling point are viewed through the eyehole. Those whose crowns extend beyond the crossarm are counted and all others ignored. The procedure is repeated until sufficient points are sampled. The counts at each point are divided by an appropriate factor called the "cover percentage factor" by Cooper (1963). For a 76.2 cm (30 in) instrument, and a crossarm of 10.8 cm (4 15/64 in), the division factor is 2. Cooper (1963) recommends using such an instrument for shrub ranges in the western United States. It should be noted that different types of vegetation require different factors.

Hyder and Sneva (1960) used a "v-shaped" angle gauge for bunchgrasses in

Oregon. The gauge was made of angle iron and could be rotated 360° at the center. Their gauge had an angle of 11° 29′ and a division factor of 1.

The major advantage of the variable plot method is the low variation associated with the method. In nearly every study reported, variability and sample size is considerably lower than other methods studied (Hyder and Sneva 1960, Kinsinger et al. 1960, Schultz et al. 1961). The method is suitable mainly for shrubs and bunchgrasses where individual plants can be distinguished rather easily. Field studies indicate a slight positive bias because of dead portions of crowns (Hyder and Sneva 1960, Kinsinger et al. 1960). The method has limitations in dense vegetation (aerial cover of >30%) because some plants tend to become obscured. Another disadvantage on rangeland is that the method requires round objects. Shrub outlines are often irregular.

Volume and Vertical Production

Many of the techniques for sampling production of herbage have included basal area and height measurements, which may be used to calculate volume. If these profile measurements are identified with life forms and species composition, they are considered an ideal means of characterizing habitat factors (food and cover) for wildlife, as well as domestic animals. Measuring segments of the vertical structure of vegetation is not new, but it has been infrequently used in range studies. Studies by MacArthur and MacArthur (1961), Anderson et al. (1977), and Nudds (1977) estimated relative abundance of vertical vegetation by the use of a white board marked at various levels above ground. Lateral distance along with vertical height covered with herbage is a measure of area (production) for each life form or layer of vegetation. Photographs of the board can also be used to relate actual area of the board covered with vegetation. The area of the board covered with vegetation is identified with the vertical increments marked on the board.

In a study by Cook (1960), it was determined that volume, which was the product of basal area of the plant multiplied by average height, accounted for 37% more variation in estimating yield than either basal area or height alone. Volume of herbage presents a useful parameter for an evaluation of the vegetation profile.

McClure, et al. (1979) made a profile study as a part of multiple resource inventory for the purpose of including information on understory structure. Layers, species composition, and relative amounts of biomass were estimated and ranked from 1 to 10 in a point system. Nystrom (1984) used a square metal frame, 1 m by 1 m with four adjustable legs so that it allowed production to be harvested at 10 cm intervals up to 1.5 m aboveground. This vertical sampling procedure required more time than two-dimensional sampling (height and area), but allowed vertical quantification of aboveground biomass by weight.

Density and Frequency

Density

Density is defined as a number of individuals per unit area (Cooper 1959,

Range Term Glossary Committee 1974). Density determinations are useful when one is more interested in the number of individuals rather than cover or biomass, such as in evaluations of seedings. Density is also useful in evaluating a shrub or tree stand. Density can be determined by the use of quadrats or distance techniques. Care must be taken when reading historical literature, because density, unfortunately, was used by early range investigators to mean cover.

Quadrats

Each individual within a quadrat is counted. Quadrat size is important in determining density. If the quadrat is too small, variation will be high. If the quadrat is too large, counting will be too time consuming. For example, Sharp and others (1957) reported as many as 1,200 individuals of medusahead rye *(Taeniatherum asperum)* per 0.1 m^2 in Idaho. Recognition of individual plants may be difficult with rhizomatous species. The perimeter to area ratio must also be considered.

Distance Techniques

Cottam and Curtis (1949, 1955, 1959) refined and used distance techniques that were developed in Europe during the previous century. Others have also described and evaluated various distance methods (Clark and Evans 1954, Moore 1954, Pielou 1959, Dix 1961, Catana 1963, Strickler and Stearns 1963, Heyting 1968, Lyon 1968, Risser and Zedler 1968, Batcheler 1971, Beasom and Haucke 1975). The methods are based on the fact that as density increases, distance between plants decreases. Six different methods have been developed: (1) random pairs, (2) closest individual, (3) nearest neighbor, (4) point-centered quarter, (5) angle order and (6) wandering quarter. For the first three methods, distances are measured from point to plants or plant to plant. For the point-centered quarter method, distances are measured to the nearest plant in each of 4 quadrants. In the angle-order method, four measurements are also made at each point, but these are often to the third nearest plant (Morisita 1957). In the wandering quarter method, the observer follows a zig-zag path with distances from plant to plant made within a 90° angle. All methods involve calculating a mean area per individual and then converting to density. For example, for the point-centered quarter method the mean distance *(d)* is calculated as:

$$d = \frac{D}{\text{No. Distances}}$$

where D = total of all distances

$$\overline{\text{M.A.}} = d^2$$

where $\overline{\text{M.A.}}$ = mean area per individual

d = mean distance

$$\text{Density} = \frac{1}{\text{M.A.}}$$

If measurements are made in meters, then density will be in number of plants per square meter. Density would be for all species. Density for each species would be determined by multiplying the relative density of that species by total density of all species (Dix 1961). Relative density is the number of measurements to a species divided by the total number of measurements. Formulas for all these methods are given in Catana (1963) and Strickler and Stearns (1963).

The angle-order and wandering quarter method were developed for non-randomly distributed populations. Consequently, some studies revealed biases for the other methods in field studies due to nonrandomness of vegetation (Risser and Zedler 1968, Becker and Crockett 1973).

Frequency

Frequency is an easy characteristic to measure since only a "yes" or "no" decision needs to be made as to whether or not a species is present or absent in a quadrat. Frequency sampling combines density and dispersion characteristics (Hyder et al. 1963), but it has not been widely used by range workers, probably because of a concern about sensitivity of the analysis.

Frequency is defined as the percentage of sample units containing the species (Cain 1943, Hyder et al. 1965). Frequency is usually determined from quadrats but sometimes also from transects or points. Quadrat size is of paramount importance in conducting frequency sampling (Cain 1938, Rice and Kelting 1955, Hyder et al. 1963). For sampling sagebrush-grass vegetation in Oregon, a quadrat size of 15 to 25 cm^2 was found suitable (Hyder et al. 1963). For blue grama *(Bouteloua gracilis)* range in Colorado, two quadrats were used: a 5$\times$5 cm for blue grama and 40$\times$40 cm for all other species (Hyder et al. 1966). Bonham (1976) described a double sampling procedure to reduce the sample size required for frequency sampling.

Hyder et al. (1966) and Hyder et al. (1975) have studied soil-plant, climate-plant, fertilizer, and grazing relations utilizing frequency sampling. They caution, however, that a large number of samples are required. Where information is needed on a large number of species, frequency sampling should be considered.

Diversity

Diversity can be defined as the richness and evenness of the species composition of plant communities (Odum 1971, Peet 1974). Richness is an expression of the number of species in the population while evenness is the distribution of abundance among species. The effects of species distribution patterns on diversity has been related to mathematical models, namely: (1) lognormal model (Whittaker 1965, May 1975), (2) random niche or broken stick model (MacArthur 1965), and (3) niche preemption model (Whittaker 1965).

Several indexes of diversity (DI) have been proposed and used in studying species distribution and importance (Odum 1971). Simpson's index as originally presented was as follows:

$$DI = \sum^{s} \frac{n_i (n_i - 1)}{N(N - 1)}$$

where s is the number of species in the sample, n_i is the number of individuals for a species, and N is the number of individuals in the sample (Simpson

1949). Modifications of the calculation have been suggested by Williams (1964), Hill (1973), and Pielou (1975).

The Shannon-Wiener index (H) is calculated from the following formula:

$$H = (\frac{n_i}{N}) \quad \log \quad (\frac{n_i}{N})$$

where n_i is actual cover of species i and N is the total actual cover of all species (Odum 1971). Certain precautions for the use of the Shannon-Wiener index were pointed out by Pielou (1975) and Routledge (1980).

MacArthur (1965) observed that richness or number of species increased with sample size. Evenness was largely independent of number of species but evenness increased with extreme dominance.

McIntosh (1967) proposed an index of diversity (DI) by the following:

$$DI = \sqrt{\Sigma n_i^2}$$

where n_i is the number of individuals for species i.

When comparing the species composition of two or more plant communities, it has been suggested that an index of similarity may be more appropriate than indexes of diversity for each of the comparisons (Odum 1971). The similarity index (SI) is calculated as follows:

$$SI = \frac{2C}{A+B}$$

where A is the number of species in community A, B the number of species in community B, and C the number of species common to both communities A and B. Note the index of dissimilarity is calculated by 1-SI.

Measuring Plant Vigor

Plant vigor is synonymous with the status or health of the plant. It denotes the relative appearance, vitality, rate of growth, and herbage production of the plant. A vigorous plant has reserve vitality and is free from defects and disease. For maximum vigor, it requires a favorable environment.

Plant vigor is a relatively abstract term and, therefore, difficult to describe, measure, or interpret precisely. It is a composite expression of the influence of all environmental growth factors. Changes or modifications of any growth factor, such as soil fertility, soil moisture, rainfall, or the biotic influences of insects, rodents, and big game or livestock grazing, affect the vigor of the plant.

On many ranges, plant vigor is closely associated with grazing intensity. Whenever ranges are overgrazed, deterioration is often first reflected in plant vigor, followed by changes in plant density, species composition, and soil stability. Plant vigor (as well as herbage yields, species density, plant composition, soil stability, and litter) has been used to classify range conditions and serve as criteria for evaluating range improvement or deterioration (Talbot

1937, Pechanec and Stewart 1949, Hutchings and Stewart 1953, Parker 1954, Evanko and Peterson 1955). Increase in plant vigor is also one of the first expressions of range improvement.

Plant vigor is manifested, or indicated, in several ways:

Physical characteristics
(1) Size and appearance of plants—plants with poor vigor may have dead centers, decadent appearance, dead branches and/or broken sod
(2) Height and number of stems
(3) Number and size of fruiting bodies or seed heads
(4) Size or area of foliage
(5) Date of renewal of spring growth and rate of foliage development
(6) Herbage production
(7) Color of foliage has also been suggested
(8) Root production

Physiological and root characteristics
(1) Manufacture and storage of plant food reserves
(2) Amount and characteristics of chlorophyll
(3) Winter and drought hardiness

Measurements or observations on any of these criteria provide information on plant vigor. However, most investigators measure and evaluate several characteristics. All possible clues to plant vigor must be considered before a final evaluation is made. The greater the number of valid factors considered and measured, the greater the confidence in the results and interpretations obtained.

Size, character, and condition of plants are the most visible and easily recognized indicators of plant vigor. Several studies (Nelson 1930, Biswell and Weaver 1933, Talbot 1937, Albertson et al. 1953), have demonstrated that frequent close clipping or grazing reduces plant size, breaks sod and crowns of grasses, injures twigs and foliage of shrubs, and leaves the plants in a decadent condition. Severe clipping or grazing of some shrubs for a period of one or two years sometimes stimulates twig growth, but continued close cropping, year after year, markedly reduces plant size and vigor (Garrison 1953, Cook 1971).

Plant height (Nelson 1930, Biswell and Weaver 1933, Nedrow 1937, Albertson et al. 1953, Hutchings and Stewart 1953, Evanko and Peterson 1955), number of flower stalks (Weaver and Hougen 1939), and amounts of seed produced (Sampson 1914, Julander 1937, Hutchings and Stewart 1953) are the most commonly used and most easily measured criteria for determining and evaluating plant vigor. These attributes are probably the most sensitive to grazing treatments and they can be measured quantitatively.

If plant vigor is appraised by plant height, all measurements should be on a comparative basis and a new set of guides established each year to eliminate differences attributable to weather. Parker (1954) recommended that yearly guides to stem length or leaf height be established.

Criteria have been established for evaluating plant vigor. For grasses, the criteria are based on plant height, leaf length, and herbage yield. For shrubs, leaf size, twig length, twig mortality, and production of fruit and flowers are used in appraising plant vigor. Julander (1937) and Garrison (1953) used twig length and herbage yield in measuring plant vigor in shrubs. They found that pruning stimulated twig growth so that twig length was not always a sensitive measure of plant vigor in shrubs. Weight of herbage produced was more sensitive in most shrubs. Cook and Child (1971) found percentage dead crown cover to be the most reliable index to low vigor in desert grasses and shrubs of Utah.

All the factors that affect plant vigor are integrated in herbage production. Therefore, herbage yield is undoubtedly a more accurate measure of plant vigor than any single vegetation character.

If accurate measurements and valid comparisons are to be made of plant vigor by herbage yield, certain restrictions are needed. All comparisons should be made under controlled treatments where plant populations are of comparable age and size. Whenever possible, individual plants of equal age should be selected for comparisons. Yearly fluctuations—precipitation and other weather factors—also influence herbage yield; therefore, comparisons must be made each year. If vigor comparisons are to be made between years, it is imperative that yield data be obtained at approximately the same phenological stage each year or when the plants reach their peak of production.

Root development and production are related to plant vigor. Root production is difficult to study and therefore is not readily usable in the field for making comparisons. When available, it adds to the information and interpretation of plant vigor.

Confining observations and studies of plant vigor to a few selected species fails to evaluate fully range condition or trend because invading or undesirable species are generally ignored. A comparative appraisal of plant vigor for desirable and undesirable forage species would produce a much more complete and effective evaluation than vigor of key species alone.

Measuring Quality of Vegetation

Forage quality may be determined from the vegetation directly or as expressed in animal products (Beaty and Engel 1980). Qualities of vegetation commonly tested are palatability, total digestible nutrients, energy values, and individual nutrients such as protein, phosphorus, and vitamin A. Since animals require certain quantities of food for maintenance, growth, and reproduction, animal responses that are manifested in milk, wool, meat, hides, or offspring are useful criteria for measuring forage quality. Measurements of forage quality may be obtained from field grazing trials, laboratory analyses, or a combination of both. Combined field and laboratory methods involve digestion, balance, and grazing trials, which on large range areas are often not practicable. A somewhat modified technique has been followed wherein a range forage representative of larger range types is grazed in small enclosures where the animals can be closely observed.

Grazing trials are a practical means of indirectly evaluating forage quality, but provide little quantitative information on nutritional composition of the forage. Hence, laboratory tests are commonly used to measure the nutritional level of the range forage. Much has been published on the chemical composition and digestibility of various range forages. Chemical composition and digestibility vary according to species, site, season, and other factors (Watkins 1955, Wilson 1981, and Van Soest 1982). Knowledge of adequacies or shortages that exist enables a range manager to supplement during critical periods to sustain animal production.

Development of several techniques has made possible expanded research into the area of measuring vegetation quality. These include the development of the esophageal fistula to obtain samples of ingested forage (Torell 1954), the refinement of the microhistological technique for determination of botanical composition of fistula or fecal samples (Sparks and Malechek 1968), development of an accurate in vitro method for determination of digestibility (Tilley and Terry 1963), electron microscope imaging (Akin and Amos 1975), and infrared reflectance spectroscopy (Norris et al. 1976).

Several review articles are available on methods of assessing diet quality (Harris et al. 1967, Harris 1968, Van Dyne 1969, Theurer 1970a, 1970b, Lesperance et al. 1974, Theurer et al. 1976, Kothmann 1980, Van Dyne et al. 1980, Holechek et al. 1982a, 1982b). Consequently, these techniques will not be reviewed in detail in this chapter.

Animal Gains

Animal gains as a measurement of quality of vegetation are the net results of specific combinations of a large number of variables. Among these is the quantity of vegetation available to the animals. Sufficient forage should be available at all times so that the total intake does not directly influence animal gains. The objective should be to provide a rate of stocking which will be near the level for sustained production. Because this level can seldom be exactly determined, it is advisable to use a stocking rate a little lighter than calculated to be proper for the experimental range. This will assure that gains are not directly influenced by the quantity of forage available. Chapter 6 provides a complete discussion of techniques to determine animal gain.

Analytical Evaluation of Range Forage

Chemical analysis of range forage plants serves as a comparative measure of differences between species and changes with season or phenology. Also, it is an index to mineral and vitamin content when evaluating deficiencies or excesses in the diet.

No one chemical constituent or any combination of chemical constituents will probably evaluate the nutritive content of range forage (Cook and Harris 1950, Van Soest 1982). No two chemical constituents are directly associated in all plant material. For instance, browse plants are comparatively high in lignin, whereas grasses are comparatively low; yet, from the standpoint of nutritional value, grasses are better in some respects and shrubs are better in others. Mature grasses generally are higher in crude fiber content than shrubs, yet they may have greater total digestible nutrients.

Chemical content of plant species may differ because of inherent ability to withdraw certain nutrients from the soil and concentrate them in the tissues. They may also vary in susceptibility to leaching, or may produce different proportions of leaves, stems, and flower stalks at various stages of maturity or because of previous grazing treatments. Chemical composition of the same species varies with state of maturity, soil conditions, or general climatic conditions. Collection technique and analytical procedure should recognize these effects.

Cook et al. (1977) found that digestible protein was the most closely associated with animal response when single nutrients were considered, and digestible energy and digestible protein together were the best combination of nutrients when a total of 14 independent factors were compared to animal response. Vitamin A (carotene), phosphorus, and digestible energy are related to digestible protein, especially while plants are growing to maturity.

Collecting Forage Samples

The portion of the plant collected and stage of growth should always be identified. In addition, it is important to collect samples from several sites where the plant is commonly found. A statistician should be consulted as the experimental design is being developed (see Chapter 10).

Generally, it is desirable to collect material representative of what the animals are eating (Cook 1964). The grazing animal harvests range forage in an assortment of species and portions of plants. The selectivity of the animals may be influenced by kind of animal, intensity of grazing, plant species present, stage of growth, and general climatic conditions.

Several methods of collecting samples representing the material being consumed by the grazing animal or the nutrients ingested are available (Cook 1964). These methods include hand plucking to simulate grazing, cage clipping, strip harvesting, collecting plant units before and after grazing, and by the esophageal fistula.

Hand plucking method. In the hand plucking method, plant samples representing ingested forage are obtained by observing individual grazing animals for several hours daily and hand plucking material comparable to the forage actually being consumed. Many small plucks should be taken over the area. For accuracy it requires from four to six man-hours daily and gentle animals that can be approached closely.

Cage method. With the cage method, chemical content of the diet may be determined by difference between a grazed sample and ungrazed sample. Usually a number of portable cages are located randomly over the range to prevent grazing on small plots. Ungrazed herbage samples are collected from these plots and chemical contents are compared to samples from adjacent grazed range. Then the cages are moved to protect an area from grazing for the next sampling period. The intervals between sampling periods should be short, especially on rapidly growing forage. Otherwise plants in cages will be in more advanced growth stages than the plants grazed (Amer. Soc. Agron. et al. 1952). This method has a distinct disadvantage on heterogeneous range since it is impractical to sample enough plots to obtain representative samples of the general area. In addition, the abundant species are oversampled and the minor species are greatly undersampled if composition by species is desired.

Strip harvesting. A similar method involves the use of mowed strips. In several areas, a strip is harvested by mowing before grazing, and an adjacent strip is harvested after grazing. Samples from each strip may be separated into individual species or analyzed as a composite sample. The difference in weight and chemical content between the before-grazing strip and the after-grazing strip represents the diet. The interval between samples should be brief or the vegetation should not be growing or weathering appreciably (Amer. Soc. Agron. et. al. 1952). This method is better adapted to homogeneous pastures rather than to usual range conditions.

Before and after grazing. A before-and-after method suitable to heterogeneous range was used by Cook et al. (1948). This method of collecting material to determine the botanical and nutritional content of the diet consists of collecting a number of distinct plant units of each dominant species before grazing and another comparable group of units after grazing. These two samples are weighed and analyzed chemically. Chemical composition of the diet can be approximated by determining the volume that each species contributed to the entire range (usually an estimate), multiplying this by utilization (based on "before" and "after" weights), and finally multiplying this by the chemical content.

Esophageal fistula. It has often been stated that a representative sample could be obtained only by letting the animal forage it. This has been accomplished by use of an esophageal fistula (Torell 1954, Cook et al. 1958). The technique is discussed in detail by McManus (1981).

Chemical Determinations

Some of the common chemical determinations for plant material are: total digestible nutrients, crude protein (percentage nitrogen $\times 6.25$), gross energy, ether extract, ash, lignin, cellulose, other carbohydrates, crude fiber, nitrogen-free-extract, calcium, phosphorus, and carotene (precursor of vitamin A). For a more detailed discussion of chemical analyses of plant material see Van Soest (1982). It has been found in domestic feeds that a close relation exists between digestible energy and total digestible nutrients. Thus, by using gross energy determinations of feeds and feces, energy values for feeds can be appraised more simply and more economically. Gross energy determinations are necessary to calculate metabolizable energy. To determine metabolizable energy, losses of gross energy through the feces, urine, and gases are subtracted from the gross energy consumed in the feed. Metabolizable energy is the most suitable index to energy-furnishing qualities for range forages (Cook et al. 1952).

Total digestible energy, or total digestible nutrients, can be used as an index to energy of grasses. In some cases, it is inaccurate for shrubs or forbs because of the presence of ether extract material, other than fatty acids, that is passed off in the urine of the animal, and thus is not available for body use.

Proximate analysis of feeds includes ether extracts, crude protein, ash crude fiber, and nitrogen-free-extract. The latter is determined by difference. A weakness is the assumption that the ether extract fraction consists largely of fatty acids. This is not the case with many species of forbs and browse which are high in various oils and resin. These are extracted by ether but do not furnish energy that is available to the animal. As well, it has been suggested that crude fiber and nitrogen-free-extract determinations be replaced by determinations of lignin, cellulose, and other carbohydrates (Van Soest 1982). Digestibility of crude fiber and nitrogen-free-extract may be nearly equal for many forages, whereas lignin is relatively indigestible. Other carbohydrates, and usually cellulose, are highly digestible. Crude fiber and nitrogen-free-extract determinations are of value to compare relative content of these constituents in range plants with domestic feeds since most feed analyses, until recently, included these determinations. Analyses of lignin, cellulose, and other carbohydrates are more meaningful from the standpoint of interpreting the nutrient value of range forage.

Recommended analytical procedures can be found in the Association of Official Agricultural Chemists' guide (1975), published periodically to keep analytical procedure as nearly standard as possible. Van Soest (1982) describes analytical procedures for many suggested systems of identifying nutrient content of forage plants.

Inorganic elements in plant material such as calcium, phosphorus, magnesium, potassium, iodine, cobalt, copper, iron, selenium, and molybdenum can be measured directly by chemical analysis. Analysis of vegetation for its content of the various vitamins is not well developed.

Digestibility

The value of a forage to the grazing animal depends on the digestibility of the ingested nutrients. The digestion coefficients are the average percentage of each nutrient digested. These coefficients are a direct means of determining available nutrients to the animal. They may vary slightly according to the animal's age, species, condition, sex, nutrient intake (nutrient level of the ration), and activity. Therefore, even when the diet and digestibility are accurately determined, the evaluation of the nutrient is only approximate for all animals.

Some digestion trials have been made on range plants by standard procedure using digestion crates. Such studies involving controlled feeding of clipped or hand plucked forage have been described by Maynard (1948). These have distinct disadvantages because the animal is not allowed to select normally among species and plant parts, and because the animal is not naturally active.

Field digestion trials have been used to measure nutritive value of native range plants. With this method, it is necessary to use as an indicator a plant constituent that appears in the forage and is indigestible so that it can be recovered in the feces. In the indicator method, animals select the forage in a normal manner and from the ratios between the indicator (lignin) and other constituents in the feed and feces, digestion coefficients can be determined. Since the entire amount of the indigestible indicator is recoverable in the feces, the percentage of each nutrient that is digested is determinable by the following formula:

$$100 - \left[100 \times \frac{\% \text{ indicator in forage}}{\% \text{ indicator in feces}} \times \frac{\% \text{ nutrient in feces}}{\% \text{ nutrient in forage}} \right] = \% \text{ digestibility}$$

The entire fecal output can be collected in specially designed fecal bags, or representative samples can be collected from intermittent defecations. In the latter method, small samples are taken from several defecations from several animals or from a single animal during each day of the collection period. Urine samples likewise can be collected from male animals in specially devised bags. If the total quantity of both feces and urine is collected, nutrient balance trials can be conducted and metabolizeable energy values determined (Cook et al. 1952).

Cook et al. (1963), studying sheep grazing on winter range plants, found that lignin gave satisfactory results. Reid et al. (1950) suggested that plant chromogens (plant pigments absorbing light at a wavelength of 406 μm) could be used as an indicator substance. However, Cook et al. (1951) found that the chromogen method was not satisfactory for some range species. Fecal nitrogen concentration has also been used as an indicator (Cordova et al. 1978). Vallentine (1956), Harris et al. (1959), Kartchner and Campbell (1979), and Van Soest (1982) reviewed the use of indicator methods in digestion trials in range research, and these sources are recommended to the researcher desiring to employ such methods.

Digestibility trials can be carried on by grazing pure stands of a single species or by grazing mixtures of many species. It is important to determine accurately the chemical intake of the grazing animal.

In vitro techniques may also be used to determine digestibility. Plant material is ground and placed in nylon bags preparatory to being placed in an artificial rumen or in the rumen of an animal through a fistula. The time of fermentation is usually 48 hours for digestibility estimations. When using a fistulated (rumen) animal it is usually fed a feed comparable to the feed being tested. The size of the bag, fineness of the grind, and quantity of material per bag can all affect the disappearance during fermentation (Uden et al. 1974, Van Hellen and Ellis 1973, Van Soest 1982). Optimum pore size of the bag is 30 to 50 microns and fineness of grind is 1 mm (ground to pass through a 20 to 30 mesh screen). Dry matter disappearance is a common in vitro technique known as the Tilley-Terry method (Tilley and Terry 1963) and later modified by Goering and Van Soest (1970). Various endpoint procedures are used which include gas production, volatile fatty acid (VFA) production, cellulose disappearance, residual dry matter, residue after pepsin digestion and the neutral-detergent residue (Van Soest 1982).

Palatability and Preference

Palatability is defined as a plant characteristic or condition which stimulates a selective response by animals (Heady 1964) or the relish with which a particular species or plant part is consumed by an animal (Range Term Glossary Committee 1974). Preference, on the other hand, refers to selection by the animal and is largely a behavioral response (Heady 1964).

Several factors influence palatability (Tribe 1952). Animal factors which influence palatability are:

(1) Grazing preferences of different kinds or species of animals.

(2) Age, degree of maturity, stage of pregnancy, and general physical condition of the animal.

(3) Hunger of the animal.

Nonanimal factors include:

(1) Season and growth stage of the plant.

(2) Palatability and relative abundance of associated plants.

(3) Differences in locations, sites, and climates.

(4) Physical characteristics of the plant.

Methods used to indicate palatability such as diet composition or utilization by species do not indicate preference. Preference indices have been used to take into account availability. A simple ratio of percentage of the plant in the diet to percentage in herbage has been expanded to include frequency measurements (Krueger 1972). Including frequency in the formula may provide more realistic ratios for species with irregular distributions.

Krueger gave four possible formulas for preference indices:

$$RP_1 = \frac{(\% \text{ diet freq.}) \, (\% \text{ diet comp.})}{(\% \text{ range freq.}) \, (\% \text{ range comp.})}$$

$$RP_2 = \frac{\% \text{ diet com.}}{\% \text{ range comp.}}$$

$$RP_3 = \frac{(\% \text{ diet freq.}) \, (\% \text{ diet comp.})}{(\% \text{ range comp}) \, (100)}$$

$$RP_4 = \frac{(\% \text{ range comp.}) \, (100)}{(\% \text{ range freq.}) \, (\% \text{ range comp.})}$$

Krueger's (1972) data indicate that RP_1 and RP_2 gave similar base values for ranges in southern Montana. However, he stated that including frequency in diet and range samples provided the best estimate of preference. Many shortcomings of these indices were discussed by Loehle and Rittenhouse (1982).

Literature Cited

Ahmed, J., and C.D. Bonham. 1982. Optimum allocation in multivariate double sampling for biomass estimation. J. Range Manage. 35:777-779.

Ahmed, J., C.D. Bonham, and W.A. Laycock. 1983. Comparison of techniques used for adjusting biomass estimates by double sampling. J. Range Manage. 36:217-221.

Akin, D.E., and H.E. Amos. 1975. Rumen bacterial degradation of forage cell walls investigated by electron microcscopy. J. Appl. Microbiol. 19:692-701.

Albertson, F., W.A. Riegel, and J.L. Launchbaugh. 1953. Effects of different intensities of clipping on short grasses in west central Kansas. Ecology. 34:1-2.

Alcock, M.B. 1964. An improved electronic instrument for estimation of pasture yield. Nature. 103:1309-1310.

Alcock, M.B., and J.V. Lovett. 1967. The electronic measurement of the yield of growing pasture: I.A. statistical assessment. J. Agr. Sci. 68:27-38.

Alder, F.E., and J.A. Richards. 1962. A note on the use of the power driven sheep shearing head for measuring herbage yield. J. Brit. Grassland Soc. 17:101.

American Society of Agronomy, American Dairy Science Association, American Society of Animal Production, and American Society of Range Management Joint Committee. 1952. Pasture and range research techniques report.

Anderson, B.W., R.W. Engel-Wilson, D. Wells, and R.D. Ohmart. 1977. Ecological study of southwestern riparian habitats: Techniques and data applicability, *In:* Symposium on the importance, preservation and management of riparian habitat. RM-43. Rocky Mountain Forest and Range Exp. Sta., Forest Service, USDA, Fort Collins, Colorado.

Arny, A.C. 1944. Alfalfa and grass percentage determinations with the inclined point quadrat apparatus at different stages of development of the mixtures. J. Amer. Soc. Agron. 36:996-998.

Arny, A.C., and A.R. Schmid. 1942. A study of the inclined point quadrat method of botanical analysis of pasture mixtures. J. Amer. Soc. Agron. 34:238-247.

Association of Official Agricultural Chemists. 1975. Official methods of analysis. 12th ed. Washington, D.C.

Bartolome, J.W., and B.H. Kosco. 1982. Estimating browse production by deerbrush *(Ceanothus integerrimus).* J. Range Manage. 35:671-672.

Basile, J.V., and S.S. Hutchings. 1966. Twig diameter-length-weight relations for bitterbrush. J. Range Manage. 19:34-38.

Batcheler, C.L. 1971. Estimation of density from a sample of joint point and nearest neighbor distances. Ecology. 52:703-709.

Beasom, S.L., and H.H. Haucke. 1975. A comparison of four distance sampling techniques in south Texas live oak mottes. J. Range Manage. 28:142-144.

Beaty, E.R., and J.L. Engel. 1980. Forage quality measurements and forage research-a review, critique, and interpretation. J. Range Manage. 33:49-54.

Becker, C.F. 1959. Equipment for harvesting short-grass rangeland plots. Agron. J. 51:430-431.

Becker, D.A., and J.J. Crockett. 1973. Evaluation of sampling techniques on tall-grass prairie. J. Range Manage. 26:61-65.

Billings, W.D. 1964. Plants and ecosystem. Wadsworth Publ. Co., Belmont, California.

Biswell, H.H., and J.E. Weaver. 1933. Effect of frequent clipping on the development of roots and tops of grasses in prairie sod. Ecology. 14:368-390.

Bitterlich, W. 1948. Die Winkelzahlprobe (In German). Allg. Forst. Holzwirtsh. Ztg. 59:4-5.

Blackman, G.E. 1935. A study of statistical methods of the distribution of species in grassland association. Ann. Bot. 49:729-777.

Blankenship, J.O., and D.R. Smith. 1966. Indirect estimation of standing crop. J. Range Manage. 19:74-77.

Bobek, B., and R. Bergstrom. 1978. A rapid method of browse biomass estimation in a forest habitat. J. Range Manage. 31:456-458.

Bonham, C.D. 1976. An optimum sampling strategy for plant species frequencies. J. Range Manage. 29:160-165.

Brown, D. 1954. Methods of surveying and measuring vegetation. Commonwealth Agr. Bur. Farnham Royal, Bucks, England.

Bryant, F.C., and M.M. Kothmann. 1979. Variability in predicting edible browse from crown volume. J. Range Manage. 32:144-146.

Brun, J.M., and T.W. Box. 1963. A comparison of line intercepts and random point frames for sampling desert shrub vegetation. J. Range Manage. 16:21-25.

Burzlaff, D.F. 1966. The focal point method of vegetation inventory. J. Range Manage. 19:222-223.

Cable, D.R. 1975. Influence of precipitation on perennial grass production in the semidesert southwest. Ecology. 56:981-986.

Cain, S.A. 1938. The species-area curve. Amer. Midland Natur. 19:578-581.

Cain, S.A. 1943. Sample plot technique applied to alpine vegetation in Wyoming. Amer. J. Bot. 30:240-247.

Campbell, A.G., D.S.M. Phillips, and E.D. O'Reilly. 1962. An electronic instrument for pasture yield estimation. J. Brit. Grassland Soc. 17:89-100.

Campbell, J.B., and R.W. Lodge. 1955. Sturdy cage for range and pasture study. J. Range Manage. 8:128.

Canfield, R.H. 1941. Application of the line interception method in sampling range vegetation. J. Forest. 39:388-394.

Carpenter, L.H., O.C. Wallmo, and M.J. Morris. 1973. Effect of woody stems on estimating herbage weights with a capacitance meter. J. Range Manage. 26:151-152.

Catana, A.J., Jr. 1963. The wandering quarter method of estimating population density. Ecology. 44:349-360.

Clark, P.J., and F.C. Evans. 1954. Distance to nearest neighbor as a measure of spatial relationships in populations. Ecology. 35:445-453.

Conrad, P.W. 1969. Magnetic pin brakes and a base mounting for point frames. J. Range Manage. 22:424-425.

Cook, C.W. 1960. The use of multiple regression and correlation in biological investigations. Ecology. 41:556-560.

Cook, C.W. 1964. Symposium on nutrition of forages and pastures: collecting forage samples representative of ingested material of grazing animals for nutritional studies. J. Anim. Sci. 23:265-270.

Cook, C.W. 1970. Energy budget of the range and range livestock. Bull. TB109. Colorado Agr. Exp. Sta.

Cook, C.W. 1971. Effect of season and intensity of use on desert vegetation. Bull. 483. Utah Agr. Exp. Sta.

Cook, C.W., and C.D. Bonham. 1977. Techniques for vegetation measurements and analysis for a pre- and post-mining inventory. Sci. Ser. No. 28. Range Sci. Dep., Colorado State Univ.

Cook, C.W., and R.D. Child. 1971. Recovery of desert range plants in various states of vigor. J. Range Manage. 24:339-343.

Cook, C.W., and L.E. Harris. 1950. The nutritive content of the grazing sheep's diet on summer and winter ranges of Utah. Bull. 342. Utah Agr. Exp. Sta.

Cook, C.W., and L.A. Stoddart. 1953. The quandary of utilization and preference. J. Range Manage. 6:329-331.

Cook, C.W., J.T. Blake, and J.W. Call. 1963. Use of esophageal-fistula cannulae for collecting forage samples from both sheep and cattle grazing in common. J. Anim. Sci. 22:579-581.

Cook, C.W., R.D. Child, and L.L. Larson. 1977. Digestible protein in range forages as an index to nutrient content and animal response. Sci. Ser. No. 29. Range Sci. Dep., Colorado State Univ.

Cook, C.W., L.E. Harris, and L.A. Stoddart. 1948. Measuring the nutritive content of the foraging sheep's diet under range conditions. J. Anim. Sci. 7:170-180.

Cook, C.W., L.A. Stoddard, and L.E. Harris. 1951. Measuring consumption and digestibility of winter range plants by sheep. J. Range Manage. 4:335-346.

Cook, C.W., L.A. Stoddard, and L.E. Harris. 1952. Determining the digestibility and metaboliz-able energy of winter range plants by sheep. J. Anim. Sci. 11:578-590.

Cook, C.W., J.L. Thorne, J.T. Blake, and J. Edlefsen. 1958. Use of an esophogeal-fistula cannula for collecting forage samples by grazing sheep. J. Anim. Sci. 17:189-193.

Cook, C.W., J.W. Walker, M.H. Ebberts, L.R. Rittenhouse, E.T. Bartlett, D.A. Cramer, P.T. Fagarlin, and M.C. McKean. 1983. Alternative grass and grain feeding systems for beef production. Bull. 579S. Colorado Agr. Exp. Sta.

Cooper, C.F. 1957. The variable plot method for estimating shrub density. J. Range Manage. 10:11-115.

Cooper, C.F. 1959. Cover vs. density. J. Range Manage. 12:215.

Cooper, C.F. 1963. An evaluation of variable plot sampling in shrub and herbaceous vegetation. Ecology. 44:565-569.

Cordova, F.J., J.D. Wallace, and R.D. Pieper. 1978. Forage intake by grazing livestock: a review. J. Range Manage. 31:430-438.

Cottom, G., and J.T. Curtis. 1949. A method for making rapid surveys of woodlands by means of randomly selected trees. Ecology. 30:101-104.

Cottom, G., and J.T. Curtis. 1955. Correction for various exclusion angles in the random pairs method. Ecology. 36:767.

Cottom, G., and J.T. Curtis. 1956. The use of distance measures in phytosociological sampling. Ecology. 37:451-460.

Cowlishaw, S.J. 1951. The effect of sampling cages on the yields of herbage. J. Brit. Grassland Soc. 6:179-184.

Culley, M. 1938. Densimeter, an instrument for measuring the density of ground cover. Ecology. 10:588-590.

Culley, M., R.S. Campbell, and R.H. Canfield. 1933. Values and limitations of clipped quadrats. Ecology. 14:35-39.

Currie, P.O., and G. Peterson. 1966. Using growing-season precipitation to predict crested wheatgrass yields. J. Range Manage. 19:284-288.

Daubenmire, R.F. 1940. Exclosure technique in ecology. Ecology. 21:514515.

Daubenmire, R.F. 1959. A canopy-coverage method of vegetational analysis. Northwest Sci. 33:43-64.

Dayton, W.A. 1950. Glossary of botanical terms commonly used in range research. Misc. Pub. 110, USDA, Washington, D.C.

Dean, S., J.W. Burkhardt, and R.O. Meeuwig. 1981. Estimating twig and foliage biomass of sagebrush, bitterbrush, and rabbitbrush in the Great Basin. J. Range Manage. 34:224-227.

Dix, Ralph L. 1961. An application of the point-centered quarter method to the sampling of grassland vegetation. J. Range Manage. 14:63-69.

Dowling, E.J., K. Spencer, and D. Bouma. 1965. The performance of a capacitance measuring instrument in estimating yield of subterranean clover pastures. Field Sta. Rec. CISRO. 4:103-106.

Drew, W.B. 1944. Studies on the use of the point-quadrat method of botanical analysis of mixed pasture vegetation. J. Agr. Res. 69:289-297.

Driscoll, R.S. 1958. A loop method for measuring ground cover characteristics on permanent plots. J. Range Manage. 11:94.

Duncan, D.A., and R.G. Woodmansee. 1975. Forecasting forage yield from precipitation in California's annual rangeland. J. Range Manage. 28:327-329.

Duvall, V.L., and R.M. Blair. 1962. Terminology and definitions, p. 8-11. *In:* Range Research Methods. Misc. Pub. 940. Forest Service, USDA, Washington, D.C.

Evanko, A.B., and R.A. Peterson. 1955. Comparison of protected and grazed mountain rangelands in southwestern Montana. Ecology. 36:71-82.

Evans, R.A., and R.M. Love. 1957. The step point method of sampling-a practical tool in range research. J. Range Manage. 10:208-212.

Ferguson, R.B., and M.A. Marsden. 1977. Estimating overwinter bitterbrush utilization from twig diameter-length-weight relations. J. Range Manage. 30:231-236.

Fisser, H.G. 1961. Variable plot, square foot plot, and visual estimate for shrub crown cover measurements. J. Range Manage. 14:202-207.

Fisser, H.G., and G.M. Van Dyne. 1966. Influence of number and spacing of points on accuracy and precision of basal cover estimates. J. Range Manage. 19:205-211.

Fletcher, J.E., and M.E. Robinson. 1956. A capacitance meter for estimating forage weight. J. Range Manage. 9:96-97.

Francis, R.C., R.S. Driscoll, and J.N. Reppert. 1972. Loop-frequency as related to plant cover, herbage production, and plant density. Res. Paper RM-94, Forest Service, USDA, Washington, D.C.

Frischknecht, N.C., and P.W. Conrad. 1965. Adaptable transportable utilization cages. J. Range Manage. 18:33-34.

Frischknecht, N.C., P.W. Conrad, and P.E. Hansen. 1970. Improved folding utilization cages. J. Range Manage. 23:215-218.

Garrison, G.A. 1953. Effects of clipping on some range shrubs. J. Range Manage. 6:309-317.

Goebel, C.J. 1955. The weight-estimate method at work in Southeastern Oregon. J. Range Manage. 8:212-213.

Goebel, C.J., L. DeBano, and D. Lloyd. 1958. A new method of determining forage cover and production on desert shrub vegetation. J. Range Manage. 11:244-246.

Goering, H.K., and P.J. Van Soest. 1970. Forage fiber analysis. Handbook No. 379. ARS, USDA, Washington, D.C.

Goodall, D.W. 1952. Some considerations in the use of point quadrats for the analysis of vegetation. Aust. J. Sci. Res. Ser. B. 5:1-41.

Greig-Smith, P. 1964. Quantitative plant ecology. Butterworth Sci. Publ., London, England.

Grosenbaugh, L.R. 1958. Point sampling and line sampling: probability theory geometric implications, synthesis. Southern Forest Exp. Sta. Occas. Paper 160:34.

Halls, L.K., and R.F. Harlow. 1971. Weight-length relations in flowering dogwood twigs. J. Range Manage. 24:236-237.

Hanley, T.A. 1978. A comparison of the line-interception and quadrat estimation methods of determining shrub canopy coverage. J. Range. Manage. 31:60-62.

Harniss, R.O., and R.B. Murray. 1976. Reducing bias in dry leaf weight estimates of big sagebrush. J. Range Manage. 29:430-432.

Harris, L.E. 1968. Range nutrition in an arid region. Honor Lecture 36. Utah State Univ.

Harris, L.E., C.W. Cook, and J.E. Butcher. 1959. Intake and digestibility techniques and supplemental feeding in range forage evaluation. Agron. J. 51:226-234.

Harris, L.E., C.J. Kercher, G.P. Lofgreen, R.J. Raleigh, and V.R. Bohman. 1967. Techniques of research in range livestock nutrition. Bull. 271. Utah Agr. Exp. Sta.

Heady, H.F. 1957a. Effect of cages on yield and composition in the California annual type. J. Range Manage. 10:175-177.

Heady, H.F. 1957b. The measurement and value of plant height in the study of herbaceous vegetation. Ecology 38:313-320.

Heady, H.G. 1964. Palatability of herbage and animal preference. J. Range Manage. 17:76-82.

Heady, H.F., and L. Rader. 1958. Modifications of the point frame. J. Range Manage. 11:95-96.

Heady, H.F., and G.M. Van Dyne. 1965. Prediction of weight composition from point samples on clipped herbage. J. Range Manage. 18:144-148.

Heady, H.F., R.P. Gibbens, and R.W. Powell. 1959. A comparison of the charting, line intercept, and line point methods of sampling shrub types of vegetation. J. Range Manage. 12:180-188.

Heyting A. 1968. Discussion and development of the point-centered quarter method of sampling grassland vegetation. J. Range Manage. 21:370-380.

Hill, M.O. 1973. Diversity and evenness: a unifying notation and its consequences. Ecology 54:427-432.

Hilmon, J.B. 1959. Determination of herbage weight by double-sampling: weight estimate and actual weight, p. 20-25. *In:* Techniques and methods of measuring understory vegetation. Forest Service, USDA, Tifton, Georgia.

Hinnant, R.T., and M.M. Kothmann. 1982. Durable livestock exclosure for herbage production and utilization sampling. J. Range Manage. 35:127128.

Holechek, J.L., M. Vavra, and R.D. Pieper. 1982a. Botanical composition determination of range herbivore diets: a review. J. Range Manage. 35:309-315.

Holechek, J.L., M. Vavra, and R.D. Pieper. 1982b. Methods for determining the nutritive quality of range ruminant diets: a review. J. Anim. Sci. 54:364-376.

Hormay, A.L. 1949. Getting better records of vegetation changes with line interception method. J. Range Manage. 1:67-69.

Hutchings, S., and R.C. Holmgren. 1959. Interpretation of loop-frequency data as a measure of plant cover. Ecology. 4:668-677.

Hutchings, S., and L.R. Mason. 1970. Estimating yields of gambel oak from foliage cover and basal area. J. Range Manage. 23:430-434.

Hutchings, S., and G. Stewart. 1953. Increasing forage yields and sheep production on intermountain winter ranges. Circ. 925. USDA, Washington, D.C.

Hyder, D.N., and F.A. Sneva. 1960. Bitterlich's plotless method for sampling basal ground cover of bunchgrasses. J. Range Manage. 13:6-9.

Hyder, D.N., R.E. Bement, E.E. Remmenga, and D.F. Hervey. 1975. Ecological responses of native plants and guidelines for management of shortgrass range. Tech. Bull 1503. USDA, Washington, D.C.

Hyder, D.N., R.E. Bement, E.E. Remmenga, and C. Terwilliger, Jr. 1965. Frequency sampling of blue grama range. J. Range Manage. 18:90-93.

Hyder, D.N., R.E. Bement, E.E. Remmenga, and C. Terwilliger, Jr. 1966. Vegetation soils and vegetation-grazing relations from frequency data. J. Range Manage. 19:11-17.

Hyder, D.N., C.E. Conrad, Paul T. Tueller, L.D. Calvin, C.E. Poulton, and Forrest A. Sneva. 1963. Frequency sampling in sagebrush-bunchgrass vegetation. Ecology. 44:740-746.

Johns, G.G., G.R. Nicol, and B.R. Watkin. 1965. A modified capacitance probe technique for estimating pasture yield. I. Construction and procedure for use in the field. J. Brit. Grassland Soc. 20:212-217.

Johnston, A. 1957. A comparison of the line interception, vertical point quadrat, and loop methods as used in measuring basal area of grassland vegetation. Can. J. Plant Sci. 37:34-42.

Joint Committee of Agriculture Societies. 1962. Pasture and range research techniques. Comstock Publ. Assoc., Ithaca, New York.

Julander, O. 1937. Utilization of browse by wildlife. Trans. North Amer. Wildlife Conf. 2:276-287.

Kartchner, R.J., and C.M. Campbell. 1979. Intake and digestibility of range forages consumed by livestock. Bull. 718. Montana Agr. Exp. Sta.

Kinsinger, F.E., R.E. Eckert, and P.O. Currie. 1960. A comparison of the liner interception, variable plot, and loop methods as used to measure shrub crown cover. J. Range Manage. 12:17-21.

Kingman, D.L., S.R. Miles, G.O. Mott. 1943. The cage method for determining consumption and yield of pasture herbage. J. Amer. Soc. Agron. 35:739-746.

Kothmann, M.M. 1980. Nutrition of livestock grazing on range and pasture lands, *In:* Church, D.C. (ed.) Digestive physiology and nutrition in ruminants. Vol. 3 (2nd ed.) O. and B. Books, Inc., Corvallis, Oregon.

Krueger, W.C. 1972. Evaluating animal forage preference. J. Range Manage. 25:471-475.

Lesperance, A.L., D.C. Clanton, A.B. Nelson, and C.B. Theurer. 1974. Factors affecting the apparent chemical composition of fistula samples. Bull. T18. Nevada Agr. Exp. Sta.

Levy, E.B. 1927. Grasslands of New Zealand. N.Z.J. Agr. 34:143-164.

Levy, E.B., and E.A. Madden. 1933. The point method of pasture analysis. N.Z.J. Agr. 46:267-279.

Loehle, C., and L.R. Rittenhouse. 1982. An analysis of forage preference indices. J. Range Manage. 35:316-319.

Ludwig, J.A., J.F. Reynolds, and P.D. Whitson. 1975. Size-biomass relationships of several Chihuahuan desert shrubs. Amer. Midland Natur. 94:451-461.

Lyon, L.J. 1968. An evaluation of density sampling methods in a shrub community. J. Range Manage. 21:16-20.

Lyon, L.J. 1970. Length-and weight-diameter relations of serviceberry twigs. J. Wildlife Manage. 34:456-460.

MacArthur, R.H. 1965. Patterns of species diversity. Biol. Rev. 40:510-533.

MacArthur, R.H., and J.W. MacArthur. 1961. On bird species diversity. Ecology. 42:594-598.

Matches, A.G. 1963. A cordless hedge trimmer for herbage sampling. Agron. J. 55:309.

May, R.M. 1975. Patterns of species abundance and diversity, p. 81-120. *In:* M.L. Cody and J.M. Diamond (ed.) The ecology and evaluation of communities. Harvard Univ.

Maynard, L.A. 1948. Animal nutrition. McGraw-Hill Book Co., Inc., New York, New York.

McClure, J.P., N.D. Cost, and H.A. Knight. 1979. Multi-resource inventories—a new concept of forest survey. Res. Paper SE 191. Southeast Forest Exp. Sta., Forest Service, USDA.

McGinnies, W.J. 1959. A rotary lawn mower for sampling range herbage. J. Range Manage. 12:203-204.

McIntosh, R.P. 1967. An index of diversity and the relation of certain concepts to diversity. Ecology. 48:392-404.

McManus, W.R. 1981. Oesophageal fistulation technique as an aid to diet evaluation of the grazing ruminant, p. 249-260. *In:* J.L. Wheeler and R.D. Mochrie (eds.). Forage evaluation: concepts and techniques. Amer. Forage and Grassland Counc., Lexington, Kentucky.

Medin, D.E. 1960. Physical site factors influencing annual production of true mountain mahogany, *Cercocarpus montanus.* Ecology. 41:454-460.

Milner, C., and R.E. Hughes. 1968. Methods of the measurement of primary production of grassland. Blackwell Sci. Publ., Oxford, England.

Moore, P.G. 1954. Spacing in plant populations. Ecology. 35:222-227.

Morisita, M. 1957. A new method for the estimation of density by the spacing method applicable to non-randomly distributed populations (in Japanese). Physiol. and Ecol. 7:134-144.

Mueller-Dombois, D., and H. Ellenberg. 1974. Aims and methods of vegetation ecology. John Wiley and Sons, New York, New York.

Murphy, A.H. 1970. Predicted forage yield based on fall precipitation in California annual grasslands. J. Range Manage. 23:363-365.

Myers, R.M. 1960. Range utilization exclosure. J. Range Manage. 13:40.

Nadabo, S., R.D. Pieper, and R.F. Beck. 1980. Growth patterns and biomass relations of *Xanthocephalum sarothrae* (Pursh) Shinners on sandy soils in southern New Mexico. J. Range Manage. 33:394-397.

National Academy of Sciences. 1962. Range Research. Basic Problems and Techniques. Nat. Acad. Sci., Nat. Res. Council Pub. 890. Washington, D.C.

Neal, D.L., and J.L. Neal. 1973. Uses and capabilities of electronic capacitance instruments for estimating standing herbage. J. Brit. Grassland Soc. 28:81-89.

Neal, D.L., and L.R. Neal. 1965. A new electronic meter for measuring herbage yield. Res. Note PSW-56. Forest Service, USDA, Washington, D.C.

Neal, D.L., P.O. Currie, and M.J. Morris. 1976. Sampling herbaceous native vegetation with an electronic capacitance instrument. J. Range Manage. 29:74-77.

Neal, D.L., R.L. Hubbard, and C.E. Conrad. 1969. A magnetic point frame. J. Range Manage. 22:202-203.

Nedrow, W.W. 1937. Studies on the ecology of roots. Ecology. 18:27-52.

Nelson, E.W. 1930. Method of studying shrubby plants in relation to grazing. Ecology. 11:764-769.

Nerney, N.J. 1960. A modification for the point-frame method of sampling range vegetation. J. Range Manage. 13:261-262.

Norris, K.H., R.F. Barnes, J.E. Moore, and J.S. Shenk. 1976. Predicting forage quality by infrared reflectance spectroscopy. J. Anim. Sci. 43:889-897.

Nudds, T.D. 1977. Quantifying the vegetation structure of wildlife cover. Wildlife Soc. Bull. 5:113-117.

Nystrom, T.E. 1984. Vertical vegetative production sampling for pre- and post-mining inventory. M.S. Thesis, Colorado State Univ.

Odum, E.P. 1959. Organic production and turnover in old field succession. Ecology. 41:34-49.

Odum, E.P. 1971. Fundamentals of ecology. W.B. Saunders, Philadelphia, Pennsylvania.

Oosting, H.J. 1956. The study of plant communities. W.H. Freeman and Co., San Francisco, California.

Owensby, C.E. 1969. Effect of cages on herbage yield in true prairie vegetation. J. Range Manage. 22:131-132.

Owensby, C.E. 1973. Modified step-point system for botanical composition and basal cover estimates. J. Range Manage. 26:302-303.

Papanastasis, V.P. 1977. Optimum size and shape of quadrat for sampling herbage weight in grasslands of northern Greece. J. Range Manage. 30:446-448.

Parker, E.E. 1963. Estimating grass herbage production on desert plains grassland range. M.S. Thesis, New Mexico State Univ.

Parker, K.W. 1951. A method for measuring trend and range condition on national forest ranges. Forest Service, USDA, Washington, D.C.

Parker, K.W. 1954. Application of ecology in the determination of range condition and trend. J. Range Manage. 7:14-23.

Parker, K.W., and R.W. Harris. 1959. The 3-step method for measuring condition and trend of forest ranges: a resume of its history, development and use, p. 55-69. *In:* Forest Exp. Sta. Proc. USDA, Washington, D.C.

Parker, K.W., and D.A. Savage. 1944. Reliability of the line interception method in measuring vegetation on the Southern Great Plains. J. Amer. Soc. Agron. 36:97-110.

Payne, G.F. 1974. Cover-weight relationships. J. Range Manage. 29:403-404.

Pechanec, J.F., and G.D. Pickford. 1937. A weight estimate method for determination of range or pasture production. J. Amer. Soc. Agron. 29:894-904.

Pechanec, J.F., and G. Stewart. 1949. Grazing spring-fall sheep ranges in southern Idaho. Circ. 808. USDA, Washington, D.C.

Peet, R.K. 1974. The measurement of species diversity. Ann. Rev. Ecol. and Syst. 5:285-307.

Pielou, E.C. 1959. The use of point-to-point distance in the study of the pattern of plant distribution. J. Ecol. 47:607-613.

Pielou, E.C. 1975. Ecological diversity. John Wiley and Sons, New York, New York.

Pieper, R.D. 1978. Measurement techniques for herbaceous and shrubby vegetation. New Mexico State Univ.

Pieper, R.D., J.R. Montoya, and V.L. Groce. 1971. Site characteristic on pinyon-juniper and blue grama ranges in south-central New Mexico. Bull. 573. New Mexico Agr. Exp. Sta.

Pino, R. 1954. Comparative efficiency of various lengths of belt transects in estimating forage production on semidesert grassland range. M.S. Thesis, New Mexico State Univ.

Poulton, C.E., and E.W. Tisdale. 1961. A quantitative method for the description and classification of range vegetation. J. Range Manage. 14:13-21.

Provenza, F.D., and P.J. Urness. 1981. Diameter length-weight relations for blackbrush *(Coleogyne ramosissima)* branches. J. Range Manage. 34:215-217.

Pumphrey, F.V. 1980. Precipitation, temperature, and herbage relationships for a pine woodland site in northeastern Oregon. J. Range Manage. 33:307-310.

Range Term Glossary Committee. 1974. A glossary of terms used in range management. Soc. Range Manage., Denver, Colorado.

Reese, G.A., F.L. Bayn, and N.E. West. 1980. Evaluation of double-sampling estimators of subalpine herbage production. J. Range Manage. 33:300-306.

Reid, J.T., P.G. Woolfolk, C.R. Richards, R.W. Kaufmann, J.K. Loosli, K.L. Turk, J.I. Miller, and R.E. Blaser. 1950. A new indicator method for determination of digestibility and consumption of forages by ruminants. J. Dairy Sci. 33:60-71.

Reppert, J.N., R.H. Hughes, and Don Duncan. 1962. Herbage yield and its correlation with other plant measurements. *In:* Range Research Methods. Misc. Pub. No. 940. Forest Service, USDA, Washington, D.C.

Rice, E.L., and R.W. Kelting. 1955. The species area curve. Ecology. 37:7-11.

Risser, P.G. 1984. Methods for inventory and monitoring vegetation, litter, and soil surface conditions. *In:* Developing stratagies for rangeland management. Westview Press, Boulder, Colorado.

Risser, P.G., and D.H. Zedler. 1968. An evaluation of the grassland quarter method. Ecology. 49:1006-1009.

Rittenhouse, L.R., and F.A. Sneva. 1977. A technique for estimating big sagebrush production. J. Range Manage. 30:68-70.

Robertson, J.H. 1954. A low-cost portable cage for range and pasture plots. J. Range Manage. 7:42.

Roe, R. 1947. Preliminary survey of the natural pastures of the New England district of New South Wales and a general discussion of their problems. Res. Bull. 210. New South Wales Counc. Sci. Industr.

Routledge, R.D. 1980. Bias in estimating the diversity of large uncensused communities. Ecology. 61:276-281.

Rutherford, M.C. 1979. Plant based techniques for determining available browse and browse utilization: A review. Bot. Rev. 45:203-228.

Ruyle, G.B., J.E. Bowns, and A.F. Schlundt. 1983. Estimating snowberry *(Symphoricarpos oreophilus)* utilization by sheep from twig diameter-weight relations. J. Range Manage. 36:472-474.

Sampson, A.W. 1914. Natural revegetation of range lands based upon growth requirement of life history of the vegetation. J. Agr. Res. 3:93-148.

Schultz, A.M., R.P. Gibbens, and L. De Bano. 1961. Artificial populations for teaching and testing range techniques. J. Range Manage. 14:236-242.

Schuster, J.L. 1965. Estimating browse from twig and stem measurements. J. Range Manage. 18:220-223.

Shafer, E.L. 1963. The twig-count method for measuring hardwood deer browse. J. Wildlife Manage. 27:428-437.

Sharp, L.A. 1954. Evaluation of the loop procedure of the 3-step method in the salt-desert shrub. J. Range Manage. 7:83-88.

Sharp, L.A., M. Hironaka, and E.W. Tisdale. 1957. Viability of medusa-head (*Elymus caputmedusae* L.) seed collected in Idaho. J. Range Manage. 10:123-126.

Sharrow, S.H., and D.A. Tober. 1979. A simple, lightweight point frame. J. Range Manage. 32:75-76.

Shiflet, T.N., and H.E. Dietz. 1974. Relationship between precipitation and annual rangeland herbage production in southeastern Kansas. J. Range Manage. 27:272-276.

Shoop, M.C., and E.H. McIlvain. 1963. The micro-unit forage inventory method. J. Range Manage. 16:172-179.

Short, L.R. 1953. New equipment for the 3-step method. J. Range Manage. 6:184-186.

Simpson, E.H. 1949. Measurement of diversity. Nature. 163:688.

Smith, A.D. 1944. A study of the reliability of range vegetation estimates. Ecology. 25:441-448.

Smith, J.G. 1959. Additional modifications of the point frame. J. Range Manage. 4:204-205.

Smith, J.G. 1962. An appraisal of the loop transect method for estimating root crown area changes. J. Range Manage. 15:72-78.

Smoliak, S. 1956. Influence of climatic conditions on forage production of shortgrass rangeland. J. Range Manage. 9:89-91.

Sneva, F.A., and C.M. Britton. 1983. Adjusting and forecasting range yields in the intermountain big sagebrush portion of the steppe region. Bull. 659. Oregon Agr. Exp. Sta.

Sneva, F.A., and D.N. Hyder. 1962. Estimating herbage production on semiarid ranges in the Intermountain Region. J. Range Manage. 15:88-93.

Society of American Foresters. 1950. Forestry terminology. Soc. Amer. Forest., Washington, D.C.

Soplin, H., H.D. Gross, and J.O. Rawlings. 1975. Optimum size of sampling unit to estimate coastal Bermudagrass yield. Agron. J. 67:533-537.

Sparks, D.R, and J.C. Malechek. 1968. Estimating percentage dry weights in diets using a microscope technique. J. Range Manage. 21:264-265.

Stelfox, H.B. 1957. Two types of cages found satisfactory for pasture studies. J. Range Manage. 10:210-231.

Stewart, G., and S.S. Hutchings. 1936. The point observation-plot (square-foot density) method of vegetation survey. Amer. Soc. Agron. J. 28:714-726.

Strickler, G.S., and F.W. Stearns. 1963. The determination of plant density. In: Range research methods. Misc. Pub. No. 940. Forest Service. USDA, Washington, D.C.

Stubbendieck, J., and C.R. Fenster. 1981. A versatile flail-type forage plot harvester. J. Range Manage. 34:90-91.

Sylvestre, P.E. and S.B. Williams. 1952. Methods of measuring the relative productivity of pasture experiments with livestock. Husb. Div. Central Exp. Farm, Ottawa, Canada. Mimeo.

Tadmor, N.H., A. Brieghet, I. Noy-Meir, R.W. Benjamin, and E. Eyal. 1975. An evaluation of the calibrated weight-estimate method for measuring production in annual vegetation. J. Range Manage. 28:65-69.

Talbot, M.W. 1937. Indicators of southwestern range conditions. Farmers' Bull. 1782. USDA, Washington, D.C.

Terry, W.S., D.H. Hunter, and B.F. Swindel. 1981. Herbage capacitance meter: an evaluation of its accuracy in Florida rangelands. J. Range Manage. 34:240-241.

Theurer, C.B. 1970a. Chemical indicator techniques for determining range forage consumption. In: Range and Wildlife Habitat Evaluation. Mis. Pub. 1147. Forest Service, USDA, Washington, D.C.

Theurer, C.B. 1970b. Determination of botanical and chemical composition of the grazing animals diet, In: Nat. Conf. Forage Quality Evaluation and Utilization. Univ. Nebraska.

Theurer, C.B., A.L. Lesperance, and J.D. Wallace. 1976. Botanical composition of the diet of livestock grazing native ranges. Tech. Bull. 233. Arizona. Agr. Exp. Sta.

Tilley, J.M.A., and R.A. Terry. 1963. A two-stage technique for the in vitro digestion of forage crops. J. Brit. Grassland Soc. 18:104-110.

Tinney, F.W., O.S. Aamodt, and H.L. Ahlgren. 1937. Preliminary report of a study on methods used in botanical analyses of pasture swards. J. Amer. Soc. Agron. 29:835-840.

T'Mannetje, L., and K.P. Haydock. 1963. The dry-weight-rank method for the botanical analysis of pasture. J. Brit. Grassland Soc. 18:268-275.

Torell, D.J. 1954. An esophageal fistula for animal nutrition studies. J. Anim. Sci. 13:878-884.

Tribe, D.E. 1952. The relation of palatability to nutritive value and its importance in the utilization of herbage by grazing animals. Proc. 6th Int. Grassland Congr. II:1265-1270.

Uden, P., R. Parra, and P.J. Van Soest. 1974. Factors influencing reliability of the nylon bag technique. J. Dairy Sci. 57:622.

Uresk, D.W., R.O. Gilbert, and W.H. Richard. 1977. Sampling big sagebrush for phytomass. J. Range Manage. 30:311-314.

Vallentine, J.F. 1956. Use of indicator methods in range digestion trials. J. Range Manage. 9:235-239.

Van Dyne, G.M. 1966. Use of a vacuum-clipper for harvesting herbage. Ecology. 47:624.

Van Dyne, G.M. 1969. Measuring quantity and quality of the diet of large herbivores, In: Golley, F.B., and H.K. Buechner (eds). A Practical Guide to the Study of the Productivity of Large Herbivores. Blackwell Sci. Publ., Oxford, England.

Van Dyne, G.M., W.G. Vogel, and H.G. Fisser. 1963. Influence of small plot size and shape on range herbage production estimates. Ecology. 44:746-759.

Van Dyne, G.M., N.R. Brockington, Z. Szocs, J. Duek, and C.A. Ribic. 1980. Large herbivore subsystem, In: Breymeyer, A.I., and G.M. Van Dyne (eds.) Grasslands systems analysis and man. Cambridge Univ. Press, Cambridge, England.

Van Hellen, R.W., and W.C. Ellis. 1973. Membranes for rumen in situ digestion techniques. J. Anim. Sci. 37:358.

Van Soest, P.J. 1982. Nutritional ecology of the ruminant. O & B Books, Inc., Corvallis, Oregon.

Warren Wilson, J. 1959. Analysis of the distribution of foliage area in grassland, In: Measurement of grassland productivity. Acad. Press, New York, York York.

Warren Wilson, J. 1960. Inclined point quadrats. New Phytol. 59:8-10.

Warren Wilson, J. 1963a. Errors resulting from thickness of point quadrats. Aust. J. Bot. 11:178-188.

Warren Wilson, J. 1963b. Estimation of foliage denseness and foliage angle by inclined point quadrats. Aust. J. Bot. 1:95-105.

Watkins, W.E. 1955. Digestibility of range grasses and grass-legume mixtures. Bull. 400. New Mexico Agr. Exp. Sta.

Weaver, J.E., and V.H. Hougen. 1939. Effect of frequent clipping on plant production in prairie and pasture. Amer. Midland Natur. 21:396-414.

Whisenant, S.G., and D.F. Burzlaff. 1978. Predicting green weight of mesquite (*Prosopis glandulosa* Torr.). J. Range Manage. 31:396-397.

Whittaker, R.H. 1965. Dominance and diversity in land plant communities. Science. 147:250-260.

Whitman, W.C., and E.I. Siggeirsson. 1954. Comparison of line interception and point contact methods in the analysis of mixed grass range vegetation. Ecology. 35:431-436.

Wiegert, R.G. 1962. The selection of an optimum quadrat size for sampling the standing crop of grasses and forbs. Ecology. 43:125-129.

Wight, J.R. 1967. The sampling unit and its effect on saltbush yield estimates. J. Range Manage. 20:323-325.

Wilbert, D.E. 1961. A durable, economical cage for utilization or production studies. J. Range Manage. 14:337-338.

Williams, C.B. 1964. Patterns in the balance of nature. Acad. Press, New York, New York.

Wilm, H.G., D.F. Costello, and G.E. Klipple. 1944. Estimating forage yield by the double sampling method. J. Amer. Soc. Agron. 36:194-203.

Wilson, J.R. 1981. Environmental and nutritional factors affecting herbage quality, *In:* J.B. Hacker (ed.). Symposium on nutritional limits to animal production from pastures. Commonwealth Agr. Bur., Farnham Royal, England.

Winkworth, R.H. 1955. The use of point quadrats for the analysis of heathland. Aust. J. Bot. 3:68-81.

Winkworth, R.E., and D.W. Goodall. 1962. A crosswire sighting tube for point-quadrat analyses. Ecology. 43:342-343.

Young, V.A., and G.F. Payne. 1948. Utilization of "key" browse species in relation to proper grazing practices in cutover western white pine in northern Idaho. J. Forest. 46:35-40.

Chapter 4
Studies of Root Habits and Development

Introduction

An understanding of the principles of range management depends on a basic knowledge of plants. This includes knowledge about their below ground parts—the roots—an important component that has not been fully appreciated until rather recently. Few ecologists have studied the root systems of plants growing in nature. A beginner who wishes to embark on root investigations will soon learn why this has been so. But, it should be remembered that whenever methods are cumbersome and tedious, potential for innovation is great.

In 1957 Troughton published a book on "The Underground Organs of Herbage Grasses." This text includes 25 chapters divided into three parts: description of underground organs, factors influencing growth, and effect of the plant upon the soil. Two more recent books of interest that deal with methods of studying root systems are: "The Root System" by Kolesnikov (1971) and "Methods of Studying Root Systems" by Bohm (1979). These are recommended for study by those investigators interested in the detailed analysis of roots. In addition to general methods of studying root systems, Kolesnikov (1971) describes innovative methods for recording lateral roots and for determining root diameter, and Bohm (1979) presents techniques for measuring root surface, root volume, and root length.

Value of Knowledge of Root Reactions

Roots have one or more of the following functions: (1) absorption of nutrients and water, (2) anchorage and support, (3) propagation, (4) storage of food reserves and (5) synthesis of some of the growth regulators. They also play a prominent role in the growth and welfare of other organisms through (6) soil development, nitrogen fixation, and root exudates.

Studies of plant responses to drought, fertility, competition, and other environmental conditions can be aided by, and are often entirely dependent upon, a thorough knowledge of root habits: depth of penetration, extent of branching, distribution through the soil profile, rate of growth, ratio of roots to shoots, and other characteristics which determine the absorptive ability of the plant. Investigations concerning the role of the root systems in anchorage of the plant can be of great importance to range management. Examples to be cited are the value of depth, quantity, and tensile strength of the roots to resist frost heaving of seedlings, washing or blowing of soil by erosive agents, and pulling upon the plants by grazing animals.

In the strict sense, roots of grasses and other plants encountered on range-lands rarely act as organs of propagation. On the other hand, rhizomes, which are root-like in appearance but actually are underground stems, are important means of propagation among perennial plants. While studies of rhizomes will not be included in this chapter on roots, it should be emphasized that they occupy major interest in weed control techniques [e.g., eradication of bind-weeds (*Convolvulus* spp.)], plant breeding programs [e.g., development of creeping alfalfa *(Medicago sativa)*], and revegetation research.

The role of roots as a storage place for food reserves is the basis of many of our present-day range management concepts and practices. Principles of range readiness, range condition and trend, rotation grazing, and selective spraying are associated with distribution of food materials in the plant from season to season. The subject of plant vigor is important from both ecological and production phases of range management research. Another important area of root study could concern the effects of roots on the habitat itself. This is the study of plant root influences, and includes effects of plant roots on soil formation, soil fertility, and erosion control.

Methods of Studying Roots

Root Excavations and Descriptions of Root Systems

The following methods involve the description of natural root systems *in situ,* their removal from the soil intact, or a sample of the system removed. Variations of these methods can be found; the specific methods required will depend upon the type of plant or community, soil type, topography, and resources available. It may be practical to employ mechanized ditch-digging or back hoe equipment to open the trenches before using the more meticulous ice pick and hand trowel where a large number of roots are to be studied in place.

Trench Tracing Method

This method has great variations in its application, depending upon type of plant roots (tap or fibrous), age of plants (mature or seedlings), and type of soil (Weaver 1926, Albertson 1937, Kolesnikov 1971). Before digging the trench a careful survey of plants should be made to find a typical site with respect to topography and soil type. Also, proper spacing and species of plants present is desired. When the site is selected, stakes are set and a string stretched to mark one edge of the trench. This trench should be at least 60 cm wide and as long and deep as required for safety and to study the lateral spread and depth of roots. It is desirable, but not always possible, to have all the study plants located on one side of the trench. Soil can then be placed on the opposite side of the trench to avoid damage to the plants.

When the trench is dug, a flat spade is used to provide a vertical trench wall where root studies are to be made. With the trench completed, ice picks, sharp trowels and spades are used to remove the soil from roots, beginning at the top and working in a perpendicular rather than a horizontal direction to a depth of 10–30 mm into the soil profile. As the roots are exposed, they are drawn to scale on paper with type of growth, diameter, and direction indi-cated (Fig. 4-1). A frame with thin wire or string forming 5- to 10-cm squares when placed against the profile aides in marking off the roots according to scale.

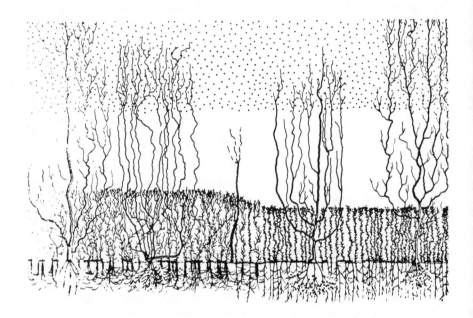

Figure 4-1. Bisect of prairie plants showing root habits of forbs and grasses (Courtesy of J.E. Weaver).

The vertical trench wall (profile) method permits the determination of the distribution of roots in the soil horizons, the zone of root concentration, and both lateral spread and depth of roots. Such a method was used by Cook and Lewis (1963) and Cook et al. (1965) to study competition between grasses and shrubs on foothill ranges of Utah.

Root Photography in Situ

Spraying roots with paint from pressurized cans has been effective in the photography of grass, shrub, and tree roots *in situ* (Haas and Rogler 1953, Schultz and Biswell 1955). The first step is to make an excavation on one side of the plant. A portion of the root system is then isolated from the surround-ing soil with an ice pick. Enough roots should remain imbedded in the soil to hold the plant top in its normal, upright position. The roots are then sprayed with paint. Either aluminum paint or yellow enamel are satisfactory for black and white photography (Fig. 4-2). Other paint colors can be used effectively for color film. The paint which has adhered to the soil behind the exposed roots is removed by chipping off a thin layer of soil with an ice pick. Thus a dark background is restored giving the needed contrast for photographs.

Figure 4-2. Photographing roots of brush plants *in situ* (Courtesy of A.M. Schultz).

Trench Washing Method

This method is similar to the trench tracing method except that water under pressure is employed to aid in softening and removing the soil (Stoechler and Kluender 1938, Tharp and Muller 1940, Upchurch and Lovvorn 1951). The ice pick may be effectively used to supplement action of water in exposing roots. Using water will make it possible to separate soil from the finer roots while the roots remain in a fairly natural position until drawn on scaled paper. It is usually impossible to make drawings of roots in exactly the same number per unit area as actually found in the soil. Drawings, however, should show such factors as relative abundance, diameter, and type and extent of growth. Filling the trench with water several days before washing may soften the soil around the roots. Extraction is more effective in sandy than in clay soils. A disadvantage is the production of mud in the trench.

Hydraulic Method

For the hydraulic method, it is desirable to locate the excavation sites along road cuts or faces of gullies accessible to tank trucks equipped with power pumps. The pumps are fitted with two types of nozzles—a high-pressure, single stream type and a fine spray type. The bulk of the soil or parent material around the plant being studied is removed with the high-pressure nozzle. The fine spray is then used to wash the soil away from the smaller roots (Hellmers et al. 1955, Singer and Hutnick 1973). Caution must be used with high-pressure nozzles or the delicate root systems will be torn apart. It is helpful if the terrain below the exposed embankment drains the excess mud and water away from the working area.

Excavation with Air

Air pressure from a compressor or suction from a vacuum such as a heavy-duty vacuum cleaner used by industry have been used with some success. Both of these techniques work reasonably well on moderately-dry friable soils of a sandy loam texture. These techniques using air are discussed briefly by Bohm (1979).

Soil Prism Washing Method

In this method a trench is dug entirely around a prism of soil 100 cm square (Fig. 4-3) and as long and deep as is required to include full root depth of plants studied (Weaver 1926). Wire netting or a nylon net can then be stretched securely over the sides and ends of the prism. Next, sharpened wires or thin rods are driven through the prism of soil in parallel rows along the meshes of netting, or a needle board can be driven into one side of the prism (Bohm 1979). The needle board helps support the soil column and aids in keeping the roots in place while the plant is washed or removed from the trench.

Figure 4-3. A soil prism exposed and ready for removal to be soaked for easy removal of the soil from the roots by gently spraying with water (Courtesy of C.W. Cook).

The loose surface soil is then removed, with the plant crowns left exposed. One technique is to replace a thin layer of surface soil with plaster of paris to support the plants during the soaking and washing process. Soil around the roots is washed away by water from a force pump or allowed to soak away in a canal or small streambed with gentle agitation by fingertips. Washing should proceed from top of the plants downward. Care should be taken to preserve as many small roots as possible during washing. This method, however, is not designed to remove all roots of any plant but only those concentrated in the prism studied.

Schuurman and Goedewaagen (1971) suggested drying the prism at 100°C, followed by soaking in a solution of sodium pyrophosphate, and finally washing the roots free with a water spray. These authors suggested that soils with a high clay content might be treated with a combined method of soaking in water and freezing the prism followed by the process of soaking in a solution of sodium pyrophosphate.

Soil-block Washing Method

This method is sometimes used when the entire root system of a plant is being studied (Pavlychenko 1937). If the progress in root development is to be followed, soil blocks of various sizes should be used. For the 5- to 20-day old plants, soil blocks 38×38×38 cm are usually sufficiently large. For 20- to 30-day old plants, blocks 60×30×80 cm are generally satisfactory. When root systems of mature plants are studied, the blocks should be considerably larger, often 100×100×170 cm for 3-year-old plants. Extent of roots will depend upon species, age, and type of soil in which the plants are growing.

When the block is marked out in the field, a trench is dug around it to the desired depth. The block is then encased by a wooden frame of sufficient strength to support the weight of soil. The block is hoisted from the pit and hauled to a tank of water. After soaking for several hours, a spray of water is applied slowly and carefully to wash the soil from the roots.

When all soil has been removed from the roots, the entire plant is placed in a tank of water large enough for the roots and tops to be spread in a natural position for analysis. It is helpful if the tank is painted black on the inside and a scale with 2.5-cm divisions or cross sections marked along the bottom. Floodlights may be used to increase illumination. This arrangement makes it possible to float the plant in water for the most efficient analysis (Cook 1943).

Modifications of this method are in common use. Half square meters of sod 10 cm deep may be employed effectively for determining the amount of plant material (roots and rhizomes) in the upper 10 cm for various kinds of prairie sod (Shively and Weaver 1939).

Cylinder or Box Method

Galvanized iron cylinders, plastic pipe, or boxes have many uses and modifications in application. They may be used for studies pertaining to soil-root relations as influenced by soil type, age of plants, or treatments. The containers can be filled with soil, seeded to various plants, and later used for studies on root development in relation to such factors as clipping, rate of growth, and amount of soil water (Weaver and Clements 1938). Metal or plastic cylinders (phytometers) for this work will vary considerably in size depending upon the questions which the investigator wishes to answer.

For example, galvanized cans 15×60×60 cm could be used to study root growth on lifted sods of prairie grasses as it relates to degree of utilization during past years. Sods 15×60×20 cm transplanted in these cans with 40 cm of soil beneath them permits the study of rate and amount of root growth that takes place below the transplanted sod. Similar cylinders may be used to determine root growth of seedlings of various species. Cylinders may be made by rolling sheets of galvanized iron into cylinders held tightly in position by iron bands. The cylinders are often placed in tin containers, such as four-liter cans. When the growing period is completed, the cylinder is lifted from the can, the bands removed, and the galvanized sheet unrolled to permit washing of soil from roots. Some galvanized, rectangular containers are made so that one side can be removed to expose the profile. Roots then may be floated in water while drawings and calculations are made, after which they may be removed from the tops for drying and weighing. Plastic pipe may also be used where roots are sampled at the end of the study by cutting through the pipe and exposing the soil.

Soil Core Method

As early as in the 1950's, Ruby and Young (1953) and Kinsinger (1955) used power-driven machines to force tubes into the soil to rather deep depths to remove cores containing plant roots (Fig. 4-4). Cores of grassland sod were

Figure 4-4. A soil core 210 cm in length taken with a conventional soil coring machine used by Soil Conservation Service to sample soils. Roots are removed from the soil by soaking and gently removing soil from the roots of each 15-cm section.

obtained by driving cylinders of 5- to 15-cm diameter into the soil to a depth of 10 to 150 cm. When removed, the cores furnish such information as number of roots that penetrate beyond certain depths and volume of roots in the cylinder. These cores can be taken quite rapidly, allowing many samples to be obtained over a relatively short period of time. This method has been effectively used to determine rooting habitat in relation to drought and intensity of grazing (Weaver and Albertson 1943). Soil cores, 8 cm or less in diameter, can be taken by forcing a steel tube several centimeters into the soil.

Cores thus obtained can be used to determine behavior of roots in relation to such factors as soil texture, bulk density, or intensity of clipping of vegetation (Ruby and Young 1953).

The core method has been used extensively at the Grassland Research Institute in England with fertility experiments (Williams and Baker 1957). In these experiments, no attempt was made to separate roots from attached rhizomes and stem bases. The initial disposal of clay, silt, and fine sand has been mechanized with a root washing machine. This consists of a 60-mesh sieve in a rotating funnel and under a spray of water. After washing in this manner, the sample is dried, weighed, and ashed. The plant ash is dissolved by sulfuric acid, leaving the residual mineral ash which is subtracted from the sample dry weight to calculate root weight on an ash free basis.

One important advantage of the core method is that the relatively small holes left in the sod have little effect on grass growth in small experimental plots, a large part of which might be disturbed with root excavation method. Stony soils make the core sampling procedure difficult, if not impossible.

Bartos and Sims (1974) used root sampling instruments such as a pneumatic hammer, a T-shaped core sampler (Fig. 4-5), and a hydraulic coring

Figure 4-5. A pneumatic hammer (left front) and T-shaped samplers (right front) used to obtain root samples from shortgrass prairies (Courtesy of D.L. Bartos and P.L. Sims).

machine mounted on a truck. The T-shaped sampler facilitated taking cores to a depth of 10 cm with a diameter of 7.5 cm. To collect a depth of 1 m with a 5-cm diameter core, a pneumatic hammer and core cylinder were used. For deeper depth samples, a hydraulic coring instrument mounted on a truck was used. The soil cores were divided into various depth increments. The cores were soaked in containers of water for several minutes prior to washing. Soil cores were then hand washed on the same day they were collected. Cores were washed over a 32-mesh screen to prevent loss of root material. Root material was oven-dried for 48 hours at 105°C, weighed, ashed at 610° for 4 to 8 hours, and reweighed. Root biomass was then expressed on an ash-free basis and presented in grams per depth and area of soil.

Wyatt et al. (1980) and Holechek (1982) used a modification of the method described by Bartos and Sims (1974). Roots were separated from soil by placing segments of the soil cores into screen cages or over a 1 mm sieve for soaking and washing with water.

Bowns and Box (1964) described a core sampling device that was used effectively to excavate grass roots in fine sandy soils. Box (1966) later described a core sampling implement that could be used for a wide variety of soil conditions to extract roots from shallow soil depths. This apparatus was of low-cost material made from aluminum irrigation pipe.

A portable coring tool for collection of root and soil samples in roadless areas was presented by Brown and Thilenius (1977). The coring tool could be used to sample to a 50-cm depth conveniently. Again, moist soils of lighter texture are considerably easier to sample than the dry or heavy soils. Frequently, sampling is easier if the area is soaked with water a day or two before sampling. After the water has had time to penetrate to the desired depth and the soil is moist, the coring tool can easily be inserted into the soil to obtain the sample core, but soil compression may be a problem.

Monolith Method

The monolith was designed to provide for a more detailed study of plant roots than may be accomplished by most of the other methods. For example, detailed information may be obtained on such factors as relation of main root growth to growth of branch roots and root growth of one species of plant as related to growth of other plants with which the species is associated. Roots freed from soil can easily be mounted and placed on exhibit or they may be cut at various depths and root weight determined. A trench is dug 0.5-1 m wide alongside the plants included in the study. The wall of the trench is made smooth and plumb. Then a shallow wooden box 30 cm wide, 8-12 cm deep, and the desired length with the top open is placed against the side of the trench and tapped into the soil face with a sledge hammer. With the impression of the box made in the side of the trench, the monolith is marked and 30 cm or more of soil cut away. The box is then fitted tightly over the protruding block. After the box is carefully braced, the soil behind the box and on the side of the trench is cut away until the box can be lifted from the trench. Soil on the open side of the box is now trimmed to the desired depth. The monolith of soil can then be transported to the laboratory.

Repeated soaking and washing of the monolith with a spray of water will eventually remove the soil from the roots (Fig. 4-6). Roots can be teased into their natural positions and measured when covered with about 1 cm of water over dark colored blotter paper laid on the bottom surface of the tank. The blotter paper along with the root mass can then be raised slowly from the top of the root system until free from the water. The blotter paper holding the roots can then be laid on a flat surface to dry, after which the roots can be

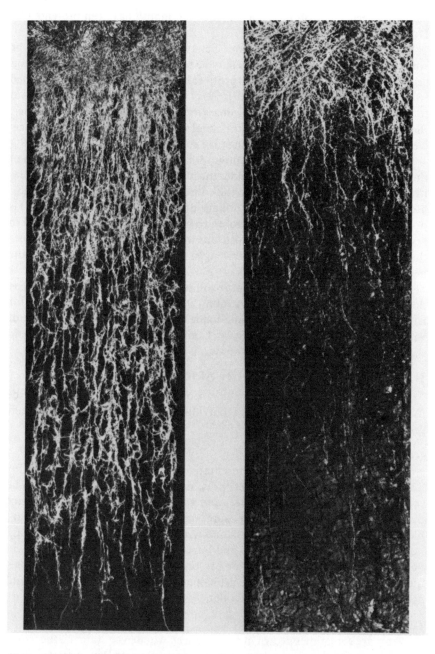

Figure 4-6. Left: root system washed from a soil monolith and arranged in natural position on black felt or blotter paper for photographing. Right: monolith of soil showing roots partially washed out (Courtesy of J.E. Weaver).

mounted under Plexiglas for display. Roots may be mounted for permanent display, or cut as desired to obtain root weights at various levels (Weaver and Darland 1949). An outline of procedures along with a complete list of materials needed for obtaining a range-soil monolith has been presented by Donaldson and Beck (1973).

Where the relation between root behavior and soil structure is to be studied, permanent soil monoliths may be prepared by using vinyl resin and cellulose acetate to impregnate the profile and to keep the monolith attached to a supporting board (Smith et al. 1952). The monolith method can be used for measuring comparative root biomass among treatments or plant species, the zone of root concentration, the axial length, the functioning surface, weights, and lengths of active or inactive roots.

One major disadvantage of the monolith method is that only a portion of the root system, usually directly under the plant, is sampled. Thus, extrapolation of any measurements taken to the entire plant is difficult, if not impossible. Sometimes a board with pins or nails driven into it in rows (pinboard) is positioned along the side of a monolith to help stabilize the monolith and to keep the roots near their natural positions while the soil is being washed from the roots. Schuurman and Goedewaagen (1971) described the use of the needleboard or pinboard in detail.

A round monolith, or a rather large soil core, can be taken from the soil by powered machines or by spades. A round steel ring is required as a guide for trimming the core to size. The spade-made core can be removed in a cage of wire netting stretched tightly around it. Cook (1943), Gooderham (1969), and Bloomberg (1974) used a version of such a method to study root systems.

Rate of Growth and Longevity of Roots

In studying the growth of individual roots, a number of methods may be used. These involve the marking of individual roots and later observing their growth.

Root Blacking Method

This method requires that representative new main roots be exposed for observation by means of trenches, pots, or boxes with removal sides. The roots remain in their natural state, and the rest of the root system is not disturbed. With a minimum of exposure, small apical sections of the roots are blackened with moist carbon black and wrapped immediately in wet sphagnum with burlap. The sphagnum and burlap are reinforced with styrofoam board, and the excavation is covered to protect it from the weather. Subsequent examinations to determine growth are made by lifting the burlap and gently removing the sphagnum (Crider 1955).

Glass-box Window Method

Plants are sometimes grown in narrow, deep wooden containers, the fronts of which are fitted with windows of heavy plate glass or Plexiglas. A convenient size for the boxes is 6 cm wide, 30 cm long, and 30 cm deep. Small holes in the bottom of the boxes and about 2 cm of pebbles provide drainage. The boxes are filled 2 to 3 cm from the top with screened, uniformly mixed, fine sandy loam soil. The grasses or forbs are seeded (or seedlings may be transplanted) into the boxes. During growth, the windows should be covered with aluminum foil, tar paper, black plastic, or wooden panels. When kept tilted forward at an angle of 30°, most of the roots will grow along the glass surface. Day-to-day record of root elongation is made directly on the glass by marking apexes with a grease pencil (Fig. 4-7) (Crider 1955).

Figure 4-7. Roots showing through glass window, marked for measuring growth increments (Courtesy of J.F. Crider).

Majerus (1975) measured the responses of root growth to decreased soil water potential with glass-front root observation boxes in the greenhouse. The glass surface of the root boxes was divided vertically into four equal 10-cm soil horizons. Thermocouple psychrometers were inserted through the back of the boxes and centered at 5, 15, 25 and 35-cm depths in each of the four soil levels. Soil water potential, soil temperature, and root elongation were measured periodically.

Ares (1976) studied the growth of roots under field conditions by means of windows in field excavations. The vertical observation surface was fitted with a glass plate 0.5 cm thick. A fine layer of sieved soil was applied to the inner surface between the face of the original soil and the glass. The glass was braced against the observation surface and covered with a black plastic sheet and then supported by a thick plastic foam sheet. This excluded light and provided insulation but could be removed readily for observation. The entire excavation was covered to prevent damage from wind and moisture.

Taylor and Bohm (1976) studied root distribution and root density behind glass rhizatron windows and concluded that root densities were considerable higher in the 2-mm layer near the plastic-soil interface than in the bulk soil behind it. Thus, plastic windows are useful in descriptive or demonstrational experiments, but are not recommended for quantitative evaluations of the root mass.

Photoelectric Cell Method

Rowse and Phillips (1974) devised a method for determining length of roots by employing a photoelectric cell to count the number of intersections between the root sample and a set of parallel straight lines. Roots from the sample are cut into segments and spread uniformly under water on a transparent glass plate which is illuminated from below. A second glass sheet etched with 1 cm grid is placed over the root samples. The intersections between the roots and the parallel lines are counted by moving the root sample beneath a modified binocular microscope fitted with a photoelectric counting device. Whenever a root passes beneath the microscope, a count is accumulated on a scaler (electronic counter). A metal disc with a small hole in the center is fitted to the eyepieces below the lens to reduce the field to about 100 μm. With no root in the microscope field the light shines through the scope on to a silicon photo-transistor mounted on a housing above the eyepiece. A root that enters the field of view reduces the light intensity on the photo-transistor and thus produces a count on the scaler. An estimate of root length is obtained from the count of number of intersections between the root sample and a set of parallel lines. The length = $1/2 \, \pi DN$, where D is the distance between the parallel lines and N is the total number of intersections counted. Richards et al. (1979) used a somewhat similar method which is referred to as an optoelectronic scanner.

Banding Method

The life span of individual roots can be determined by banding while some of the roots are young (Weaver and Zink 1945, 1946). This method is effective for plants in containers where the roots can later be washed out easily. However, under field conditions the technique is not satisfactory since natural conditions are disturbed when the roots are first banded.

Grasses are prepared for banding by washing away the sand or loam from the roots with a spray of water. Bands 8 to 10 mm long and 2 to 3 mm wide are cut from material obtained from new, unpainted toothpaste, ointment tubes, or similar material. The thickness of this material is only about 0.12 mm, so it

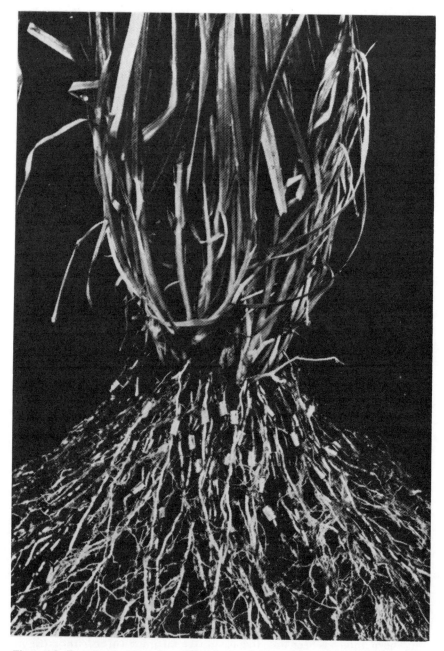

Figure 4-8. Roots washed from the soil showing banded ones using small strips of tin cut from tooth paste tubes (Courtesy of J.E. Weaver).

is pliable, yet durable. Banding is done on damp or rainy days, and over a wet floor. Roots must be moistened frequently by spraying with a hand sprayer. Grasses are not injured by exposure to this treatment.

The tin is formed into an open band by rolling it into a cylinder around the small end of a pipette, then fitting it over the root. With thumb and forefinger, it is then gently, but tightly, rolled until it fits closely around the root (Fig. 4-8). When the banding procedure is finished, the roots are again covered with soil and immediately watered. The band can partly unroll itself when the root grows in diameter.

For examination after an interval of growth, the entire banded (upper) portion of the root system is removed. Each banded root is examined to determine whether it is still alive. Living roots generally are yellow, white, or brown in color. Their tensile strength is good, and they are not brittle. The same test is not valid for each species and this must be learned by experience. Sometimes the root will have decayed so that the band lies free in the soil mass. The proportion of living to dead roots should be noted. If desired, part of the system may be exposed for examination at one time and the remainder saved for another date. Replicated plants can be used to achieve the same purpose.

Banding is unsatisfactory for species with fine roots, such as Kentucky bluegrass *(Poa pratensis)* and lovegrasses (*Eragrostis* spp.), or where the number of roots is great and the roots are compact, exemplified by smooth brome *(Bromus inermis)* and crested wheatgrass *(Agropyron cristatum).* With others, such as switchgrass *(Panicum virgatum)* and big bluestem *(Andropogon gerardii),* the technique is relatively easy.

Tracer Method

This is an "indirect" method which depends on the uptake of certain chemical elements or compounds from the soil or entrance to the plant through the stomata and the subsequent detection of those materials in the plant tissue. Dyes, rare elements, or isotopes of common elements can be used.

Knievel (1973), Bartos and Sims (1974), and Ward et al. (1978) used triphenyltetrazolium chloride (TTC) reduction techniques to determine the amount of living tissue in soil core samples. Relationship between TTC reduction per gram of roots and dry weight ratios of living to dead root tissue can be determined. Viable root cells reduce 2,3,5-triphenyltetrazolium chloride (colorless) to formazan (red) which identifies living roots from dead ones.

Some of the rarer elements not normally found in soils are lithium and ribidium. Lithium, for example, is easily absorbed and accumulated by plants, much like sodium and potassium. It is not toxic to plant tissues so concentration used is of little consequence. However, even dilute amounts can be detected by a spectroscope. No other element absorbs light at 67090 nm. The method has been used to measure lateral growth of corn roots (Sayre and Morris 1940). Lithium chloride, the salt most convenient to use, is immobile in the soil so it can easily be adapted for depth studies.

Radioactive tracers and other isotopes are ideal for root studies (Fox and Lipps 1964). They are usually detectable in all organs of the plant, can be located in the soil where probability of entering the plant is high, and remain near the point of placement in the soil throughout the period of study. Commonly used isotopes include phosphorus (^{32}P), carbon (^{14}C), and nitrogen (^{15}N). The technique will be described using ^{32}P as the example.

The isotope ^{32}P can be applied to the soil in a statistically designed pattern of horizontal and vertical distribution (Mathis et al. 1965, Wyatt et al. 1980). The concentration should not be so high as to change the level of soil phosphorus by the ^{32}P carrier. Ordinarily a solution of 4 to 20×10^5 Bq/ml is sufficient. Detectability of ^{32}P will be reduced where the soil phosphorus level is already high so the concentrations should be higher, or perhaps another isotope used.

The specific activity of the plant (as determined by Geiger counter or liquid scintillation counter) is a measure of the ^{32}P uptake from a given locus in the soil. The specific activity of P in the soil changes as some of the ^{32}P is withdrawn and also with time, hours after placement. To determine when roots have appeared in given zones, information on the change in specific activity of a system in which part of the ^{32}P is withdrawn with a subsequent redistribution of the remaining ^{32}P should be obtained.

At different soil horizons, the variation in specific activity will be great since vertical distribution of soil phosphorus varies. When more soil phosphorus is present, specific activity will be less. This is equalized by the greater absorption from the loci having the higher amounts of phosphorus. Thus, the activity of the plant is the product of the specific activity of the test locus and the total amount of P withdrawn from that locus. Contributions made by the ^{32}P of the different zones of placement can then be interpreted as representing proportionate amounts of root growth in those zones at a given time. An illustration of the technique is given by Hall et al. (1953) for corn, cotton, peanuts, and tobacco and by Burton et al. (1954) for a group of eight important southern range and pasture grasses.

Baldwin et al. (1971) developed an *in situ* method that used autoradiography by means of injecting radiophosphorus (^{32}P) into plants which was translocated into the roots. By inserting (X-ray) film supported by steel backing plates into the soil, cut ends of roots labeled with radiophosphorus could be found from the location of the spots (points of exposure) on the film. Equations were used to estimate root length per unit volume of soil from the number of roots crossing the cutting plane in the soil.

If the intertwining of roots of different plant species were of interest, pairs of isotopes such as ^{32}P and ^{33}P that emit beta particles of contrasting energy could be injected into inter-penetrating root systems (Baldwin and Tinker 1972). The isotope ^{14}C which shows up in root reserves from shoot injection could also be used as a third tracer element (Ellern et al. 1970).

Harris (1967) used ^{32}P to identify roots of a species and also to calculate the distribution of roots grown in greenhouse boxes. Radio-autographs were made of the root systems by placing X-ray film in contact with one side of the soil column. Only the roots near the soil-box interface when the side of the box was removed activated the film. Each plant received about 4×10^5 Bq of radioactivity. At this level, satisfactory exposure was reached within 6-8 hours.

Singh and Coleman (1973) used $^{14}CO_2$ released inside polyethylene tents to determine the root biomass in grassland ecosystems. Root samples from exposed plants were mounted on sheets of paper, exposed to X-ray film, and separated into functional and non-functional groups through autoradiography.

Barber and Martin (1976) grew plants in a chamber where $^{14}CO_2$ was used. The ^{14}C and total carbon contents of the roots and shoots, and of the water-soluble and insoluble material present in the soil, were measured. This procedure allowed for both the amount of organic materials released into the soil by the roots and the effects of microorganisms in the rhizosphere to be determined. From 18 to 25% more photosynthetically fixed carbon was released in unsterilized soils from the roots, as compared to sterilized soils. Root turnover can be measured successfully by pulse labelling with $^{14}CO_2$ when administered and monitored over a 2- to 6-year period (Coleman 1976).

In a study of nitrogen cycling Clark et al. (1980) used ^{15}N to measure the movement of nitrogen into live roots and subsequently into the aerial parts of plants and the recycling of N in future years from plant material into the soil and into the plant again. Such a technique can also be used to study extent of root growth by uptake of the ^{15}N by placement of the labelled material at different spacing both laterally and vertically in the soil.

Ellis and Barnes (1973) described a method for estimating distribution of living roots under field conditions. Rubidium (^{86}Rb) was injected into the base of shoots; within 24 hours the concentration of the tracer was sufficiently uniform throughout the root system for the volume of roots in different zones of soil to be inferred as a result of the tracer content. No ^{86}RB entered the dead roots from outward diffusion from the live roots. Energy of the gamma radiation from ^{86}Rb enables it to be measured accurately in soil samples approximating 3 kg. Thus, quantifying root distribution at different soil depths is possible. The advantage of this method is that labelled roots can be monitered without being extracted from the soil core, but care must be taken in handling radioactive isotopes and special safety clearances are required.

Willatt and Struss (1979) studied root growth by taking neutron radiographs using Indium collector foils of roots growing in enclosed boxes. Plants were grown in rectangular aluminum cans that were transparent to thermal neutrons. The reactor facility had a beam of thermal energy (0.04 eV) neutrons with an intensity of approximately 10^7 n•$cm^{-1}s^{-1}$. The indirect technique of total exposure using Indium collector foils required some 5×10^9 n•cm^{-2}. The collector foils are used to expose X-ray films, in this case Kodak Industrial AA film for three half-lives of decay of the foil.

Non-destructive Stain Technique

A technique that lends itself to studying the length and weight of seminal and adventitious roots was presented by Carman (1982). Red, blue, and yellow chorotriazinyl dyes are used. These were individually applied as a soil drench at three infrequent intervals. A rather porous growth media is desirable because the dye is leached from the rooting medium after a brief time. At the end of the growth period, the roots are washed and differentiated by color.

Indirect Method by Mathematical Calculation

Newman (1966) has described a method whereby roots from a core or prism of known volume or area are separated from the soil by washing and storing in a container of water. Lengths of the roots are determined by pouring the sample into a flat dish. Roots are dissected if necessary so that they do not tangle into a mass, but rather float apart with perhaps some mechanical assistance. The roots are arranged to occupy the whole of an area marked off on the face of the dish. Fields within the area occupied by the roots are viewed through a microscope; the center point of a hairline is placed in turn over each random point or grid intersection. After each position has been reached, the microscope eyepiece containing the hairline disk is rotated to give the hairline a random direction. Then a count is made of the number of intersections between the line and the roots. An intersection is only counted if the hairline crosses the center line of the root.

Example of calculation (Newman 1966).

Microscope fields regularly spaced; roots arranged in area 10×20 cm; 40 fields examined; apparent length of hair-line (=diameter of field) = 1.88 cm; 344 intersections. Using equation $R = \frac{\pi N A}{2H}$ where R is the total length of root, N is the number of intersections between the root and the straight lines, A is the area of the rectangle, and H is the total length of the straight lines, the total length of root is:

$$R = \frac{3.14 \times 344 \times 10 \times 20}{2 \times 40 \times 1.88} = 1436 \text{ cm}$$

Tennant (1975) presented a somewhat simplified formula for determining root length as accomplished by Newman (1966). When based upon a grid of indeterminate dimensions, the intersection counts could be converted to centimeter measurements.

Soil-moisture Measurement Method

Root penetration can be determined by measuring soil moisture at intervals through the soil profile (Veihmeyer and Hendrickson 1948). It must be assumed that decrease in soil moisture below field capacity is largely caused by absorption of roots and ultimate transpiration (Kramer 1983). This is true except in the surface soil where evaporation will take place. By inference, any horizon or lateral zone where a measurable change (decrease) in soil water occurs indicates plant water uptake from that zone. This method was developed and used in California where there is little or no rain from May to October to confound soil water withdrawal patterns.

Continuous methods for measuring soil moisture involve the use of electrical-conductance blocks (Bouyoucos and Mick 1940), fiberglass units (Colman 1950), or soil psychrometers (Brown 1970). The readings on the resistance meters or microvoltmeters must be calibrated with actual moisture percentages determined by the older gravemetric or neutron probe methods, if conversions are to be considered. Where soils are of similar texture and organic matter content, it is probable that no recalibration is necessary between soil types. Various methods of soil-moisture measurement are discussed by Lull and Reinhart (1955).

Optic in Situ Technique

Waddington (1971) described a technique that can be used to determine root penetration, distribution, and density with little or no disturbance to the plant. This technique is sometimes referred to as a minirhizotron. A small diameter transparent tube (glass or Plexiglas) is inserted into the soil at a 30° angle. A fiber optics probe inside the tube is used to observe the roots along the wall at various depths, thus allowing for an estimate of their distribution

Figure 4-9. Inserting the fiber optic duodenoscope into a transparent Plexiglas tube which is imbedded in the root zone at a 30° angle (Courtesy of D.A. Brown).

and density. The probe consists of a light source and fiber bundle for illumination, a coherent fiber bundle for image transfer to the surface, and a right-angle viewing attachment (mirror) at the objective end along with adjustable lenses.

Sanders and Brown (1978) used an optical *in situ* method for measuring root growth that involved the use of a refined fiber optic duodenoscope

Figure 4-10. A mini-nitizotron borescope designed with video tape for measuring root growth during the entire growing season (Courtesy of B.L. McMichael).

similar to the technique used by Waddington (1971). The root growth was monitored by inserting the unit into a transparent Plexiglas tube which was imbedded in the root zone (Fig. 4-9). This permitted quantitative characterization of the root systems throughout the growing season. The duodenoscope method can be used to measure density distribution and length of roots in the soil profile.

Recently, B.L. McMichael (1983; personal communication) developed and used an apparatus which was referred to as a borescope that was equipped with a light source and a low-light sensitive television camera to record the images of each section inside the Plexiglas tube on video tape (Fig. 4-10). A videotape machine was then used to redisplay the image in the laboratory where intersections of roots in each scene were counted on a superimposed grid on the television monitor. Calculations for total root length were then made according to the method described by Newman (1966).

Root Reserve Analyses

Storage of carbon or energy reserves is an important function of perennial plants. An understanding of this storage function, and its response to environmental factors and management practices is indispensable for proper management of pasture or rangeland. Not only is such information needed to maintain composition and high yields of desirable forage species, but also to control undesirable plants.

The significance of energy or food reserves in the management of perennial forage plants was early emphasized by Graber et al. (1927) and Graber (1931). Aldous (1930) was among the first to stress importance of food reserve levels in relation to time of applying measures to control undesirable pasture plants. Sampson and McCarty (1930), McCarty (1935, 1938), Bukey and Weaver (1939), McCarty and Price (1942), McIlvanie (1942), and Benedict and Brown (1944) were some of the early researchers to conduct studies of food reserves of western range grasses in relation to phenological stages and management practices.

Maximum levels of carbohydrate storage generally occur when plants are approaching maturity or have gone through the reproductive stage. A slight decline in reserves usually occurs during the quiescent or dormant period because of maintenance respiration. A substantial drawdown in reserves occurs during the formation of new tissue following dormancy. This general U- or V-shaped cycle in carbohydrate reserves has been found in range plants by a number of authors (Weinmann 1961, Cook 1966, McConnell and Garrison 1966, Donart 1969, Coyne and Cook 1970, Trlica and Cook 1971, Boo and Pettit 1975, Wilson et al. 1975, Menke and Trlica 1981).

Early work by Steinke and Booysen (1968) and Steinke (1969) showed that translocation of labeled materials from storage organs to new leaves occurred immediately following defoliation until sufficient photosynthetic tissue was formed for self-support. Roots were deprived of their normal supply of carbohydrates during this time. Chung and Trlica (1980) indicated that a large portion of the carbon in storage was, however, used in both aboveground and belowground respiration. Jameson (1963) and Caldwell et al. (1981) indicated that reserves were only needed until sufficient leaf area was produced to sustain respiration and growth demands.

Carbohydrates and Defoliation

Reserve compounds are used for initial growth, maintenance during stress, construction demands, maintenance respiration, and for regrowth following defoliation. Many studies have shown that plant vigor and carbohydrate reserves have been markedly affected by frequency, intensity and season of defoliation (Aldous 1930, Sampson and McCarty 1930, Graber 1931, Biswell and Weaver 1933, Bukey and Weaver 1939, Hanson and Stoddart 1940, McCarty and Price 1942, McIlvanie 1942, Sullivan and Sprague 1943, 1953, Weinmann 1943, 1949 Holscher 1945, Smith and Graber 1948, Blaisdell and Pechanec 1949, Sprague and Sullivan 1950, Waite and Boyd 1953, Thaine 1954, Broughman 1956, Neiland and Curtis 1956, Wolf et al. 1962, Welch 1968, Trlica and Cook 1971, 1972, Owensby et al. 1977, Miller and Donart 1981, Menke and Trlica 1983). Defoliation at any period during the year usually affects levels of carbohydrate reserves (Cook et al. 1958, Hyder and Sneva 1963, Cooper and Watson 1968, Donart and Cook 1970, Owensby et al. 1970, Trlica and Cook 1971 Willard and McKell 1973, Menke and Trlica 1983). Defoliation during maturity or reproductive stages is usually more detrimental to reserve concentrations than is defoliation during quiescence or early growth (Owensby et al. 1970, Trlica and Cook 1971 and 1972, Miller and Donart 1981, Menke and Trlica 1983).

Regrowth following defoliation is often related to carbohydrate levels and, in general, rate of growth is slower and amount of biomass is less for plants with lowered reserves as a result of defoliation (Baker and Garwood 1961, Ward and Blaser 1961, Reynolds 1962, Smith 1962, Hyder and Sneva 1963, Alcock 1964, Alberda 1966, Wolf 1967, Albuquerque 1968, Steinke and Booysen 1968, Laycock and Conrad 1969, Ueno and Smith 1970, Grueb and Wedin 1971, Booysen and Nelson 1975).

Reserve Substances

Reserve food substances may be defined as organic substances elaborated and stored at certain times to be utilized later by the plant for energy and production of new tissues. From this generally accepted viewpoint, food reserves of vegetative organs are composed primarily of certain groups of carbohydrates.

Certain minerals and nitrogen are essential nutrients but are not sources of energy, nor reserve substrate in the true sense. Protein may be included among the food reserves (Sheard 1968), but evidence indicates that carbohydrates far overshadow protein as a reserve substance in vegetative plant organs.

Various classifications of carbohydrates exist, and terminology differs somewhat between the physiologists and the chemists. For more adequate information on reserve compounds and their characteristics, the investigator should refer to textbooks on plant physiology (Bonner and Galston 1952, Meyer et al. 1966, Sosebee 1977, Salisbury and Ross 1978) and on biochemistry (Bonner 1950, Robinson 1975). Reviews of literature concerning carbohydrates which function as reserves may be found in several articles such as those by Sullivan and Sprague (1943), Eaton and Ergle (1948), Weinmann

(1948b, 1952), Smith and Grotelueschen (1966), Grotelueschen and Smith (1968), and White (1973).

Carbohydrate compounds which have been found to be important as reserves—the so-called "available carbohydrates"—in higher green plants are sugars, starch, and dextrins (glucosans), inulin, and fructosans. The more complex polysaccharides, such as hemicelluloses and pentosans, are apparently structural materials which probably cannot readily be utilized by the plant as reserves. Recent work by Chung and Trlica (1980) and Deregibus and Trlica (1985) indicate that compounds other than sugars, starches, and fructosans may also serve as reserve substrates. These compounds may make up as much as 40 to 60% of the reserve constituents of some grasses.

Three sugars are of major importance as carbohydrate reserves; two monosaccharides ("simple" sugars): (1) glucose (dextrose or grape sugar) and (2) fructose (levulose or fruit sugar), and the disaccharides: (3) sucrose (saccarose or cane sugar). Glucose and fructose have a reducing action in alkaline solutions on certain metallic compounds (e.g., cupric hydroxide to cuprous oxide) and are commonly reported as "reducing sugars." The mixture of these two sugars, which results from the hydrolysis of sucrose, has also been termed "invert sugar." Sucrose, a "nonreducing" sugar, is not only a major storage substance, but also the principal form of carbohydrate translocation within the plant. Other sugars occur in various types of chemical combination in plants but are often not considered important reserve substances.

Starch is the most abundant reserve carbohydrate of the plant world and is found under favorable conditions in most plant organs. Hydrolysis of starch yields glucose as the end product, which is a major substrate for construction and respiration.

Dextrins, which are composed of short chains of glucose molecules, are transition products in the hydrolysis of starch and do not often accumulate to any extent in the plant. In some cases, considerable amounts have been reported in early work (Graber 1931), perhaps because of the laboratory techniques employed. However, other workers have considered dextrins to be significant as reserve substances in those grasses that stored large amounts of starch (Weinmann and Reinhold 1946, Weinmann 1947, 1948a, 1952).

Fructosans and inulin are known to be important reserve substances in certain plants, but have been studied less intensively than other reserve carbohydrates. Inulin, a specific polysaccharide (polyfructoside) in which fructose is the repeating unit, might be considered comparable to starch, where glucose is the repeating unit. Fructosans include a group of short-chain polysaccharides of fructose having in common the property of cold water solubility (inulin is soluble in hot water). In a sense, fructosans are intermediate between the disaccharides on the one hand and the polysaccharides on the other. Inulin replaces starch as the reserve carbohydrate of some plants; others may store both inulin and starch. Although inulin does not occur in the more common forage species, it is particularly prominent in the composite family *(Compositeae)* and occurs also in a number of other families of dicotyledonous plants and the families *Liliaceae* and *Amaryllidaceae* of the monocotyledons. It has been found in relatively large amounts in *Helianthus, Parthenium, Solidago, Cichorium, Dahlia, Inula, Lappa, Iris,* and numerous other genera.

Fructosans occur widely in grasses (Bonner 1950, Sullivan and Sprague 1943, Smith 1969) and are important reserve substances in some species of grass, but not in other common forage plants such as legumes. Weinmann (1948b, 1952) pointed out that grasses native to cool temperature (C_3 plants) climates stored fructosans, while grasses of warm regions (C_4 plants) stored more starch. A large proportion of the fructosans present may be lost through using laboratory methods of hydrolysis for the breakdown of dextrins and starch but resulting in the partial destruction of fructose (Weinmann 1952).

Suzuki (1971a) suggested that potassium may be vital to the accumulation of fructosan storage in some plants. Grazing or defoliation may stimulate the change of fructosans to one of the sugars, perhaps for mobilization. Other minerals have also been associated with carbohydrate accumulation (Deregibus et al. 1982). Most carbohydrate fractions can be readily transformed from one to another, therefore determination of total nonstructural carbohydrates (TNC) is probably more important as a reserve index than individual carbohydrate fractions. However, care must be taken to insure that the TNC fraction contains most of the reserve substrates utilized by the plant for maintenance and growth. Abiotic and biotic factors affecting the formation, transfer, and utilization of carbohydrates along with their redistribution in roots and stems was reviewed in Range Science Series No. 4 (Sosebee 1977).

Procedures for Chemical Analysis

In the chemical determinations of reserve substances, the standard methods recognized by the Association of Official Analytical Chemists (1975) are usually recommended and used. Also recommended is "Modern Methods of Plant Analysis" by Paech and Tracey (1955-56) and the article by Smith (1969). Based on extensive experience at the U.S. Regional Pasture Research Laboratory, State College, Pennsylvania, Sullivan (1951) prepared a succinct guide to the analysis of carbohydrates in forage plants. Investigators will still find this guide helpful in selecting methods suitable for their circumstances.

A major problem in plant chemistry is in separating the wanted constituent from interfering substances. Once that is accomplished, the standard chemical procedures give satisfactory results. Experienced biochemists recognize the analytical procedures must be "tailored" to fit the specific type of plant material being studied, as well as the equipment available. Consequently, innumerable variations in procedures are reported in the literature.

In selecting appropriate methods, the types of carbohydrate reserves involved must first be ascertained, and methods chosen which will give reliable results for all reserve substances present. The same procedures may not apply to all grasses because some store fructosans and others starch. Therefore, preliminary trials will be necessary to work out details of analysis for species where little is known about their reserve stores.

The purpose and nature of the study will also influence the relative efficiency of analytical methods. When the investigator is primarily interested in total nonstructural carbohydrates, rather than the individual compounds, recent methods for directly determining this total have been used successfully for grasses and legumes (Weinmann 1947, Sullivan 1951, Grotelueschen and Smith 1967, Smith 1969, Suzuki 1971b, Ford 1973, Wolf and Ellmore 1973, 1975).

Storage Organs

Consideration of food reserves should not be restricted to underground organs alone. Storage occurs, temporarily at least, in all portions of the plant (Bonner and Galston 1952). Most pertinent to research related to forage plants or range management are those portions which remain unutilized or alive through the dormant period: the roots, rhizomes, stolons, and crowns or stem bases (stubble) of herbaceous species, and also the aerial parts of shrubs. In grasses, and perhaps other herbaceous plants, reserve carbohydrates tend to accumulate in the basal portions of the aerial parts even during vegetative growth stages. Intensive studies on perennial ryegrass *(Lolium perenne)*, orchardgrass *(Dactylis glomerata)*, and bluebunch wheatgrass *(Agropyron spicatum)* have shown that greatest concentrations of soluble carbohydrates occur in the lower parts of the leaf blades, sheaths, and stems (Sullivan and Sprague 1943, Caldwell et al. 1981).

Rather high concentrations (percentages) of reserve substances are found in both rhizomes and stolons. Mooney's review (1972) showed that rhizomes of plants contained as much as 60% TNC at the end of the growing season. However, the total amount is often greatest in the roots because of their greater mass.

Balasko and Smith (1973) found that stems and inflorescences accumulated most of the labeled carbohydrate when plants were fed labeled carbon ($^{14}CO_2$) at initiation of stem elongation. Stems and roots together contained 73% of the total ^{14}C. Bamberg et al. (1972) found that about 22% of the fixed ^{14}C was found in the roots of desert shrubs, and about 76% of the fixed ^{14}C was found in the stems. For these reasons, procedures should be adopted which not only insure estimates of carbohydrates in various portions of the plant, but also provide estimate of the mass of the different plant parts involved.

Recommendations for Field Procedures

Field procedures to be followed in studies of reserves will necessarily be dictated by the nature of the problem, the plants under consideration, and the specific information desired. However, a few guides gleaned from the literature or from experience may be helpful to those contemplating such studies for the first time.

Advanced thorough consideration of the kind and amount of data required to meet the specific objectives of the study, together with detailed plans for collecting, analyzing, and interpreting the data, will do much toward insuring positive results and also toward saving time, effort, and money. Procedures appropriate and necessary for studying the basic physiological aspects of reserve substances may be unnecessarily refined in studies of an applied nature, such as investigating reserve levels in relation to season or management practices. Sampling requirements will also vary widely. Whereas frequent sampling is necessary to establish seasonal trends and critical levels of reserves, one sampling at an appropriate period may be adequate in evaluating different management practices (Trlica and Cook 1971). Use of uniform potted plants is often more efficient than working with field-grown material (Santos and Trlica 1978).

Preliminary tests not only should check field and laboratory techniques but also provide an estimate of the variability to be expected and the possibilities for reducing it. Care in segregating different plant parts, living and dead material, and in removing foreign matter will give greater consistency in results.

To permit adequate interpretation, study design must provide an estimate of experimental error. As a result of compositing field samples before chemical analysis and lack of replication, investigators often have not been able to distinguish between biological variation and significant trends or treatment effects. Consequently, interpretations have sometimes been difficult, weak, or erroneous.

Plant samples should be fixed immediately after harvesting to stop enzymatic action and chemical changes and then preserved until analysis can be completed. Such quick killing can readily be achieved by autoclaving for 5 minutes at 2.4 kg pressure, quick freezing with liquid nitrogen, or by drying the samples at 100°C for an hour, followed by drying at 50 to 70°C. For alcohol preservation, a standard procedure is to immerse the fresh tissue in sufficient boiling 95% ethanol (roughly 4 cc/gm of tissue) to obtain a final concentration of 70-80% after dilution by water in the sample. A small amount of calcium carbonate may be added to neutralize plant acidity if it is important to prevent any change from one form of carbohydrate to another by acid hydrolysis. Ethanol may also be used to reduce enzyme activity and to fix field samples until they can be brought into the laboratory for drying.

Glass jars with glass or enameled-metal lids (such as Mason, Kerr, or Atlas) are convenient containers for alcohol-preserved samples. Dried material can be stored for a reasonable time in paper bags before grinding. For finely ground material, air-tight containers are necessary to prevent excessive absorption of hygroscopic moisture, chemical changes, or spoilage caused by microbial activity in humid climates.

The appropriate sample size will depend upon the uniformity of plant materials, chemical determinations to be made, and methods employed. Ordinarily, 10- to 20-g samples of ovendry material will provide enough material for chemical analyses.

Complete records should be kept that include rate and state of growth, pertinent climatic factors such as temperature and moisture conditions, time and procedures of sampling, and other measurable or observable conditions that might affect the physiology of the plants or the composition of the samples. Such records are helpful and often essential for adequate interpretation of results.

Interpretation and Application of Data on Food Reserves

Data on food reserves have been used most widely in the past to support and explain effects of various management practices, such as herbage yield at various seasons and intensities of grazing. More recently, they have also been used as a primary basis for developing and evaluating management requirements of range and cultivated forage plants. For the latter purpose, studies of reserves offer a direct fundamental approach which can be quicker, more efficient, and often less expensive than usual empirical methods. For example, reserve levels and trends, which can often be established in a single year, provide perhaps the best indication of the most and least appropriate times for grazing or harvesting a particular species. Also, effects of management practices involving defoliation can often be detected much earlier through food reserve analysis than through herbage yields or other secondary responses (Trlica and Cook 1971). Reserve levels at dormancy, quiescence, or before initial growth should offer an objective, quantitative measure of plant vigor among plants from various treatments.

Because carbohydrate reserves readily change from one form to another in the plant, the total amount is more pertinent and meaningful than the amount of the separate components for interpreting studies of an applied nature. Commonly all fractions, including starch and fructosans, are reported as equivalents of the sugars, glucose, fructose, or sucrose. The standard to use will depend upon the dominant storage carbohydrates within the species.

Total carbohydrate reserves represent net difference between gain through photosynthesis and loss through respiration and growth. Consequently, all factors which influence these processes should be considered when interpreting fluctuations in carbohydrate levels. Rate of photosynthesis is predominantly governed by the effective leaf area interacting with abiotic variables. The general relation between photosynthetic area and the accumulation or depletion of reserves is well known, but quantitative relations have yet to be established. It is known, however, that the leaf area necessary to balance substrate utilization for growth and respiration will vary with environmental factors such as light, temperature, and soil water that influence these latter processes. It will also vary among species.

Respiration apparently utilizes the bulk of the products of photosynthesis. For perennial ryegrass plants that were clipped and placed in darkness, weight loss from the stubble and roots was five times the weight of new growth produced (Sullivan and Sprague 1943). Even in the light, weight loss from stubble and roots was 74% greater than the weight of new growth 40 days after clipping (Sullivan and Sprague 1949). Such results indicate that the major amount of carbohydrate reserves disappearing after defoliation enters into the process of respiration (Sullivan and Sprague 1953, Chung and Trlica 1980).

Although rapid respiration necessarily accompanies rapid growth, respiration also is a continuing process, and the rate appears to be even more closely correlated with temperature than with growth rate. At high temperatures, utilization of reserves increases a plant's tolerance to high temperatures (Julander 1945). However, there is great variation among species regarding optimum and critical temperature in relation to reserve storage and survival.

It is important to recognize that the total weight of storage organs fluctuates as reserves are withdrawn or stored, and this necessarily changes the percentages of components other than reserves. Growth of underground organs is also markedly influenced by the level of organ reserves and, conversely the total amount of reserves is necessarily related to the total amount of underground organs. Therefore, evaluation of reserves on the basis of percentage composition alone is less informative than on the basis of absolute amount or weight (White 1973, Trlica 1977, Caldwell et al. 1981, Deregibus et al. 1982). Several investigators working with pasture species have found relatively small differences among experimental treatments at the end of the season on the basis of percentage of reserves, but pronounced differences in absolute amounts of reserves as a result of differences in total biomass of the storage tissue (Graber et al. 1927, Smith and Graber 1948, Sprague and Sullivan 1950, Tesar and Ahlgren 1950, Weinmann 1952, Santos and Trlica 1978).

Until more information is accumulated on critical, adequate, or optimum levels of reserves, results must necessarily be interpreted on a comparative basis (Deregibus et al. 1982). After dormancy or following defoliation, reserve levels characteristically exhibit a U-or V-shaped curve when plotted against time as the abscissa (Cook 1966). However, maximum and minimum levels as well as rates of change vary with species, with initial levels of reserves, and with environmental factors mentioned previously.

Reserves may comprise over 40% of the root weight or other storage organ at maximum levels of storage in some forage plants, although maximums of 10 to 25% are more common. Critical minimum levels have not been well defined. Several investigators have reported that seasonal new growth of native forage species reduced reserves to minimum concentrations amounting to 20 to 30% of the maximum (McCarty 1938, McCarty and Price 1942, McIlvanie 1942). The degree of depletion of reserves by new growth of forage plants has been shown to be related to the initial concentration at the time of cutting and other environmental conditions (Moran et al. 1953, Sprague and Sullivan 1950, Donart 1969, Trlica and Cook 1971, Menke and Trlica 1981, 1983).

Mycorrhizal Fungi

Mycorrhizal fungi grow into cortical cells of the roots of host plants with their hyphae extending into the soil, thus forming a mycorrhizal-fungus root. As a result, they serve as extensions of the root system and are, in some cases, more efficient in absorbing and translocating nutrients from the soil to the plant than the roots themselves. A rather detailed review of the benefits of mycorrhizal fungi for plant growth is presented by Gerdemann (1974) and Smith (1980).

It is generally accepted that the presence of vesicular- arbuscular (VA) mycorrhizal fungi benefits native range plants that serve as hosts. These symbiotic fungi increase the plant's ability to absorb phosphorus and many other minerals. Plants supporting mycorrhizal fungi may also have an increased capability to absorb water from the soil. Mycorrhizae fungi appear in the soil as spores or as symbiotic organisms on plant roots. The number of spores present is not always an accurate index to the mycorrhizal inoculum potential because many are nonviable. There are several distinct kinds of mycorrhizae, but VA mycorrhizal fungi are found on more plant species than any of the other types. Only a few plant associations do not contain species of VA mycorrhizal fungi (Gerdemann 1974).

Moorman and Reeves (1979) measured vesicular-arbuscular (VA) mycorrhiza inoculum potential (MIP) of soils from western ranges using a corn bioassay method. The bioassay consists of determining the percentage of colonization in corn root systems grown for 30 days in soil collected from various range sites and conditions. Corn is frequently used as the bioassay plant because of its ability to serve as a host to many of the endomycorrhizal fungi commonly found on rangelands. In the bioassay procedure, only live inoculum units are used (spores and infected roots). About 30 days after planting, roots from several corn plants per situation or condition are washed, cut into small sections, and mixed. Randomly selected 1 cm root sections are removed and stained in trypan blue-lactophenol according to the method described by Phillips and Hayman (1970). Only segments containing mycorrhizal hyphae and either vesicles or arbuscules are counted as infected. Thus, the mean percentage root infection can be determined and expressed as MIP (Moorman and Reeves 1979).

Kormanik et al. (1980) stated that ectomycorrhizae are readily visible to the naked eye and are rather easily assessed, but endomycorrhizae must be verified through a more refined process requiring microscopic examination. Common staining techniques that are suitable for non-pigmented roots are frequently unsatisfactory for the more heavily pigmented roots from woody plants. A detailed procedure for clearing and staining plant root samples from the field for endomycorrhizal assay is presented in the publication by Kormanik et al. (1980). Clearing and staining make the roots opaque, but the VA mycorrhizae stain bright red or pink. For the most part, root fungi evaluation can then be made under a dissecting microscope equipped with transmitted light. Results can be expressed as percentage of roots infected and intensity of infection within the root (Kormanik and McGraw 1982).

Assessment of colonization after clearing and staining is reported by Giovannetti and Mosse (1980). Their study follows four rather distinct methods: (1) visual estimate, (2) slide length of colonized tissue in root segments, (3) presence or absence on the slide of colonization in the root segment, and (4) gridline intersect counts of mycorrhizae on the roots. The authors concluded that it was still unknown which procedure most accurately estimated root colonization.

Radiotracer methods are being using to measure the movement of compounds from fungus to host and from host to fungus. The use of ^{32}P and ^{14}C has been rather extensive since both are vitally concerned in mycorrhizal symbiosis (Rhodes and Hirrel 1982). Moawad (1979) reported that temperature appeared to affect physiological activity of mycorrhizae more than mycorrhizae development. Partial shading of mycorrhizal plants decreased the efficiency of the mycorrhizae as measured by phosphorus uptake and plant growth, but this shading had no effect upon nonmycorrhizal plants.

Root Exudates

A large number of known compounds are exuded from intact roots. These include sugars, amino acids, peptides, enzymes, vitamins, organic acids, nucleotides, fungal stimulants, growth regulators, attractants, and many miscellaneous substances. The amount and kind of exudates from roots differ greatly among plant species (Rovira 1969). Other factors affecting exudation from plant roots even within a species are: (1) age of plant or phenology, (2) ambient air and soil temperatures both affect root exudates markedly during growth, (3) daily irradiance at which plants grow affects the kind and quantity of root exudates of species differentially, (4) plant nutrient level may affect the exudates of roots depending upon the species of plant and the degree of nutrient deficiency, (5) defoliation level, and (6) soil moisture content greatly affects exudation of plant roots by either increasing or decreasing the release of compounds depending upon the plant species in question. Hale et al. (1971) presented an excellent review on the factors affecting root exudation.

Microorganisms and Root Exudates

Root exudates may affect the microorganism population and activity rather dramatically. On the other hand, microorganisms of the rhizosphere may modify the exudation process and the nature of the exudates. Such interactions are not well understood because of the complexity and the perplexing problems of studying these interrelationships under natural field conditions (Rovira 1969).

However, $^{14}CO_2$ has been used successfully by Warembourg and Paul (1977) to measure the root and rhizosphere microflora respiration in the soil. It was later suggested in a study by Warembourg and Billes (1979) that a time sequence of root and microbial respiration in the rhizosphere, based upon a time delay for the appearance and utilization of root and microbial respiratory substrates (labelled assimilates and root exudates, respectively), could be used as a means to estimate root and microbial activity separately. These authors (Warembourg and Billes 1979) used a pulse labelling system whereby $^{14}CO_2$ was released intermittently in a closed system allowing the plant to photosynthetically fix the ^{14}C. The labeled carbon can then be detected in various organs and in respired $^{14}CO_2$ over extended time periods.

Method of Studying Root Exudates

The root zone immediately behind the tip is considered the major source of exudate, but entire root systems of plants grown in aqueous solutions or sand culture are known to produce exudates. The exudates can be measured by progressively changing the solution. Both the solution and the sand culture technique lack the ability to extrapolate to natural field conditions. Use of heat sterilized soils causes the formation of phytotoxins, but soils sterilized by gamma radiation contain only minor phytotoxins. These phytotoxins only affect some species. A synthetic soil of sand, fieldspar, and kaolinite was used rather successfully by Harmsen and Jager (1962).

Compounds labled with ^{14}C were applied to leaves, and ^{14}C was found in the soil and even adjacent plants as a result of exudation and sloughing from roots (Linder et al. 1964, Kansouh and Hopkins 1968). The authors were able to measure the amount of ^{14}C lost from roots during progressive periods following treatment of the leaves. However, measurement of root exudates under natural field conditions is difficult and costly.

Nitrogen-fixing Root Nodules

Determining the importance of the number of root nodules on plants, especially legumes, is part of root research. The number of nodules on excavated roots is expressed on the basis of total root biomass in the sample or in terms of total root length in the sample. Intermittent sampling by seasons over a period of a few years can be used as an expression of root nodule dynamics. Sampling during the growing season appears to be best because the active nodules are swollen and flesh-colored. As a consequence, the symbiotic nitrogen-fixing bacteria tubercles are more easily located and counted (Bohm 1979, Daniels and Skipper 1982). The isolation of bacteria and determination of species of bacteria involved in nodule formation and atmospheric nitrogen fixation by legume and nonlegume plants is presented by Mishustin and Shil'nikova (1971), Becking (1975), and Dart (1975).

Literature Cited

Alberda, T. 1966. The influence of reserve substances on dry-matter production after defoliation, p. 140-147. *In:* Tenth Int. Grassland Congr. Proc.

Albertson, F.W. 1937. Ecology of mixed prairie in west-central Kansas. Ecol. Monogr. 7:481-547.

Albuquerque, H.E. 1968. Leaf area, and age, and carbohydrate reserves in the regrowth of tall fescue (*Festuca arundinacea* Schreb.) tillers. Diss. Abstr. Sec. B 28:3968B.

Alcock, M.B. 1964. The physiological significance of defoliation on the subsequent regrowth of grass-clover mixtures and cereals, p. 24-41. *In:* D.J. Crisp (ed.), Grazing in terrestrial and marine environments. Blackwell Sci. Publ., Oxford, England.

Aldous, A.E. 1930. Relation of organic food reserves to the growth of some Kansas pasture plants. Amer. Soc. Agron. J. 22:385-392.

Ares, J. 1976. Dynamics of the root system of blue grama. J. Range Manage. 29:208-213.

Association of Official Analytical Chemists. 1975. Official methods of analysis, 12th ed. Assoc. Offic. Anal. Agr. Chem. Washington, D.C.

Baker, H.R., and E.A. Garwood. 1961. Studies on root development of herbage plants. V. Seasonal changes in fructosan and soluble-sugar contents of cocksfoot herbage, stubble, and roots under two cutting treatments. J. Brit. Grassland Soc. 16:263-267.

Baldwin, J.P., and P.B. Tinker. 1972. A method of estimating the length and spatial patterns of two interpenetrating root systems. Plant & Soil. 37:209-213.

Baldwin, J.P., P.B. Tinker, and F.H.C. Mariott. 1971. The measurement of length and distribution of onion roots in the field and the laboratory. J. Appl. Ecol. 8:543-554.

Balasko, J.A., and D. Smith. 1973. Carbohydrates in grasses: V. Incorporation of ^{14}C into plants parts and nonstructural carbohydrates of timothy (*Phleum pratense* L.) at three developmental stages. Crop Sci. 13:19-22.

Bamberg, S., A. Wallace, G. Kleinkopf, and A. Vollmer. 1972. Gas exchange and assimilate distribution in Mojave desert shrubs. US/IBP Desert Biome Program Rep.

Barber, D.A., and J.K. Martin. 1976. The release of organic substances by cereal roots into the soil. New Phytol. 76:69-80.

Bartos, D.L., and P.L. Sims. 1974. Root dynamics of a shortgrass ecosystem. J. Range Manage. 27:33-36.

Becking, J.H. 1975. Root nodules in non-legumes, p. 507-566. *In:* J.G. Torrey and D.T. Clarkson (eds.). Development and function of roots. Acad. Press, London, England.

Benedict, H.M., and G.B. Brown. 1944. The growth and carbohydrate responses of *Agropyron smithii* and *Bouteloua gracilis* to changes in nitrogen supply. Plant Physiol. 19:481-494.

Biswell, H.H., and J.E. Weaver. 1933. Effect of frequent clipping on the development of roots and tops of grasses in prairie sod. Ecology. 14:368-389.

Blaisdell, J.P., and J.F. Pechanec. 1949. Effect of herbage removal at various dates on vigor of bluebunch wheatgrass and arrowleaf balsamroot. Ecology. 30:209-305.

Bloomberg, W.J. 1974. Two techniques for examining root distribution. Can. J. Plant Sci. 54:865-868.

Bohm, W. 1979. Methods of studying root systems. *In:* W.D. Billings, F. Golley, O.L. Lange, and J.S. Olson (eds.), Ecological studies analysis and synthesis. Vol. 33. Springer-Verlag, New York., New York.

Bonner, J. 1950. Plant biochemistry. Academic Press, New York., New York.

Bonner, J., and A.W. Galston. 1952. Principles of plant physiology W.H. Freeman, Co., San Francisco, California.

Boo, R.M., and R.D. Pettit. 1975. Carbohydrate reserves in roots of sand shin oak in west Texas. J. Range Manage. 28:469-472.

Booysen, P. de V., and C.J. Nelson. 1975. Leaf area and carbohydrate reserves in regrowth of tall fescue. Crop Sci. 15:262-266.

Bouyoucos, G.J., and A.H. Mick. 1940. An electrical resistance method for continuous measurement of soil moisture under field conditions. Tech. Bull. 172. Michigan Agr. Exp. Sta.

Bowns, J.E., and T.W. Box. 1964. A core sampler for excavating grass roots. J. Range Manage. 17:43-44.

Box, T.W. 1966. A low cost apparatus for taking undisturbed soil cores. J. Range Manage. 19:142-143.

Brougham, R.W. 1956. The effect of intensity of defoliation on regrowth of pastures. Aust. J. Agr. Res. 7:377-387.

Brown, G.R., and J.F. Thilenius. 1977. A tool and method for extracting plant-root-soil cores on remote sites. J. Range Manage. 30:72-74.

Brown, R.W. 1970. Measurement of water potential with thermocouple psychrometers: construction and application. Res. Paper INT-80. USDA, Washington, D.C.

Bukey, F.W., and J.E. Weaver. 1939. Effects of frequent clipping on the underground food reserves of certain prairie grasses. Ecology. 20:246-252.

Burton, G.W., E.H. DeVane, and R.L. Carter. 1954. Root penetration, distribution and activity in southern grasses measured by yields, drought symptoms and P^{32} uptake. Agron. J. 46:229-233.

Caldwell, M.M., J.H. Richards, D.A. Johnson, R.S. Nowak, and R.S. Dzurec. 1981. Coping with herbivory: Photosynthetic capacity and resource allocation in two semiarid *Agropyron* bunchgrasses. Oecologia. 50:14-24.

Carman, J.G. 1982. A non-destructive stain technique for investigating root growth dynamics. J. Appl. Ecol. 19:873-879.

Chung, H-H., and M.J. Trlica. 1980. ^{14}C distribution and utilization in blue grama as affected by temperature, water potential and defoliation regimes. Oecologia. 47:190-195.

Clark, F.E., C.V. Cole, and R.A. Rowman. 1980. Nutrient cycling, p. 659-712. *In:* A.J. Breymeyer and G.M. Van Dyne (eds.), Grasslands, systems analysis and man. Cambridge Univ. Press, London, England.

Coleman, D.C. 1976. A review of root production processes and their influence on soil biota in terrestrial ecosystems, p. 417-434. *In:* J.M. Anderson and A. Macfadyen (eds.), The role of terrestrial and aquatic organisms in decomposition processes. Blackwell Sci. Pub., Oxford, England.

Colman, E.A. 1950. Manual of instructions for use of fibergrass soil-moisture instrument. California Forest and Range Exp. Sta. (1947, Revised 1950).

Cook, C.W. 1943. A study of the roots of *Bromus inermis* in relation to drought resistance. Ecology. 24:169-182.

Cook, C.W. 1966. Carbohydrate reserves in plants. Resource Ser. 31. Utah Agr. Exp. Sta.

Cook, C.W., and C.E. Lewis. 1963. Competition between big sagebrush and seeded grasses and foothill ranges in Utah. J. Range Manage. 16:245-250.

Cook, C.W., P.D. Leonard, and C.D. Bonham. 1965. Rabbitbrush competition and control on Utah rangelands. Bull. 454. Utah Agr. Exp. Sta.

Cook, C.W., L.A. Stoddart, and F.E. Kinsinger. 1958. Responses of crested wheatgrass to various clipping treatments. Ecol. Monogr. 28:237-272.

Cooper, C.S., and C.A. Watson. 1968. Total available carbohydrates in roots of sainfoin (*Orobrychis viciaefolia* Scop.) and alfalfa (*Medicago sativa* L.) when grown under several management regimes. Crop Sci. 8:83-85.

Coyne, P.I., and C.W. Cook. 1970. Seasonal carbohydrate reserve cycles in eight desert range species. J. Range Manage. 23:438-444.

Crider, F.J. 1955. Root-growth stoppage resulting from defoliation of grasses. Tech. Bull. 1102, USDA, Washington, D.C.

Daniels, B.A., and H.D. Skipper. 1982. Methods for the recovery and quantitative estimation of propagules from soil, Chapter 3. *In:* N.C. Schenck (ed.), Methods and principles of mycorrhizal research. Amer. Phytopathol. Soc., St. Paul, Minnesota.

Dart, P.J. 1975. Legume nodule initiation and development, p. 467-506. *In:* J.G. Torrey and D.T. Clarkson (eds.), The development and function of roots. Acad. Press, London, England.

Deregibus, V.A., and M.J. Trlica. 1985. Above- and below-ground biomass dynamics and organic reserves in two warm-season grasses as affected by defoliation regimes. J. Range Manage. (submitted).

Deregibus, V.A., M.J. Trlica, and D. Jameson. 1982. Organic reserves in herbage plants: Their relationship to grassland management, p. 315-334. *In:* Miloslav Rechcigl, Jr. (ed.), Handbook of agricultural productivity, Vol. I. CRC Press, Inc., Boca Raton, Florida.

Donaldson, N.C., and D.J. Beck. 1973. How to prepare a range soil monolith. J. Range Manage. 26:460-462.

Donart, G.B. 1969. Carbohydrate reserves of six mountain plants as related to growth. J. Range Manage. 22:411-415.

Donart, G.B., and C.W. Cook. 1970. Carbohydrate reserve content of mountain range plants following defoliation and regrowth. J. Range Manage. 23:15-19.

Eaton, F.M., and D.R. Ergle. 1948. Carbohydrate accumulation in the cotton plant at low moisture levels. Plant Physiol. 23:169-187.

Ellern, S.J., J.L. Harper, and G.R. Sagar. 1970. A comparative study of the distribution of the roots of *Avena fatua*. J. Ecol. 58:865-868.

Ellis, F.B., and B.T. Barnes. 1973. Estimation of the living roots of plants under field conditions. Plant & Soil 39:81-91.

Ford, C.W. 1973. Semimicro quantitative determination of carbohydrates in plant material by gas-liquid chromatography. Anal. Biochem. 57:413-420.

Fox, R.L., and R.C. Lipps. 1964. A comparison of stable Sr and ^{32}p as tracers for estimating alfalfa root activity. Plant & Soil 20:337-350.

Gerdemann, J.W. 1974. Mycorrhizae, p. 205-217. *In:* E.W. Carson (ed.), Plant root and its environments. Univ. Press Virginia, Charlottesville, Virginia.

Giovannetti, M., and B. Mosse. 1980. An evaluation of techniques for measuring vesicular-arbuscular mycorrhizal infection of roots. New Phytol. 84:489-500.

Gooderham, P.T. 1969. A simple method for the extraction and preservation of an undisturbed root system from the soil. Plant & Soil 31:201-205.

Graber, L.F. 1931. Food reserves in relation to other factors limiting the growth of grasses. Plant Physiol. 6:43-72.

Graber, L.F., N.T. Nelson, W.A. Leukel, and W.B. Albert. 1927. Organic food reserves in relation to the growth of alfalfa and other perennial herbaceous plants. Res. Bull. 80. Wisconsin Agr. Exp. Sta.

Grotelueschen, R.D., and D. Smith. 1967. Determination and identification of nonstructural carbohydrates removed from grass and legume tissue by various sulfuric acid concentrations, takadiastase and water. J. Agr. Food Chem. 15:1048-1051.

Grotelueschen, R.D., and D. Smith. 1968. Carbohydrates in grasses. III. Estimations of the degree of polymerization of the fructosans in the stem bases of timothy and bromegrass near seed maturity. Crop Sci. 8:210-212.

Grueb, L.J., and W.F. Wedin. 1971. Leaf area, dry-matter production, and carbohydrate reserve levels of birdsfoot trefoil as influenced by cutting height. Crop Sci. 11:734-738.

Haas, H.J., and G.A. Rogler. 1953. A technique for photographing grass roots *in situ*. Agron. J. 45:173.

Hale, M.G., C.L. Fory, and F.J. Shay. 1971. Factors affecting root exudation. Advance. Agron. 23:89-109.

Hall, N.S., W.F. Chandler, C.H.M. van Bavel, P.H. Reid, and J.H. Anderson. 1953. A tracer technique to measure growth and activity of plant root system. Tech. Bull. 101. North Carolina Agr. Exp Sta.

Hanson, W.R., and L.A. Stoddart. 1940. Effects of grazing upon bluebunch wheatgrass. J. Amer. Soc. Agron. 32:278-289.

Harmsen, G.W., and G. Jager. 1962. Determination of the quality of carbon nitrogen in the rhizosphere of young plants. Nature 195:1119-1120.

Harris, G.A. 1967. Some competitive relationships between *Agropyron spicatum* and *Bromus tectorum*. Ecol. Monogr. 37:89-111.

Hellmers, H., J.S. Horton, G. Juhren, and J. O'Keefe. 1955. Root systems of some chaparral plants in southern California. Ecology 36:667-678.

Holechek, J.L. 1982. Root biomass on native range and mine spoils in southeastern Montana. J. Range Manage. 35:185-187.

Holscher, C.E. 1945. The effects of clipping bluestem wheatgrass and blue grama at different heights and frequencies. Ecology 26:148-156.

Hyder, D.N., and F.A. Sneva. 1963. Morphological and physiological factors affecting and grazing management of crested wheatgrass. Crop Sci. 3:267-271.

Jameson, D.A. 1963. Responses of individual plants to harvesting. Bot. Rev. 29:532-594.

Julander, O. 1945. Drought resistance in range and pasture grasses. Plant Physiol. 20:573-579.

Kansouh, A.S.H., and T.L. Hopkins. 1968. Diazinon absorption, translocation and metabolism in bean plants. J. Agr. Food Chem. 16:446-450.

Kinsinger, F.E. 1955. Extracting plant root samples with the Kelley Core Sampler. J. Range Manage. 8:222.

Knievel, D.P. 1973. Procedure for estimating ratio of live to dead root dry matter in root core samples. Crop Sci. 13:124-126.

Kolesnikov, V. 1971. The root system of fruit plants. Mir. Publ., Moscow, U.S.S.R. (Translation).

Kormanik, P.P., and A.C. McGraw. 1982. Quantification of vesicular-arbuscular mycorrhizae in plant roots, Chapter 4. *In:* N.C. Schenck (ed.), Methods and principles of mycorrhizal research. American Phytopathol. Soc., St. Paul, Minnesota.

Kormanik, P.P., W.C. Bryan, and R.C. Schultz. 1980. Procedures and equipment for staining large numbers of plant root samples for endomycorrhizal assay. Can. J. Microbiol. 26:536-538.

Kramer, P.J. 1983. Water relations of plants. Acad. Press. New York. New York.

Laycock, W.A., and P.W. Conrad. 1969. How time and intensities of clipping affect tall bluebell. J. Range Manage. 22:299-303.

Linder, P.J., J.W. Mitchell, and G.D. Freeman. 1964. Persistance and translocation of exogenous regulating compounds that exude from roots. J. Agr. Food Chem. 12:437-438.

Lull, H.W., and K.G. Reinhart. 1955. Soil-moisture measurement. Occasional Paper 140. USDA Forest Serv., Southern Forest Exp. Sta.

Majerus, M.E. 1975. Response of root and shoot growth of three grass species to decreases in soil water potential. J. Range Manage. 28:473-476.

Mathis, G.W., C.J. Jaynes, and G.W. Thomas. 1965. Root development of plains bristlegrass as measured by soil placement of radiophosphorus. J. Range Manage. 18:30-32.

McCarty, E.C. 1935. Seasonal march of carbohydrates in *Elymus ambiguus* and *Muhlenbergia gracilis*, and their reaction under moderate grazing use. Plant Physiol. 10:727-728.

McCarty, E.C. 1938. The relation of growth to the varying carbohydrate content in mountain brome. Bull. 598. USDA, Washington, D.C.

McCarty, E.C., and R. Price. 1942. Growth and carbohydrate content of important mountain forage plants in central Utah as affected by clipping and grazing. Tech. Bull. 818. USDA, Washington, D.C.

McConnell, B.R., and G.A. Garrison. 1966. Seasonal variations of available carbohydrates in bitterbrush. J. Wildlife Manage. 30:168-172.

McIlvanie, S.K. 1942. Carbohydrate and nitrogen trends in bluebunch wheatgrass, *Agropyron spicatum*, with special reference to grazing influences. Plant Physiol. 17:540-547.

Menke, J.W., and M.J. Trlica. 1981. Carbohydrate reserve, phenology, and growth cycles of nine Colorado species. J. Range Manage. 34:269-277.

Menke, J.W., and M.J. Trlica. 1983. Effects of single and sequential defoliations on the carbohydrate reserves of four range species. J. Range Manage. 36:70-74.

Meyer, B.S., D.B. Anderson, and R.H. Bohning. 1966. Introduction to plant physiology. D. Van Nostrand Co., New York.

Miller, R.F., and G.B. Donart. 1981. Response of *Muhlenbergia porteri* Scribn. to season of defoliation. J. Range Manage. 34:91-94.

Mishustin, E.N., and V.K. Shil'nikova. 1971. Biological fixation of atmosphere nitrogen. Macmillan Co., New York. New York.

Moawad, M. 1979. Ecophysiology of vesicular-arbuscular mycorrhiza in the tropics, p. 197-209. *In:* J.L. Harley and R. Scott Russell (eds.) The soil-root interface. Academic Press, London, England.

Mooney, H.A. 1972. The carbon balance of plants. Annu. Rev. Ecol. System. 3:315-346.

Moorman, T., and F.B. Reeves. 1979. The role of endomycorrhizae in revegetation practices in the semi-arid west. II. A bioassay to determine the effect of land disturbance on endomycorrhizal populations. Amer. J. Bot. 66:14-18.

Moran, C.H., J.G. Sprague, and J.T. Sullivan. 1953. Changes in the carbohydrate resources of Ladino white clover following defoliation. Plant Physiol. 28:467-474.

Neiland, B.M., and J. Curtis. 1956. Differential response to clipping of six prairie grasses in Wisconsin. Ecology 37:355-365.

Newman, E.I. 1966. A method of estimating the total length of root in a sample. J. Appl. Ecol. 3:139-145.

Owensby, C.E., G.M. Paulsen, and J.D. McKendrick. 1970. Effect of burning and clipping on big bluestem reserve carbohydrates. J. Range Manage. 23:358-362.

Owensby, C.E., E.F. Smith, and J.R. Rains. 1977. Carbohydrate and nitrogen reserve cycles for continuous, season-long and intensive-early stocked Flint Hills bluestem range. J. Range Manage. 30:258-260.

Paech, K., and M.V. Tracey. 1955-1956. Modern methods of plant analysis. 4 vols. Springer-Verlag, Berlin, Germany.

Pavlychenko, T.K. 1937. The soil-block washing method in quantitative root study. Can. J. Res., Sect. C. Bot. Sci. 15:33-57.

Phillips, J.M., and D.S. Hayman. 1970. Improved procedures for clearing roots and standing parasitic and vesicular-arbuscular mycorrhizal fungi for rapid assessment of infection. Trans. Brit. Mycol. Soc. 55:158-161.

Reynolds, J.H. 1962. Morphological development and trends of carbohydrate reserves in alfalfa, smooth bromegrass and timothy under various cutting schedules. Diss. Abstr. 23:1855-1856.

Rhodes, L.H., and M.C. Hirrel. 1982. Radio tracer methods of mycorrhizal research, p. 189-200. *In:* N.C. Schenck (ed.), Methods and principles of mycorrhizal research. Amer. Phytopathol. Soc., St. Paul, Minnesota.

Richards, D., F.H. Goubran, W.N. Garwoli, and M.W. Daly. 1979. A machine for determining root length. Plant & Soil 52:69-76.

Robinson, T. 1975. The organic constituents of higher plants, 3rd ed. Cordus Press, North Amherst, Massachusetts.

Rovira, A.D. 1969. Plant root exudates. Bot. Rev. 35:35-57.

Rowse, H.R., and D.A. Phillips. 1974. An instrument for estimating the total length of root in a sample. J. Appl. Ecol. 11:309-314.

Ruby, E.S., and V.A. Young. 1953. The influence of intensity and frequency of clipping on the root system of brownseed paspalum. J. Range Manage. 6:94-99.

Salisbury, F.B., and C. Ross. 1978. Plant physiology, 2nd ed. Wadsworth Publ. Co., Belmont, California.

Sampson, A.W., and E.C. McCarty. 1930. The carbohydrate metabolism of *Stipa pulchra*. Hilgardia 5:61-100.

Sanders, J.L., and D.A. Brown. 1978. A new fiber optic technique for measuring root growth of soybeans under field conditions. Agron. J. 70:1073-1076.

Santos, G.L., and M.J. Trlica. 1978. Clipping effects on production and carbohydrate reserves of blue grama and western wheatgrass, p. 384-386. *In:* D.N. Hyder (ed.), Proc. First Int. Rangeland Congr. Soc. Range Manage., Denver, Colorado.

Sayre, J.D., and V.H. Morris. 1940. The lithium method of measuring the extent of corn root systems. Plant Physiol. 15:761-764.

Schultz, A.M., and H.H. Biswell. 1955. A method for photographing roots. J. Forest. 53:138.

Schuurman, J.J., and M.A.J. Goedewaagen. 1971. Methods for examination of root systems and roots, 2nd ed. Pudoc, Wageningen, Germany.

Sheard, R.W. 1968. Relationship of carbohydrate and nitrogen compounds in the haplocorn to the growth of timothy (*Phleum pratense* L.). Crop Sci. 8:658-660.

Shivley, S.B., and J.E. Weaver. 1939. Amount of underground plant materials in different grassland climates. Bull. 21. Conserv. Soil Survey, Univ. Nebraska, Lincoln, Nebraska.

Singer, F.P., and R.J. Hutnick. 1973. Excavating roots with water pressure. J. Forest. 63:37-38.

Singh, J.S., and D.C. Coleman. 1973 A technique for evaluating functional root biomass in grassland ecosystems. Can. J. Bot. 51:1867-1870.

Smith, A.E. 1972. A method for quantifying carbohydrate functions in forage plants. J. Agr. Food Chem. 20:238-240.

Smith, D. 1962. Carbohydrate root reserves in alfalfa, red clover and birdsfoot trefoil under several management schedules. Crop Sci. 2:75-78.

Smith, D. 1969. Removing and analyzing total nonstructural carbohydrates from plant tissue. Res. Rep. 41. Res. Div. Coll. Agr. and Life Sci., Wisconsin.

Smith, D., and L.F. Graber. 1948. The influence of top growth removal on the root and vegetative development of biennial sweetclover. Agron. J. 40:818-831.

Smith, D., and R.D. Grotelueschen. 1966. Carbohydrates in grasses. I. Sugar and fructosan composition of the stem bases of several northern-adapted grasses at seed maturity. Crop Sci. 6:263-266.

Smith, H.W., R.A. McCreery, and C.D. Moodie. 1952. Collection and preservation of soil profiles, II. Soil Sci. 73:243-248.

Smith, S.S.E. 1980. Mycorrhizas of autotrophic higher plants. Biol. Rev. 55:475-510.

Sosebee, R.E. (ed.). 1977. Rangeland plant physiology. Range Sci. Ser. No. 4. Soc. Range Manage. Denver, Colorado.

Sprague, V.G., and J.T. Sullivan. 1950. Reserve carbohydrates in orchardgrass clipped periodically. Plant Physiol. 25:92-102.

Steinke, T.D. 1969. The translocation of ^{14}C-assimilates in *Eragrostis curvula:* An autoradiographic survey. Proc. Grassland Soc. South Afr. 4:19-34.

Steinke, T.D., and P. de V. Booysen. 1968. The utilization of carbohydrate reserves and regrowth of *Eragrostis curvula* after different frequencies of defoliation. Proc. Grassland Soc. South Afr. 3:105-110.

Stoechler, J.H., and W.A. Kluender. 1938. The hydraulic method of excavating root systems of plants. Ecology 19:355-369.

Sullivan, J.T. 1951. Guide to the carbohydrate analyses of forage plants. U.S. Reg. Pasture Res. Lab., State College, Pennsylvania.

Sullivan, J.T., and V.G. Sprague. 1943. Composition of the roots and stubble of perennial ryegrass following defoliation. Plant Physiol. 18:656-670.

Sullivan, J.T., and V.G. Sprague. 1949. The effects of temperature on the growth and composition of the stubble and roots of perennial ryegrass (*Lolium perenne).* Plant Physiol. 24:706-719.

Sullivan, J.T., and V.G. Sprague. 1953. Reserve carbohydrates in orchardgrass cut for hay. Plant Physiol. 28:304-313.

Suzuki, M. 1971a. Behavior of long-chain fructosan in the basal top of timothy as influenced by N, P, and K, and defoliation. Crop Sci. 11:632-635.

Suzuki, M. 1971b. Semi-automatic analysis of the total available carbohydrates in alfalfa roots. Can. J. Plant Sci. 51:184-185.

Taylor, H.M., and W. Bohm. 1976. Use of acrylic plastic as rhizotron windows. Agron. J. 68:693-694.

Tennant, D. 1975. A test of modified line intersect method of estimating root length. J. Ecol. 63:995-1001.

Tesar, M.B., and H.L. Ahlgren. 1950 Effect of height and frequency of cutting on the productivity and survival of ladino clover (*Trifolium repens* L.). Agron. J. 42:230-235.

Thaine, R. 1954. The effect of clipping frequency on the productivity of root development of Russian wild ryegrass in the field. Can. J. Agr. Sci. 34:299-304.

Tharp, B.C., and C.H. Muller. 1940. A rapid method for excavating root systems of native plants. Ecology 21:347-349.

Trlica, M.J. 1977. Distribution and utilization of carbohydrate reserves in range plants, p. 73-97. *In:* R.E. Sosebee (ed.), Rangeland plant physiology. Range Sci. Ser. 4. Soc. Range Manage., Denver, Colorado.

Trlica, M.J., Jr., and C.W. Cook. 1971. Defoliation effects on carbohydrate reserves of desert species. J Range Manage. 24:418-425.

Trlica, M.J., Jr., and C.W. Cook. 1972. Carbohydrate reserves of crested wheatgrass and Russian wildrye as affected by development and defoliation. J. Range Manage. 25:430-435.

Troughton, A. 1957. The underground organs of herbage grasses. Bull. 44. Commonwealth Bur. Pasture Field Crops, Hurly, Berkshire, England.

Uneo, M., and D. Smith. 1970. Growth and carbohydrate changes in the root wood and bark of different sized alfalfa plants during regrowth after cutting. Crop Sci. 10:396-399.

Upchurch, R.P., and R.L. Lovvorn. 1951. Gross morphological root habits of alfalfa in North Carolina. Agron. J. 43:493-498.

Veihmeyer, F.J., and A.H. Hendrickson. 1948. Soil density and root penetration. Soil Sci. 65:487-493.

Waddington, J. 1971. Observation of plant roots *in situ*. Can. J. Bot. 49:1850-1952.

Waite, R., and J. Boyd. 1953. The water-soluble carbohydrates of grasses. II. Grasses cut at grazing height several times during the growing season. J. Sci. Food Agr. 4:257-261.

Ward, C.V., and R.E. Blaser. 1961. Carbohydrate food reserves and leaf area in regrowth of orchardgrass. Crop Sci. 1:366-370.

Ward, K.J., B. Klepper, R.W. Rickmann, and R.R. Allmaras. 1978. Quantitative estimation of living wheat root lengths in soil cores. Agron. J. 70:675-677.

Warembourg, F.R., and G. Billes. 1979. Estimating carbon transfers in the plant rhizosphere, p. 183-196. *In:* J.L. Harley and R.S. Russell (eds.), Soil-root interface. Acad. Press, London, England.

Warembourg, F.R., and E.A. Paul. 1977. Seasonal transfer of assimilated ^{14}C in grassland: Plant production and turnover, soil and plant respiration. Soil Biol. Biochem. 9:295-301.

Weaver, J.E. 1926. Root development of field crops. McGraw-Hill Book Co., Inc., New York. New York.

Weaver, J.E., and F.W. Albertson. 1943. Resurvey of grasses, forbs and underground plant parts at end of the great drought. Ecol. Monogr. 13:65-117.

Weaver, J.E., and F.E. Clements. 1938. Plant ecology. McGraw-Hill Book Co., Inc., New York. New York.

Weaver, J.E., and R.W. Darland. 1949. Quantitative study of root systems in different soil types. Science 110:164-165.

Weaver, J.E., and E. Zink. 1945. Extent and longevity of the seminal roots of certain grasses. Plant Physiol. 20:359-379.

Weaver, J.E., and E. Zink. 1946. Length of life of roots of 10 species of perennial range and pasture grasses. Plant Physiol. 21:201-217.

Weinmann, H. 1943. Root reserves in South African highveld grasses in relation to fertilizing and frequency of clipping. J. South Afr. Bot. 10:37-54.

Weinmann, H. 1947. Determination of total available carbohydrates in plants. Plant Physiol. 22:279-290.

Weinmann, H. 1948a. Investigations on the underground reserves of South African grasses. South Afr. J. Sci. 2:12-18.

Weinmann, H. 1948b. Underground development and reserves of grasses; a review. Brit. Grassland Soc. J. 3:115-140.

Weinmann, H. 1949. Productivity of Marandellas sandveld pastures in relation to frequency of cutting. Rhodesian Agr. J. 46:175-189.

Weinmann, H. 1952. Carbohydrate reserves in grasses, p. 655-660. *In:* Sixth Int. Grassland Congr. Proc.

Weinmann, H. 1961. Total available carbohydrates in grasses and legumes. Herbage Abstr. 31:225-261.

Weinmann, H., and L. Reinhold. 1946. Reserve carbohydrates in South African grasses. J. South Afr. Bot. 12:57-73.

Welch, T.G. 1968. Carbohydrate reserves of sand reedgrass under different grazing intensities. J. Range Manage. 21:216-220.

White, L.M. 1973. Carbohydrate reserves of grasses: A review. J. Range Manage. 26:13-18.

Willard, E.E., and C.M. McKell. 1973. Simulated grazing management systems in relation to shrub growth responses. J. Range Manage. 26:171-174.

Willatt, S.T., and R.G. Struss. 1979. Neutron radiography, a technique for studying young roots growing in soil, p. 513-525. *In:* Isotopes and radiation in research on soil-plant relationships. Int. Atomic Energy Agency, Vienna, Austria.

Williams, T.E., and H.K. Baker. 1957. Studies on the root development of herbage plants. I. Techniques of herbage root investigation. Brit. Grassland Soc. J. 12:49-55.

Wilson, R.T., B.E. Dahl, and R.D. Kreig. 1975. Carbohydrate concentrations in honey mesquite roots in relation to development and reproductive condition. J. Range Manage. 28:286-289.

Wolf, D.D. 1967. Characteristics of stored carbohydrates in reed canarygrass as related to management, feed value and herbage yield. Bull. 402. Connecticut. Agr. Exp. Sta.

Wolf, D.D., and T.L. Ellmore. 1973. Total nonstructural carbohydrates in forages by semiautomated analysis. Can. J. Plant Sci. 53:551-552.

Wolf, D.D., and T.L. Ellmore. 1975. Automated hydrolysis of nonreducing sugars and fructosans from plant tissue. Crop Sci. 15:775-777.

Wolf, D.D., K.L. Larson, and D. Smith. 1962. Grass-alfalfa yields and food storage of associated alfalfas as influenced by height and frequency of clipping. Crop Sci. 2:363-364.

Wyatt, J.W., D.J. Dollhope, and W.M. Shafer. 1980. Root distribution in 1- to 48-year old stripmine spoils in southeastern Montana. J. Range Manage. 33:101-104.

Chapter 5
Methods of Measuring Herbage and Browse Utilization

Introduction

Utilization is defined as the degree to which animals have removed the current growth of herbage and is expressed in percentage of growth within reach of the grazing animals (Soc. American Forest. 1964). This concept may be applied to a single plant, group of plants, or to the range forage as a whole (Range Term Glossary Committee 1974). Cook and Stoddart (1953) suggest that since utilization refers to the percentage of current growth removed, a better term might be percentage utilization. In this chapter, utilization and percentage utilization are used interchangeably.

Correct utilization of herbage is one of the most important items in the whole field of range management. A forage cover can be maintained in vigorous, healthy condition only so long as it is utilized to such extent that it will grow and reproduce. Consequently, range technicians have given much attention to utilization and its measurement.

Numerous methods of measuring forage utilization have been developed. Some are more rapid or may be more detailed and accurate than others. For certain objectives and conditions, some methods are more suitable than others. The method adopted by a given research worker will be that which best fits the purpose of his study, manpower available, and kind of vegetation. None of the methods in this chapter may be wholly satisfactory, and the researcher may need to develop a method suitable for his/her own research. The literature on methods of measuring utilization has been reviewed by Pechanec and Pickford (1937), Dasmann (1948), and Heady (1949).

In addition to working on techniques to measure utilization accurately, the technician has directed much attention toward learning what constitutes proper utilization—i.e., developing utilization standards and proper use factors for each of the important forage plants and range types under various grazing conditions. In developing these standards, the investigator has first studied the life histories and requirements of individual plants. Later he has studied the effects and interactions of different intensities, frequencies, and grazing seasons on the health and vigor of the plants, changes in the plant community, soil compaction, runoff and erosion, animal gains, range condition and trend, and other factors related to grazing. Many of the studies have involved hand clipping the plants while actual grazing by animals has been used in others. Because of the great variability in plants and the many conditions under which they grow, it has been difficult to develop exact standards. This has led to some questions about the practical aspects of utilization measurements (Cook and Stoddart 1953, Hyder 1954).

Another phase of research has been directed toward developing more satisfactory methods of checking percentage utilization for such management practices as setting and adjusting stocking rates and in following trend in range condition. While administrators and ranchers are interested in accurate methods, they also want them to be easy and rapid (Campbell 1937).

Methods

Ocular Estimate-by-Plot

This method is an estimate of the percentage of herbage removed in terms of weight. These estimates are made on plots small enough that the entire plot is clearly visible from one point. A worker first spends considerable time checking his estimates against actual weights. Plots are clipped to simulate grazing. Then an estimate of the percentage weight removal is made, and the remaining stubble is clipped. Both clippings are weighed, and the actual percentage weight removal is computed. This method is suitable for grasses, forbs, and shrubs. In field practice, an investigator can check and improve the reliability of his/her estimates each day by clipping and weighing the herbage on several plots.

The advantages of ocular estimate by plot are listed by Pechanec and Pickford (1937) as "(1) observations are confined to a small area, which makes possible more accurate decision. (2) errors in personal judgment on individual plots frequently tend to be compensating, (3) data thus collected can be subjected to statistical analysis, and (4) data collected from these randomized samples are valuable in studying the distribution of grazing on range areas." Clark (1945) recommended this method as sufficiently rapid and accurate for general field use.

The chief disadvantage is that estimates rather than objective measurements are used. Estimates are subject to personal error among individuals and for the same individual at different times. Much emphasis should be placed on training and checking. In addition, the estimate can be adjusted by a factor developed by correcting estimates with actual data from periodically clipped plots, known as a double sampling technique. On ungrazed areas, grazing must be roughly simulated by clipping. The herbage removed is weighed. The percentage of herbage removed is then estimated, and the remainder of the herbage is clipped and weighed. The percentages removed by the simulated grazing and the error of estimation should be determined only after all plots have been estimated, since adjustments for error after each plot would influence the personal error of estimates.

Ocular Estimate-by-Average of Plants

This method is based on estimates of weight removed from individual plants, instead of the entire forage per plot as with the previous method. These estimates are then weighted and averaged by species to obtain plot ratings. Although slightly less rapid than the ocular estimate-by-plot method, there is less personal error since each observation is confined to a single plant. Its high correlation with actual weight removed adapts it to accurate range studies. It has the advantage of allowing definite sample size for each species since the plant is the sample unit and not a quadrat.

Cage Comparison Method

Paired plots protected by cages or other suitable exclosures are clipped to compare with similar plots on adjacent grazed areas. The difference in weight is considered to be the percentage of forage consumed.

Two similar quadrats are selected on the basis of composition, growth and utilization. One of these may be placed randomly and the second is selected to pair with the randomly selected one (Klingman et al. 1943). After the two quadrats are selected, a coin is tossed to indicate which unit to cage. At the end of each sampling period new areas are selected as before. Both utilization and yield may be measured by this method.

Historically, this method with slight variations was widely used on ranges and in pastures (Fuelleman and Burlison 1939, Darland and Weaver 1945, Nevens 1945, Weaver and Bruner 1948, Boyd 1949, Davies et al. 1950, Riegel et al. 1950, Bently and Talbot 1951). Instead of exclosing areas, Everson (1951) randomly clipped grazed and ungrazed spots in a pasture. He found this unsatisfactory from the standpoint of time and labor because large numbers of clipped spots were needed for acceptable accuracy in determining utilization between plots.

Types of cages were discussed in Chapter 3. The effect of the cage on the microenvironment was also discussed in that chapter.

A common objection is that differences in growth on the protected and grazed areas may distort the calculated utilization. The greater the period of time between caging and clipping the larger this becomes. Cook and Stoddart (1953) found rather large errors in interpreting utilization of crested wheatgrass *(Agropyron cristatum)* using this method during different periods of the growing season.

Weight Before and After Grazing

Difference in plant unit weight before and after grazing forms the basis for this system. It is best adapted to forage grazed for short periods where regrowth is not a factor. For example, it can be used where a band of sheep passes over an area and the forage is grazed within a few hours or a few days (Cassady 1941).

The method described by Cassady (1941) consists of collecting a given number of specific plant "units" before grazing and a similar number after grazing. The plant "unit" which is collected is an easily definable and recognizable portion of the individual plant. It varies with the species but may be a single stem or an entire plant. It must be large enough so as never to be entirely consumed, since after-grazing units must be collected to determine what percent has been removed by the grazing animal. Therefore, utilization is based upon percent of the unit selected which in some cases may include more plant material than is actually represented in the current year's growth. The sampling unit may also be paired quadrats. As mentioned previously the method works best over relatively short grazing periods when herbage weight is not changing rapidly.

Stubble Height Class

This method is based on the concept that intensity of grazing is reflected by a combination of grazed stubble heights and amount of ungrazed grass left on the ground at the end of the grazing season. Transects 15 m long are adequate on ranges supporting a grass cover of 5% or more, whereas ranges having less than 5% of the area occupied by perennial grasses require a transect 30 m long (Canfield 1944). Plants are recorded in stubble height classes. The following stubble height classes were found adequate for southern Arizona mixed grama grass ranges. However, the class intervals given here may or may not be the most suitable for areas supporting other species. When tall, coarse-stemmed grasses are the principal forage plants, it may be necessary to have more or larger class intervals.

Class No.	Stubble height in centimeters
1	0– 1
2	1– 2
3	2– 5
4	5–10
5	10–15
6	15–20
7	20–25
8	25 and over
9	Ungrazed plants

The height of each tuft or stem is measured from ground level. Its lateral extent is measured at ground level along the transect. In cases where the tufts are grazed to two or more stubble heights, the ground measurement is split between the height classes according to the portion of the tuft in each class. The data for each species are compiled by stubble height classes with the percentage of plants in each class. These can be converted to percentage utilization for all species combined to cover the range as a whole. This method does not yield percentage utilization data, but does present a good picture of utilization patterns of a pasture.

Height-Weight Ratio

Since percentage of weight removed is a commonly used standard of forage utilization, a possible approach is the conversion of some other measurement to weight through regression relationships (Lommasson and Jensen 1938). The first task is working out the relationship or developing the standard to show how weight is distributed for each species encountered. Leaves and culms of grass plants are held in place by first wrapping a string spirally around an ungrazed plant from the base upward and then removing the herbage slightly above ground level. The entire plant is cut into 2.5 cm or convenient segments which are dried and weighed. Percentage of the total weight is calculated for each segment of height. Lomasson and Jensen (1938 and 1943) found that each species has a more or less definite form as illustrated by Campbell (1942) in Figure 5-1. A detailed description of the method

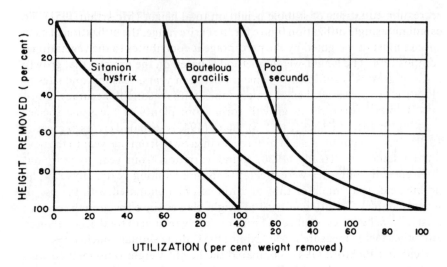

Fig. 5-1. Three types of height-weight curves of range grasses with seed stalks (courtesy R.S. Campbell.)

of constructing conversion tables and the field application is given by Lommasson and Jensen (1943) and by Campbell (1943).

Samples are taken, either systematically or at random, of both grazed and ungrazed heights to determine utilization by percentage reduction in height. This in turn is converted to weight reduction or percent utilization by weight. Consequently, one must find representative ungrazed plants to determine height reduction resulting from grazing.

The following devices have been used to make this conversion: (1) charts (Crafts 1938), (2) circular logarithmic gauges (Fig. 5-2). (Lommasson and Jensen 1943), (3) tables (Collins and Hurtt 1943), (4) cards with scales printed on them so percentage utilization may be read directly when the card is placed along side the plant (Valentine 1946), and (5) a slide rule developed from

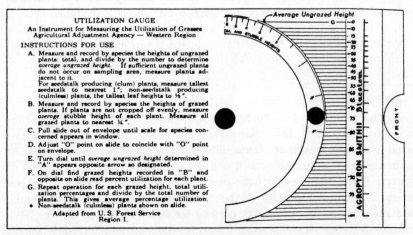

Fig. 5-2. Utilization gauge giving height-weight relationships (courtesy T. Lommasson).

regression equations of stubble height on total height (McArthur 1951). To calculate a single utilization figure for the entire range, the utilization of each species must be weighted by the percentage it contributes to the vegetational composition. The height-weight method is based on the premise that growth form of grasses is sufficiently constant between years, seasons, and sites to allow the use of average height-weight tables with reasonable accuracy. Caird (1945) found variation in growth form from plants of the same species growing on different sites (Fig. 5-3). Clark (1945) estimated errors as great as 10–25% may occur because of differences in growth from one year to the next on the same site. Heady (1950) found variation from year to year, but differences among sites were greater than those among years. However, he pointed out that much of the variation can be eliminated with the use of separate tables for different natural height classes since the growth form, at least of bunchgrasses, seemed to be more closely related to total height than to any other factor measured. McArthur (1951) drew similar conclusions.

Reid and Pickford (1941) compared the height-weight ratio method with the ocular-estimate-by-plot. Both methods gave substantially the same result when stubble height was somewhat uniform, but when stubble heights were uneven the estimates were considered low. About the same number of plots were required in both methods but the increased speed in the ocular-estimate-by-plot methods led them to recommend it. On the other hand, Lommasson and Jensen (1943) and McArthur (1951) obtained more consistent results when the height-weight ratio method was used as compared to ocular estimates.

The height-weight method has also been used on sedges (*Carex* spp.) (McDougald and Platt 1976) and for forbs (Harshman and Forsman 1978). Both these articles present details of the method in field applications.

In summary, the height-weight procedure seems to be a reliable method for determining utilization of perennial grasses. However, the construction of height-weight tables is a tedious undertaking and must be done with considerable attention to variations in growth form resulting from differences in site, weather, and genetic causes. Experience indicates that the tables need to be made for specific conditions and used in accordance with the variation encountered. Once they have been made the determination of utilization becomes a relatively accurate procedure except where grazing is primarily on leaves and the stems are left ungrazed.

Stem Count

Stoddart (1935) developed the stem count method in which he showed that percentage utilization was a direct function of the total number of stems grazed. The work was done with western wheatgrass *(Agropyron smithii)*. It required a count of grazed as well as ungrazed stems from random plots or transects. Little error results from personal or procedural causes. If proper grazing is attained when 80% of the stems have been grazed, it is a simple calculation to determine whether use has been under, proper, or over. This method was tested with thickspike wheatgrass *(Agropyron dasystachyum)* at

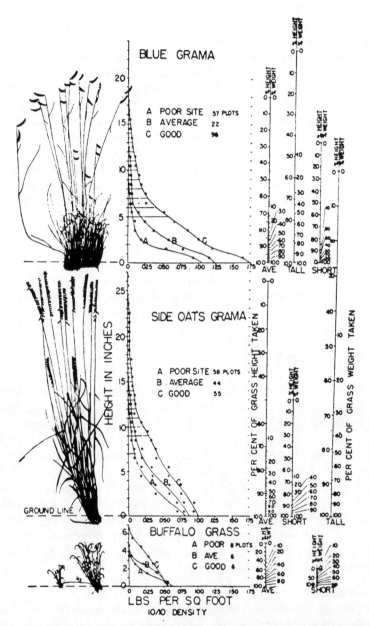

Fig. 5-3. The effects of environment on the height-weight relationships in blue grama *(Bouteloua gracilis)*, side oats grama *(Bouteloua curtipendula)* and buffalograss *(Buchloe dactyloides)* (courtesy R.W. Caird).

Dubois, Idaho, and was not sufficiently accurate for this species (Pechanec 1936). The percentage utilization was based on the volume of forage removed. The difference was due largely to the fact that all the stems grazed were not completely grazed or grazed to the same height. The error was greater with light grazing than with heavy grazing.

Short Cut

This method is based on the relation among three factors: the amount of a grass stand grazed to a stubble height of 5 cm or less, the amount of grazed above a 5 cm stubble height, and the ungrazed complement (Canfield 1942, 1944). The three height classes will total 100%. The relative amounts in terms of tuft areas, of partially grazed and ungrazed grass that are most likely to be present when various percentages of the total grass stand have been grazed to a stubble height of 5 cm are determined for each area of the grass stand.

In using the method, one estimates, in terms of basal tuft area, the average percentage of stubble grazed to 5 cm or less without regard for species or density. This estimate is then referred to the bar nearest that obtained (Fig. 5-4). The observer then looks at the upper two segments of that bar to learn the expected percentages of ungrazed plants.

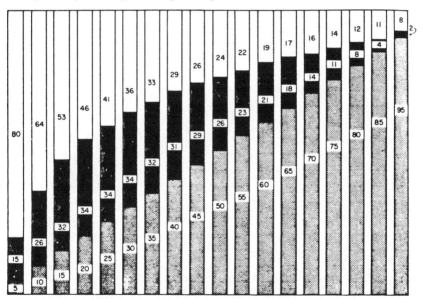

Fig. 5-4. Relation between percentage of total grass stand grazed 5 cm or less, amount grazed above 5 cm and ungrazed remainder (courtesy of R.H. Canfield).

A point of interest about the method is the constancy with which the percentage of partially grazed grass is maintained until about 50% of the cover has been grazed to a height of 5 cm or less. This may be the point where full grazing is attained and over-use begins.

Percentage of Plants Ungrazed or Grazed

This method is based on the relation between the percentage of plants ungrazed (Roach 1950) or grazed (Hurd and Kissinger 1953) and the percentage of total weight removed (Figs. 5-5 and 5-6). Basic data needed in preparing the graphs consist of the percentage of plants ungrazed or grazed

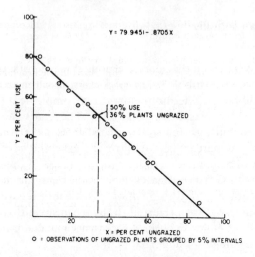

Fig. 5-5. Utilization as determined by the percentage of ungrazed plants of all important grasses on the Santa Rita Experimental Range (courtesy of M.E. Roach).

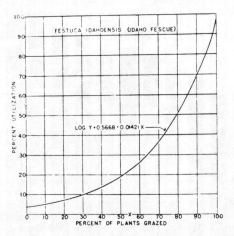

Fig. 5-6. The relation between percentage of plants grazed and utilization of Idaho fescue *(Festuca idahoensis)* on cattle ranges (courtesy of R.M. Hurd and N.A. Kissinger, Jr.).

and the associated percentage utilization by weight on areas grazed to various intensities.

Roach (1950) used straight line transects of 100 double paces. At each double pace the grass plant nearest the toe of the boot was classified as either grazed or ungrazed. At the same time, data necessary to determine the percentage utilization by the height-weight method were recorded. The data for percentage ungrazed plants and percentage utilization for each transect line were then plotted and a regression line computed. The regression equation computed from these data was $Y = 79.9451 - 0.8705X$ where X is the percentage of plants ungrazed, and Y is the percentage utilization calculated from measured stubble heights. The correlation coefficient, 0.92, indicates a strong relation.

Data obtained by Hurd and Kissinger (1953) came from forty-two 150 m transects where the ungrazed plants were counted and the percentage utilization was determined by the ocular-estimate-by-plot method. Utilization measurements on the plots ranged from 1–80%. The curve was derived from the equation Log Y = 0.5668 + 0.0142X wherein the logarithms of Y (percentage utilization) and the natural numbers of X (percentage of plants grazed) were used. The correlation coefficient was highly significant, having a value of 0.916. The method apparently works well on species which are grazed only once (Springfield 1961). However, there are many species which are apparently regrazed (Springfield and Peterson 1964; Hodgkinson 1980). In northern Utah, sheep grazed Pacific aster *(Aster chilensis)* up to 5 times in a 25-day period (Hodgkinson 1980). Consequently on those species which are grazed only lightly, they may show 100% utilization, but no increased utilization of the plants are shown when they are regrazed. Springfield and Peterson (1964) found that utilization of blue grama *(Bouteloua gracilis)* could not be estimated over 35% because at this point 100% of the plants had been grazed. Gierisch (1967) improved sensitivity of the method for Thurbers fescue *(Festuca thurberi)* by limiting counts to those plants grazed only more than 30%.

Estimates of Shrub Utilization

Several methods have been devised to determine utilization of shrubby species, but these plants pose special problems. Hormay (1943) devised a method for antelope bitterbrush *(Purshia tridentata)* which involved estimates of unbrowsed leader length, browsed leader length, percent utilization, and crown diameter. In most cases, procedures are simpler. One procedure is similar to Cassady's (1941) before-and-after method mentioned earlier with the plant unit being a twig. Twigs can be tagged at the end of the growing season and measured. The same twigs are remeasured before growth the next year. Using twig length as an index to utilization has at least three problems (Smith and Urness 1962): (1) the amount of twig taper, (2) independent utilization of leaves, and (3) complications of plant growth and regrowth. Smith and Urness (1962) showed that twigs of several Utah shrubs did exhibit some taper. Thus 50% reduction in twig length may not represent 50% utilization by weight. Several studies have shown a high correlation between twig length and weight (Basile and Hutchings 1966, Lyon 1970, Ferguson and Marsden 1977, Dean et al. 1981, Provenza and Urness 1981, and Bartolome and Kosco 1982). If animals strip leaves from the twig without nipping the twig, as much as 70% of the total weight might be removed with no reduction in twig length.

Twig diameter is also related to twig weight (Basile and Hutchings 1966, Lyons 1970). Once this relationship is determined, then utilization can be determined simply by measuring the diameter at the point of browsing and at the base and predict the amount and the total weight of the unbrowsed portion. One needs to make certain that these relationships hold from year to year and site to site.

Photographic Techniques

Using photographs provides a qualitative approach to estimating utilization (Bement and Klipple 1959, Schmutz et al. 1963). In some cases, photo guides are used for the pasture as a whole while in others photos of individual plants clipped or grazed to a certain height may be used. If the available herbage consists primarily of forbs and grasses of similar palatibility, a scaled board 50 cm × 2 m with height lines running parallel lengthwise on the board can be placed upright and photographed. The amount of the board showing through or above the parallel lines shows degree of utilization. Of course, in final analysis the method is only as reliable as the skill of the estimator.

Residue Techniques

Some workers have been rather critical of percentage utilization techniques since they estimate a quantity which is no longer present to measure directly. Hyder (1954) also states that percentage utilization methods were difficult to reconcile with the physiological needs of the plant. Consequently, the idea of using the residue or amount of herbage unused has been proposed as an index to grazing pressure. Bement (1969) has developed a stocking-rate guide for short grass vegetation in Colorado based on residue remaining at the end of the grazing period.

Literature Cited

Bartolome, J.W., and B.H. Kosco. 1982. Estimating browse production by deerbrush *(Ceanothus integerrimus)*. J. Range Manage. 35:671-672.

Basile, J.V., and S.S. Hutchings. 1966. Twig diameter-length-weight relations of bitterbrush. J. Range Manage. 19:34-38.

Bement, R.E. 1969. A stocking rate guide for beef production on blue-grama range. J. Range Manage. 22:83-86.

Bement, R.E., and G.E. Klipple. 1959. A pasture comparison method of estimating utilization of range herbage on the central Great Plains. J. Range Manage. 12:296-298.

Bentley, J.R., and M.W. Talbot. 1951. Efficient use of annual plants on cattle ranges in the California foothills. Circ. 870. USDA, Washington, D.C.

Boyd, D.A. 1949. Experiments with leys and permanent grass. J. Brit. Grassland Soc. 4:1-10.

Caird, R.W. 1945. Influence of site and grazing intensity on yields of grass forage in the Texas Panhandle. J. Forest. 43:45-49.

Campbell, R.S. 1937. Problems of measuring forage utilization on western ranges. Ecology 18:528-532.

Campbell, R.S. 1942. Preparation of grass height-weight tables for use of A.A.A. in utilization gauge. Forest Service, USDA, Washington, D.C. (mimeo).

Campbell, R.S. 1943. Ecology—progress in utilization standards for western ranges. J. Washington Acad. Sci. 33:161-169.

Canfield, R.H. 1942. Measurement of grazing use by the line interception method. J. Forest. 42:292-295.

Canfield, R.H. 1944. A short-cut method for checking degree of forage utilization. J. Forest. 42:667-671.

Cassady, J.T. 1941. A method of determining range forage utilization by sheep. J. Forest. 39:667-671.

Clark, Ira. 1945. Variability in height of forage grasses in central Utah. J. Forest. 43:273-283.

Collins, R.W., and L.C. Hurtt. 1943. A method for measuring utilization of bluestem wheatgrass on experimental range pastures. Ecology 24:122-125.

Cook, C.W., and L.A. Stoddart. 1953. The quandary of utilization and preference. J. Range Manage. 6:329-331.

Crafts, E.C. 1938. Height-volume distribution in range grasses. J. Forest. 36:1182-1185.

Dasmann, W.P. 1948. A critical review of range survey methods and their application to deer range management. California Fish and Game 34:189-207.

Darland, R.W., and J.E. Weaver. 1945. Yield and consumption of forage in three pasture types; an ecological analysis. Bull. 27. Conserv. and Soil Survey Div., Univ. Nebraska.

Davies, R.O., W.E.J. Milton, and J.R. Lloyd. 1950. Pasture productivity in mid-Wales. Pt. II. Empire J. Exp. Agr. 18:264-270.

Dean, S., J.W. Burkhardt, and R.O. Meeuwig. 1981. Estimating twig and foliage biomass of sagebrush, bitterbrush, and rabbitbrush in the Great Basin. J. Range Manage. 34:224-227.

Everson, A.C. 1951. Analysis of a forage utilization method based on the weight of plant units. J. Forest. 49:92.

Ferguson, R.B., and M.A. Marsden. 1977. Estimating overwinter bitterbrush utilization from twig diameter-length-weight relations. J. Range Manage. 30:231-236.

Fuelleman, R.F., and W.L. Burlison. 1939. Pasture yields and consumption under grazing conditions. Amer. Soc. Agron. J. 31:399-412.

Gierisch, R.K. 1967. An adaption of the grazed plant method of thurber fescue. J. Range Manage. 20:108-111.

Harshman, E.P., and R. Forsman. 1978. Measuring fireweed utilization. J. Range Manage. 31:393-396.

Heady, Harold. F. 1949. Methods of determining utilization of range forage. J. Range Manage. 2:53-63.

Heady, H.F. 1950. Studies on bluebunch wheatgrass in Montana and height-weight relationships of certain range grasses. Ecol. Monogr. 20:55-81.

Hodgkinson, K.C. 1980. Frequency and extent of defoliation of herbaceous plants by sheep in a foothill range community in northern Utah. J. Range Manage. 33:164-169.

Hormay, L.A. 1943. A method of estimating grazing use of bitterbrush. Res. Note 35. California Forest and Range Exp. Sta.

Hurd, R.M., and N.A. Kissinger, Jr. 1953. Estimating utilization of Idaho Fescue *(Festuca idahoensis)* on cattle range by percent of plants grazed. Paper No. 12:1-5. Rocky Mountain Forest and Range Exp. Sta.

Hyder, D.N. 1954. Forage utilization. J. Forest. 52:603-604.

Klingman, Dayton L., S.R. Miles, and G.O. Mott. 1943. The cage method for determining consumption and yield of pasture herbage. J. Amer. Soc. Agron. 35:739-746.

Lineham, P.A. 1952. Use of cage and mower-strip methods for measuring forage consumed by grazing animals. VI. Int. Grassland Congr. 2:1328-1333.

Lommasson, T., and C. Jensen. 1938. Grass volume tables for determining range utilization. Science 87:444.

Lommasson, T., and C. Jensen. 1943. Determining utilization of range grasses by height-weight tables. J. Forest. 41:589-593.

Lyon, L. Jack. 1970. Length- and weight-diameter relations of serviceberry twigs. J. Wildlife Manage. 34:456-460.

McArthur, J.A.B. 1951. The use of regression equations to determine utilization of little bluestem. Ph.D. Diss. Texas A&M Univ.

McDougald, N.K., and R.C. Platt. 1976. A method of determining utilization for wet mountain meadows on the summit allotment, Sequoia National Forest, California. J. Range Manage. 29:497-501.

Nevens, W.B. 1945. A comparison of sampling procedures in making pasture yield determination. J. Dairy Sci. 28:171-185.

Pechanec. J.F. 1936. Comments on the stem-count method of determining the percentage utilization on range. Ecology 17:329-331.

Pechanec, J.F., and G.D. Pickford. 1937. A comparison of some methods used in determining percentage utilization of range grasses. J. Agr. Res. 54:753-765.

Provenza, F.D., and P.J. Urness. 1981. Diameter-length-weight relations for blackbrush *(Coleogyne ramosissima)* branches. J. Range Manage. 34:215-217.

Range Term Glossary Committee. 1974. A glossary of terms used in range management. Soc. Range Manage., Denver, Colorado.

Reid, E.H., and G.D. Pickford. 1941. A comparison of the ocular-estimate-by-plot and the stubble-height methods of determining percentage utilization of range grasses. J. Forest. 39:935-941.

Riegel, D.A., F.W. Albertson, and H.H. Hopkins. 1950. Yields and utilization of forage on a mixed prairie in west-central Kansas. Kansas Acad. Sci. Trans. 53:455-472.

Range Term Glossary Committee. 1974. A glossary of terms used in range management. Soc. Range Manage., Denver, Colorado.

Reid, E.H., and G.D. Pickford. 1941. A comparison of the ocular-estimate-by-plot and the stubble-height methods of determining percentage utilization of range grasses. J. Forest. 39:935-941.

Riegel, D.A., F.W. Albertson, and H.H. Hopkins. 1950. Yields and utilization of forage on a mixed prairie in west-central Kansas. Kansas Acad. Sci. Trans. 53:455-472.

Roach, Mack E. 1950. Estimating perennial grass utilization on semi-desert cattle ranges by percentage of ungrazed plants. J. Range Manage. 3:182-185.

Schmutz, Ervin M., Gary A. Holt, and Charles C. Michaels. 1963. Grazed-class method of estimating forage utilization. J. Range Manage. 16:54-60.

Smith, A.D., and P.J. Urness. 1962. Analyses of the twig length method of determining utilization of browse. Pub. No. 62-9. Utah State Dept. Fish and Game.

Society of American Foresters. 1964. Forest terminology; a glossary of technical terms used in Forestry. Soc. Amer. Foresters. Washington, D.C.

Springfield, H.W. 1961. The grazed plant method for judging the utilization of crested wheatgrass. J. Forest. 59:666-670.

Springfield, H.W., and G. Peterson. 1964. Use of the grazed plant method for estimating utilization of some range grasses in New Mexico. Sta. Res. Note RM-22. Rocky Mountain Forest and Range Exp. Sta., Forest Service, USDA, Fort Collins, Colorado.

Stoddart, L.A. 1935. Range capacity determination. Ecology 16:531-533.

Valentine, K.A. 1946. Determining the grazing use of grasses by scaling. J. Forest. 44:528-530.

Weaver, J.E., and W.E. Bruner. 1948. Prairies and pastures of the dissected loess plains of central Nebraska. Ecol. Monogr. 18:507-549.

Chapter 6
Livestock Selection and Management
in Range Research

Introduction

Selection and management of livestock for a range research project are greatly influenced by objectives and experimental design. Experimental design and statistical aspects of sampling with animals will be treated only partially in this chapter. For additional information see Chapters 9 and 10.

Use of livestock in range research may be grouped into three general categories. First, they may be used to measure animal production under different environmental and/or management conditions, i.e., range sites, forage types, seasons of use, stocking rates, grazing systems, or supplemental feeding regimes (Morley 1978, 1981; Hacker 1982). Second, they may be used to measure animal responses to different conditions or situations (Arnold and Dudzinski 1978, Corbett 1978, Wheeler and Mochrie 1981, Dahl et al. 1982). These responses are generally behavioral or dietary in nature. The third use of livestock is to evaluate their influence on other components of range ecosystems such as plants, soils, water, and/or wildlife (Australian Rangeland Society 1977).

Livestock products are a major source of economic return from most rangelands, and measurement of animal productivity is frequently a major objective of research with grazing animals. However, to understand production responses, it is often necessary to measure non-production responses of animals, plants, and their environment. In other cases, limited resources may preclude the use of large scale studies which could provide valid animal production data. Technology for measuring animal responses under extensive grazing conditions has evolved rapidly over the past two decades, and studies with primary objectives directed towards monitoring of non-production responses of animals have become common.

Animal production can be in several forms (weight, reproduction, lactation, fiber). One universal basis for measurement is to convert animal products to economic value. Energy could also be a universal basis for comparison. Researchers should always keep these facts clearly in view when selecting animals and making management decisions. However, not all studies need to be designed to provide data suitable for economic analysis. Studies designed primarily to elucidate fundamental relationships controlling animal and range responses provide knowledge required to formulate sound theory and extrapolate research results to the general population.

Animal Selection

Species

In general, the kind(s) of animals to which research findings are to apply should be used. Physical, biological, economic, and sociological factors affect the suitability of different kinds of animals. Biological factors include kinds, proportions, and availability of plant species and both predators and competitors. Physical factors include soils, topography, and climate. Economic factors include efficiency of production by different species and relative market strength for different animal products. In many situations, socioeconomic constraints may be the overriding considerations in the choice of animal species (Ayuko 1978, Henson and Noel 1983). If research is intended to provide additional information for existing production systems, then selection of animals should be based on kinds of animals in the target system. However, researchers should carefully consider evaluating alternatives to existing systems where they offer improved production efficiency.

Common use by animal species will generally improve grazing distribution and overall forage utilization, as compared to use by single species, and will result in more efficient forage harvest from range. The mixture of animal species should be based on topographic features of the range, forage composition and degree of diet overlap to obtain maximum efficiency of forage use (Hanley and Hanley 1982, Harrington 1978, Kautz and Van Dyne 1978, Squires 1982, Theurer et al. 1976, Vavra and Sneva 1978).

Class

The class of animal (age and sex category) to be selected for a given experiment will depend on research objectives and resources available. Production systems may be based on breeding animals, stocker animals, or a combination of the two. Evaluating production from breeding animals is much more complex and generally requires more time and resources than for stocker animals. When using a representative breeding herd which includes animals at first breeding and animals to be culled because of age, a wide range of ages will, by necessity, prevail. Studies with breeding animals require several years to evaluate treatment effects on factors such as reproduction, longevity, and weight of salable animal product because of carryover effect from year to year. Studies using stocker animals have no carryover effect between years with respect to animals. Because of seasonal changes in nutrient requirements of breeding females for lactation and reproduction, it may be difficult to predict their performance based on gains of stocker animals (Launchbaugh et al. 1978).

Animal production studies directed towards production systems using breeding females should utilize comparable classes of animals. However, if many potential treatments are involved, it may be desirable to use smaller scale, short-term studies with stocker animals to screen treatments. The most promising treatments can then be selected for larger scale, longer term studies involving breeding females.

Many advantages are associated with the use of stocker animals where they are appropriate. Fewer animals and less land are required to obtain a reasonably good estimate of weight gain compared to the number of breeding females required to get a good estimate of conception rate and calf crop weaned. Studies with stockers can achieve valid results during the first year. Animal management and replacement of animals are considerably more complicated for breeding females compared to stockers. Reproductive response to a given treatment is not witnessed until the following year. The addition of bulls or rams during breeding causes temporary changes in stocking density. Total forage requirement of a breeding herd varies widely depending on the stage of productivity; whereas, forage requirements of stockers are more constant. Because of these advantages, the researcher should consider utilizing stocker animals for grazing studies whenever they are appropriate. Steers are generally preferred over heifers, since estrus in heifers may disrupt animal behavior and affect gains, thus increasing experimental error. However, objectivity should prevail over preference. Use of heifers in such studies provides valid inference to the heifer population.

Breed and Genetic Potential

Choice of breed of animal and its potential productivity may have a significant effect on the outcome of an experiment. The variety of germ plasm available has increased tremendously over the past 20 years, and crossbreeding has achieved wide acceptance among producers. Breed(s) selected should be adapted to environmental conditions, and the animal's genetic potential for production should be matched with the nutrient level available.

Researchers will be faced with selecting animals from a great diversity of breeds and types, as well as deciding whether to utilize straightbred or crossbred animals. In studies involving improved management systems, it is important to select animals typical to those that should be used by producers. The animal's genetic potential controls rates of growth, maturation, and level of lactation which, in turn, affect nutrient requirements of the animal and its offspring. If an animal's nutrient requirements greatly exceed the nutrient's availability, or if availability of nutrients exceeds the nutrient requirements of the animal, the experiment will not yield the most useful results.

In some instances, genetic-environmental interactions are known to exist. They should be taken into account in the experimental design, and in selection of appropriate breed(s) and type(s) of animal(s) for the environment.

Use of blackface rams to produce early maturing lambs off summer ranges of the western U.S. is an example of matching the animal's genotype to the pattern and level of nutrient availability. The switch from larger, slower maturing breeds to rapid maturing breeds, allows optimum conversion of nutrients on summer range to finished livestock product. Crossbred blackface lambs will fatten earlier with a much higher percentage grading choice at weaning than slower maturing breeds. Comparable examples are the use of *Bos indicus* breeds in warm humid climates where *Bos taurus* breeds are not adapted to the environmental stresses. Also, the use of medium-frame steers such as Angus and Hereford crosses which are more suited to range and sorghum grazing systems may be desirable because they mature and finish more rapidly than large-frame steers (Cook et al. 1983).

Uniformity in appearance, either in color or body conformation, does not denote uniformity of genetic potential. Wide differences exist within established breeds for most characteristics. Even when great care is exercised in selection of experimental animals, a sizeable amount of uncontrolled genetic variability may remain.

In range investigations concerned with assessment of treatments (i.e., grazing intensity, seasonal use, and vegetation composition), genetic variability among animals should be reduced as much as possible. Prime consideration should be given to obtaining experimental animals from herds or flocks in which a consistent breeding policy has been maintained. Uniform pretest environment in addition to some degree of genetic homogeneity due to the sustained selection can be obtained by this procedure.

If animals from different sources or somewhat different crosses or breeds are combined in a single grazing experiment, an equal number from each source should be assigned to each experimental treatment. Otherwise, the differences between animal sources might be confounded with treatments. In addition, such a procedure allows for statistical analysis as a stratified design which isolates these differences from experimental error.

If analysis of variance is used to estimate population parameters certain assumptions about the population and method of sampling must be made to provide results. Genetic variability may be a fixed or random effect. If inferences are made to general livestock populations, genetic differences among animals must be considered as random variables and experimental animals selected appropriately. If, on the other hand, inferences are made concerning a particular breed or type of animal, genetic differences should be considered as fixed effects. For further consideration of this topic, see Henderson (1969).

Identical twins, although difficult to locate in quantity, offer an excellent method of obtaining animal behavior patterns for paired treatments. They are particularly valuable for studies with many expensive observations per animal.

Replacement of Animals in Long-time Trials

The problem of animal replacement must be considered for grazing studies. Breeding herds may have even or uneven age composition. Extra animals should be purchased and held in reserve to serve as replacements in grazing trials, or replacements may be selected from offspring produced in the study. If replacement animals cannot be maintained under conditions similar to the treatments, losses should be replaced by animals of similar breed, sex, age, and weight. Data from replacement animals are generally excluded from statistical analyses until they have been subject to the treatment long enough to accurately reflect its effects in their level of production. In most long-term studies using a breeding herd, it is impossible to maintain equal numbers in each age class and in each treatment. In such cases investigators should use the least squares analysis for unequal subclass numbers as suggested by Harvey (1975).

The manner of selection of replacement females is somewhat controversial. Since cumulative effects of grazing are important, breeding animals should be retained on treatments as long as possible. However, replacement throughout the course of an experiment may be necessary due to disability, death, or low fertility. Losses of this nature are commonly higher in sheep and goats than in cattle. Replacements for each age group, maintained under conditions similar to those of the experiment, are the most effective answer to this problem. Local conditions determine the number of replacements to be kept.

Uneven age herd structure may be more acceptable where replacements are reared on the research station. Care should be exercised to maintain proportional numbers of each age class across treatments. However, this may not be possible if some treatments cause higher replacement rates. This approach may be more representative of most ranching operations; however, variation in level of production between different age classes will increase experimental error and make it more difficult to detect significant treatment effects. Use of age of females as a covariate in data analysis should assist in removing this undesirable source of variation.

Number of Animals Required for Optimum Precision

Sensitivity or precision of a grazing experiment is dependent upon (1) experimental error components, (2) number of animals per replication, and (3) number of replications per treatment. Decreasing experimental error by increasing number of animals per replication or by increasing number of replications will increase precision.

Animal variation may be the major source of experimental error in nutritive-value studies. However, in yield studies where results are expressed as gain, animal days of grazing, or total digestible nutrients per unit of area, pasture variation may be the larger source of experimental error. Different kinds and classes of livestock will require different numbers of animals per pasture for a given accuracy. Large numbers may be required in range studies to insure natural behavior. Precise recommendations for optimum numbers of animals to be used cannot be made unless information is available on relative sizes of experimental errors for specific conditions.

Yield studies at the Southern Great Plains Field Station (E.H. McIlvain 1958)[1] indicate a minimum of 2 stocker animals per replication and 3 replications per treatment over a period of 8 years (48 observations) gave satisfactory precision to detect a 6.8 kg difference in gain per head between treatments at <0.05 probability. Gain of suckling calves may be more variable than gain of stocker steers because of milk yield variation among dams. Numbers of animals required to estimate reproduction rates at a given level of precision is much greater than to measure gain (Table 6-1).

Optimum number of animals per pasture varies with type of study, pasture

---

[1] Personal communication

Table 6-1. Numbers of observations (animals required to detect differences in pregnancy rate or calf crop at specified probabilities, based on chi-square analysis.

Differences (%)	Probability		
	0.05	0.10	0.50
5	95	75	25
10	60	45	10

size, animal size, and length of grazing season. In addition, variability among pastures on rangelands, even when relatively small pastures of 20 to 30 hectares are used, dictates that many replications are necessary for acceptable precision. Replication is governed by economic and resource availability. Precision required from an experiment should not be overlooked at expense of the costs for achieving that precision. A question frequently asked is, "Should the design have increased replications (pastures) or increased numbers of animals within replications or pastures?" This is particularly relevant when land limits the size of the experiment. This question cannot be answered without having some knowledge of the magnitude of the components of experimental error.

Table 6-2. Analysis of variance for four grazing intensities, with five replications and eight animals per pasture or replication.

Source	D.F.	Mean Square	Components of variance
Treatment (T)	3	20.24	$(s^2 + 8s_e^2) + 40s_n^2$
Replications (R)	4	45.52	$s^2 + 8s_e^2 + 32s_r^2$
Experimental error (T×R)	12	14.11	$s^2 + 8s_e^2$
Sampling error	140	0.80	s^2

Using data in Table 6-2 as an example, experimental error is relatively high compared to sampling error, thus indicating uniformity among animals, such as possibly steers of the same breed and age. However, considerable variation remains among pastures within treatments which makes the experimental error somewhat high. Selection of replications has been good since considerable variance was removed from error.

The components of variance for error are sampling error, $s^2 = 0.80$, and the variance of a mean, $s_e^2 = (14.11 - 0.80)/8 = 1.66$, which is also included in the experimental error. With this information, it is possible to determine whether increased replications or increased animals within a replication will increase precision the most with similar effort.

Variance of a treatment mean for each decision can be calculated by

$$V_{\bar{x}} = \frac{s^2 + k_s \, s_e^2}{R \times k_s}$$

Thus, with 5 replications and 8 animals per replication or 160 total samples (animals), the variance of a treatment mean would be

$$V_{\bar{x}} = \frac{0.80 + (8)(1.66)}{5 \times 8} = 0.352$$

With 6 replications and 8 animals per replication or 192 total samples (animals), the variance of the treatment mean would be

$$V_{\bar{x}} = \frac{0.80 + (8)(1.66)}{6 \times 8} = 0.293$$

With 5 replications and 10 animals per replication or 200 total samples (animals), the variance of a treatment mean would be

$$V_{\bar{x}} = \frac{0.80 + (10)(1.66)}{5 \times 10} = 0.348$$

It is readily observed that with a small variation among animals, little is accomplished by increasing animal number per replication. However, adding one more replication with about an equal number of total animals, increased efficiency by about 16% (0.348 – 0.293 divided by 0.348). These calculations assume that s^2 and s_e^2 do not change, but $V_{\bar{x}}$ is influenced principally by the magnitude of R and k.

Similar situations based on cows and calves or ewes and lambs would be expected to give a much higher sampling error (variation among animals). Thus, if mean variance within pastures (s) remained constant or decreased, greater precision could be gained by increasing animal numbers in each replication compared to the example calculated from Table 2. Where land limits total number of animals that can be maintained, emphasis should be placed on providing adequate replication of treatments and increasing the number of samples (animals) per treatment by conducting the experiment for additional years. In arid or semi-arid conditions where spotty precipitation occurs it may be desirable to rotate treatments among pastures depending on experimental design.

When animal response to grazing treatments is being measured, it may be that the trend over several years is more important than the mean for only one or two years. If this is the case, precision will increase each year because the number of observations increases over time. Animal response to changes in primary production over time may be evaluated by means of regression of secondary production on years. Orthogonal polynomials are also a useful technique for evaluating trends across time.

Costs involved and information desired often control the number of replications used in a grazing experiment. Expected probabilities of detecting true differences of various sizes between treatments with different numbers of replications are shown in Table 6-3. A coefficient of variation of between 7 and 17% was used. Two replications will detect differences of 40% with 60 to

Table 6-3. Estimates of the probability of detecting true differences testing significance at the 5% level with a coefficient of variation of 7-17% (Lucas 1950).

Number of replications	Differences			
	10%	20%	30%	40%
2	0.1- 0.3	0.2- 0.7	0.4- 0.9	0.6->0.9
3	0.1- 0.4	0.3- 0.9	0.5->0.9	0.8->0.9
4	0.1- 0.5	0.4->0.9	0.6->0.9	0.9>0.9
8	0.2- 0.8	0.6->0.9	>0.9	>0.9
12	0.2->0.9	0.8->0.9	>0.9	>0.9

90% probability. Four replications are required to have same probability of detecting differences of 30% and eight for detecting differences of 20%. More than 12 replications are required to have the same probability of detecting differences of 10% or less.

The number of replications required for detecting various differences at a fixed probability level of 80% is given in Table 6-4. No entries are given when

Table 6-4. Estimates of the number of replications required to yield an 80% chance of detecting a significant difference at the 57% level (Cochran and Cox 1966).

Difference %x̄	Coefficient of Variance					
	4%	8%	12%	16%	20%	24%
5	11	41	—	—	—	—
10	4	11	24	41	—	—
15	3	6	11	19	29	44
20	2	4	7	11	17	23
30	2	3	4	6	8	11
40	2	2	3	4	5	7

more than 44 replications are required. In order to detect a difference of 15%, 80% of the time, the number of pastures needed assuming a coefficient of variation of 12%, is rather prohibitive. As a general statement, about 5 replications will do only a fair job of detecting differences of 20% or larger. Practical considerations often limit the number of replications to 3 or, at most, perhaps 6.

Methods of Selection and Allotment to Obtain Uniformity Between Groups

Individual animal variation constitutes an important problem in interpreting and evaluating animal response in range research. Inherent differences among individual animals include such factors as time devoted to grazing, selectivity of forage, distance traveled in a day, and basic differences in gaining ability and efficiency of feed utilization. Animals should be properly randomized so that these factors plus many others are included in the "within-lot" variation used to test treatment differences, and not confounded with treatment effects.

Animals differing as little as possible with respect to breed, age, condition, and previous treatment should be selected if uniformity is desired. However, it should be remembered that the data apply only to the mix of animals used. If animals of considerably different inherent productivity are used, stratification by groups should be used in assigning individuals to different treatments, i.e., animals with similar predicted performances are placed in separate groups. Equal numbers from each outcome are assigned at random to each treatment. Differences between outcome groups or strata are later removed from experimental error by analysis of variance.

The increase in efficiency obtained by first placing animals in outcome groups, rather than random assignment to treatments, depends on (1) size of anticipated differences between outcome groups, (2) number of treatment groups, and (3) number of animals per treatment. In general, the use of outcome groups becomes more efficient as differences between them increase; however, the possibility of an interaction between outcome groups and treatments is likely to increase. Thus, the advantage gained by having more diverse outcome groups may be somewhat offset. In some cases, previous information indicates that an interaction between outcome groups and treatments may be expected. For example, animals which vary considerably in age and weight probably will respond differently to treatments which materially affect growth. When an interaction of this type is expected, the design should be changed to one where the interaction can be measured and interpreted.

As the number of treatments increases, the value of placing animals in outcome groups before assignment to treatment groups decreases. This results because of less similarity in predicted outcome among animals in the same outcome group as the number of animals in that group increases.

If the differences expected between animals on the same treatment are associated linearly with such factors as initial weight or age, assigning animals randomly to treatments and removing the variation due to these factors by covariance may be more efficient than the use of outcome groups. A small number of degrees of freedom is removed from the error by this method, and its efficiency is not affected by the number of treatments. However, this depends upon a linear relationship between the covariate and the response variable.

In many, if not most, grazing trials, researchers are faced with uneven numbers of animals per treatment or replication. In some cases, these can be handled with replacements for missing numbers, as described by many statistical texts. It is generally more logical to handle them as unbalanced numbers (Harvey 1975).

Some animals have a nervous temperament, bad disposition, or may be habitual "fence crawlers." Unless culled from the herd, they may create much difficulty in conducting the experiment and thus cause excessive data variation. It is recommended that an effort be made to identify such animals before they are allocated to treatments. If they are unknowingly allocated to a treatment, they should be replaced as soon as they are identified. In range studies involving fistulated animals (or any research requiring intensive handling or sampling with animals in the field), it will prove extremely helpful to have animals thoroughly gentle before research begins.

Cumulative Treatment Effects

Treatments may have cumulative effects on animals, plants, and soils. Cumulative effects on plants and soils may be reflected in levels of animal production; however, it is not necessary to maintain the same animals from year to year to evaluate plant and soil responses. Cumulative effects in animals relate to body condition, reproduction, and longevity (Meyer and Garrett 1969). Longevity would generally be evaluated by culling rate for breeding females and would vary with culling policies. The most frequent causes for culling are age and reproductive failure. Animal health should be a minor effect on culling and generally would not be directly affected by the grazing treatments.

The study of cumulative effects will generally focus on body condition and reproductive success, which are closely related responses. Treatments which limit nutrient intake will reduce body condition which, in turn, may reduce reproductive capacity of both males and females. If the nonbred, or open, female is not culled, her nutrient requirements will be reduced, thus allowing improved body condition and improved probability for reproduction the following year. Where open cows are kept in an experimental treatment, their reproductive response the following year is more likely due to physiological state than to experimental treatment. Nutritional stress also will result in delayed breeding, which lengthens the calving interval or results in late lambing. This may be a major cause of reduced calf and lamb weaning weights, if weaning is practiced at a fixed time. When a fixed breeding season is utilized, calving intervals above 365 days will result in reduced calf crops over a period of several years.

A minimum of three generations is recommended to measure cumulative effects. A shorter length of time would be required if it were possible to subject the first generation to treatment differences during the prenatal and preweaning periods. Treatment differences may be obscured by maternal effects in the second generation. In general, a minimum of from 12 to 15 years is required for cattle and 9 to 12 years for sheep.

Cumulative environmental effects are difficult to measure, especially when treatment differences are not wide. Genetic variation should be minimized, not only between treatments but also between generations. Production records should be employed to select animals of similar productivity for breeding stock. A satisfactory method of sire replacement is to use sires from moderately inbred lines, i.e., closed lines in which coefficients of inbreeding change only slightly between generations. The productivity of replacement sires should be the same as that of the original sires. When using data from breeding herds (i.e., reproductive rates) it is imperative that fertile males are used in all treatments.

Differential growth between treatments may be appraised by periodic weights throughout the test period, body and wool measurements, and carcass evaluations of meat quality and bone structure. Differential reproductive rates between treatments are measured by (1) pregnancy (palpation), (2) number born alive, (3) number of stillbirths and abortions, (4) number of progeny reared to weaning, and (5) death loss after weaning. Critical autopsy data for stillborn offspring and other unexplained deaths should be obtained throughout the experiment.

Normally, longevity is measured by the lifetime of an individual. A more practical measure is the age at which individual production levels start to decline. For improved accuracy, progeny records should be adjusted to a mature age. Since improvement achieved through selection is speeded up by turning generations at a rapid rate, the importance of longevity as a selection criterion may have limited relevance.

Stocking Rate

Herbage production varies widely from year to year on rangelands. This variation will affect results of grazing studies and must be considered in design and conduction of grazing experiments (Wheeler 1962, Morley 1978).

Several techniques are available to control stocking rate to achieve desired degrees of utilization. Since stocking rate is a quantity of forage demand per unit of land area for a specified time period, it may be controlled by manipulating the forage demand rate (stocking density), the amount of land, and/or the time a given rate is applied (Scarnecchia and Kothmann 1982). The appropriate approach for controlling stocking rate will depend upon the objectives and constraints of the study.

Researchers must decide whether to use a fixed number of animals for the entire grazing season, or to "put-and-take" based on forage availability and degree of use. Other alternatives that provide flexibility in stocking rate are to use a higher stock density during rapid growth and then reduce stock density or shorten the time of grazing (Owensby and Smith 1975). When constant stock density is used, stocking rate may be adjusted by varying grazing duration.

Research directed primarily towards determining the productivity of selected forages and/or range sites should employ flexible stocking. This can assure that levels of stocking cover the range required to generate response curves during both high and low forage production years. However, research directed towards development of management practices should restrict fluctuations in stocking to levels that would be feasible to apply. Economic analysis of fixed stocking rates is relatively simple compared with "put-and-take" experiments (Jones 1981).

Studies to identify "optimum" stocking rates should be designed to cover the complete range from light, where animal performance is not affected by stocking rate, to heavy, where production per unit of area is declining (Owen and Ridgman 1968, Morely 1978, Robards 1981a). Range researchers are generally concerned with production responses of plants and animals to treatments over extended periods of time. Thus, the problem is not just one of estimating response curves, but really one of describing response surfaces (Morley 1978). Although this may require many treatments and years and generally is difficult and costly, it should not provide an excuse for poorly designed experiments. Sound principles of design, analysis, and interpretation are still required (Morely and Spedding 1968).

Several techniques have been suggested to cope with the high demands of grazing research for land resources. Morely and Spedding (1968) suggested that individual animals can be used as the experimental unit when the variance among animals within groups is not substantially greater or smaller than the variance among animals in the whole experiment. However, care should be exercised in using this technique, since it ignores the frequent problem of variation among pastures within treatments. When it is used to replace replication of treatments on pastures, it may lead to serious confounding of site effects with treatment effects.

Michalk and McFarlane (1978) suggested the use of a communal grazing design for preliminary evaluation of grazing treatments. This design requires less fencing, land and animals; thus, it may allow evaluation of many levels and combinations of treatments. While it will not provide animal production data, it will produce valid data for diet selection, plant production, and range trend. This technique deserves serious consideration by the researcher faced with the task of screening many grazing treatments and establishing base line stocking rate data.

Frequently, experimental designs are unbalanced, or treatments may be changed at intervals during long-term trials. Burns et al. (1983) used generalized least squares analysis to estimate the components of variance due to years, fields, and random error, and then used these estimates to obtain adjusted treatment means. Comparison of the adjusted means with means from balanced subsets of treatments revealed closed correspondence. This procedure offers promise for analysis of long-term studies which do not fit balanced designs and warrants further investigation.

On rangelands, concern for stability of the plant community and soils combined with the overwhelming impact of frequent droughts may limit the upper range of stocking rate so that in average or above average years production per head is little affected (Robards 1981a). The design for stocking rate studies should be chosen to facilitate evaluation of relative stability, economic viability or animal sustaining value of systems. This will require that studies be continued through a complete weather cycle and across several annual production cycles of the dominant forage species to detect trends. However, it is recommended that data from long-term experiments be analyzed and evaluated periodically to determine the relevance of data being collected.

Split-plot designs are generally required because of site variation that requires blocking and analysis over time. Years may be viewed as a random main effect and multiple observations within years as fixed split treatments. Where there are interactions of treatments and years, data should be analyzed within years. The use of years as replications should generally be avoided. Trends within years and across years can be effectively analyzed by regression or orthogonal polynomials (Draper and Smith 1966, Robards 1981a).

Methods of Obtaining Uniform Grazing Distribution

Uneven grazing distribution can be classed as area selective grazing and species selective grazing (Kothmann 1980). Area selective grazing has two principal causes. First, it is the usual concomitant of light grazing. Under light use some plants, either single plants or groups, will be fully or nearly fully used, while other plants or groups of the same species in close proximity will be entirely ungrazed. In reality, there may be little or no uniform light use of all plants; instead, light use of range is an average of nonuse and full or nearly full use of individual plants through repeated use of the same plants. Since this is the natural manner of grazing by animals, it cannot be completely eliminated.

When grazed and ungrazed plants are both well dispersed over a range, either as individual plants or as small groups, the situation may be regarded as essentially even use. Large utilization plots will reflect relatively even use. However, small square or circular plots may include mostly nonused or heavily used plants, and thus reflect patches of utilization, when, in fact, the range may be as evenly grazed as possible under light use. Increasing stocking density and use of rotational grazing may improve this type of grazing distribution problem.

Spotty or patchy grazing continued over a period of years may give rise to a fixed pattern, and as a result permanent "islands" of light or nonuse and heavy use will develop. Unused vegetation generally decreases in palatability and tends to interfere with use of new growth in subsequent years. Unutilized old growth may be removed by occasional mowing, burning, or high intensity grazing when new growth is initiated. Since these practices alter the condition of simple light use as an experimental treatment, they may not be desirable on that account. A choice exists between using one or more of them and recognizing that the experimental treatment has been modified in that way, or not using them and recognizing that patchy grazing may be one of the consequences of continued light use.

The distance-graduated type of selective grazing use occurs in varying degrees on all ranges, especially those with large pastures and limited water development, and on mountainous terrain. Areas near water, bedgrounds, or other points of livestock concentration are grazed more closely. Other factors that may induce uneven grazing use are flies and gnats in brushy areas and strong prevailing winds. Hauling water, developing temporary waters, salting and feeding, establishing insecticide-treated rubbing posts, fertilizing outlying range, mowing and burning unused feed, herding and riding, constructing trails and drift fences, intensifying stocking, and use of rotation grazing may all help reduce uneven grazing when properly administered and should be considered for use in most experimental pastures.

Selective grazing of species results when forage plant species of markedly different palatability occur on the same range. If these species are well intermingled, the resulting utilization condition may appear similar to that under light use. If, on the other hand, species of different palatability occur in distinct vegetation types or subtypes on the same range area, it may appear similar to area selective grazing. Complete correction generally cannot be made without excessive and damaging use of the more palatable plants. Mowing or burning will not always correct unevenness, since the fundamental cause of the differential grazing has not been corrected.

The problem of uneven use caused by mixed types may be met in either of two ways. First, it may be avoided by laying out experimental pastures in only one vegetation type or subtype, or, second, it may be partially corrected by rotating season of use among years. This latter method would be of value if palatability varied seasonally. Where these are not possible, utilization determinations may be recorded separately by forage types or subtypes theoretically producing relatively uniform use within a type or subtype. Under this plan, attention is concentrated only on key forage types and species.

Feeding

Two general situations arise regarding livestock feeding in grazing studies. The first is where supplement is varied as a treatment, and the second is where all animals are fed (but not as an experimental treatment) because forage is low quality or of limited availability. The first situation is usually considered in original experimental designs, but the second may not be. Thus, when droughts or severe weather occurs, or when heavily stocked treatments run short of forage, the researcher is faced with a decision regarding feeding. It is recommended that these contingencies be considered during project design and a set of guidelines established.

Feeding can be grouped into three classes: supplemental, maintenance, and emergency (Kothmann 1980). Emergency feeding is required when forage is rendered temporarily unavailable, as by ice, snow, or flood. Maintenance feeding (also called survival feeding) is required when forage availability is too low to provide adequate dry matter intake. Emergency and maintenance feeding require a balanced ration to meet the animal's nutrient requirements. Supplemental feeding provides a limited amount of a feed that is a concentrated source of one or more nutrients that are deficient in the forage, even though forage availability is adequate.

Based on these criteria, supplemental feeding will probably be included as a treatment or can be anticipated and appropriate plans made. Experiments designed to include different levels of supplemental feeding as treatments have been described by Harris et al. (1952, 1959).

Supplements fed to correct mineral deficiencies are usually provided in self-feeders for all treatments when it is not designed as a treatment effect. Salt may be put in open containers, but it is advisable to place mineral mixes containing phosphorus in covered feeders. Palatability may be greatly reduced if the mineral mix is wet with rain or dew. This is of greater concern in humid climates than in arid and semi-arid areas.

Emergency feeding is generally of short duration and can be handled uniformly across treatments. However, if snow covers short forage on heavy stocked treatments, but adequate forage is available above snow on light stocked pastures, equal feeding of both treatments would partially mask treatment effects. Not feeding on either treatment would allow full expression of treatment effects but may have little relevance to real production systems. Therefore, if the objective is to provide useful information for development of management practices, each treatment should receive feed based on need, and costs of feed and feeding should be charged to the treatment. Robards (1981a) suggested that supplemental feeding practices follow prevailing industry standards.

Studies designed to evaluate different stocking rates frequently result in forage depletion on heavier stocked pastures before the end of the planned grazing period. If stock on these pastures must be fed or removed, it would be a serious error to also feed or remove stock from pastures which have adequate forage. If the objective of the experiment is to provide animal production data, it is important to remember that biological responses have to be interpreted in economic terms (Jones 1981). If researchers will keep this fact in mind regarding feeding, they will be less likely to obscure treatment effects.

Feeding causes concentration of animals on the feed ground, which may result in trampling damage to range vegetation and soils. Also, feeding can drastically alter the animals' grazing and behavioral patterns. When animals are fed at the same time and place, considerable time may be spent in that location waiting for feed. Feeding less frequently (2 or 3 times per week) during midday after the main morning grazing period (Adams and Kartchner 1984) and feeding at different locations around the pasture will help prevent the development of poor grazing habits by supplemented animals (Melton 1960, Melton et al. 1960, McIlvain and Shoop 1962, Pearson and Whitaker 1972). If there are permanent plots for evaluation of soil or vegetation, care should be exercised not to feed directly on the plots.

General Health and Condition

Since health can have a profound effect on performance, precautions should be taken to ensure that sound and disease-free stock are placed on the experimental range unit. Any disturbance in physical condition of an animal before or during the test period will be confounded with its response to treatment.

The condition of an animal at the end of entry on test will have a bearing on its response to treatment, especially on short-term gains. In the case of shrunken yet thrifty animals, spectacular gains resulting from increased fill can be obtained over a short term. Such results often have been misconstrued. Only animals of similar condition should be placed on various treatments. In experiments extending over several years, animals should be in the same condition at times of entry in subsequent seasons.

Animals differ from one another, not only in inherent ability to convert roughage or concentrates into meat, wool, or milk, but also in the degree and type of parasite infestation and the presence of other disease-producing factors which might easily mullify experimental results. To avoid complications from infectious diseases, all animals should be immunized against diseases enzootic in the area and observed carefully for at least two weeks before placing them on the experiment. Animals should be kept reasonably free of internal and external parasites.

Measuring Livestock Performance

Productivity of livestock is frequently measured by animal weights or gains. This can present serious limitations in the evaluation of treatment effects because of variation encompassed within the weight of an animal. Gut fill, consisting of water and dry matter, and carcass composition, primarily the proportions of fat, protein, water, and minerals, can vary greatly (Meyer and Garrett 1969).

Techniques for estimating body composition of live animals have been reviewed by Stouffer (1969). Robards (1981b) reviewed and discussed techniques for evaluating forage quality through animal performance. Gain was the only measure of animal performance used in 77% of range studies surveyed by Mochrie (1981). Care should be exercised in using only animal weights and live weight gains as a measure of different husbandry systems. These measures are most applicable when they are used to compare treatments applied simultaneously to comparable sets of animals.

Before obtaining initial weights in a study, experimenters should allow animals one or two weeks to become accustomed to the experimental forage and environment. Even then, two weigh periods of a few days apart with an overnight fast is desirable. This practice will increase accuracy of actual weight gains by reducing the effect of previous treatment and any differential fill. In studies of gains, a reserve pasture similar to the experimental area usually will be necessary for the pretreatment period to prevent unmeasured use of experimental pastures.

Differentials in fill generally will not be large if periodic weights are taken at the same time of day (Whiteman et al. 1954, Heitschmidt 1982). However, severe storms just before or at the time of weighing may prevent animals from obtaining their normal fill. If type of forage or forage conditions change radically between weighings, weight data should be interpreted cautiously. False weight gains occur in spring just at the time of rapid spring growth, or at any time when animals are changing from dry to lush green forage. Likewise, false weight losses occur during fly season, hot weather, and the transition period from luxuriant or highly palatable to poor forage conditions.

The amount and rate of shrink that animals experience are affected by age and productive status of the animals, forage conditions, and environmental conditions (Heitschmidt 1982). Lactating cows shrink more than dry cows.

Calves weighing less than 50 kg experience no significant shrink or fill if left with their dams overnight. However, as they increase in age and weight, their rate of shrink or fill increases. Whiteman et al. (1954) found that water, not feed, was the major factor affecting shrink. Thus, removal from water prior to weighing is more important than removal from feed. Rate of shrink is generally highest during the first 4 hours, and then linear through 24 hours (Whiteman et al. 1954, Heitschmidt 1982). Thus, recommendations which vaguely call for overnight shrink of 12 to 24 hours or removal from feed only can lead to considerable error.

A primary benefit obtained from shrinking animals before weighing is the reduction of variance among individual animals. Animals that produce the highest gains may be those with the greatest fill. Whiteman et al. (1954) found a significant reduction in variance among animals after shrinking compared to before the shrink. It is generally assumed that an overnight shrink (no feed or water for 12 hours) is desirable to obtain gain from grazing range forages.

Animals on spring pasture, e.g., lush green feed, experience greater shrink than animals on dry or mature pasture (Whiteman et al. 1954, Heitschmidt 1982). Increased temperature and reduced humidity are also associated with greater shrink. When returned to feed and water, animals that have been shrunk, rapidly regain their weight loss.

In the absence of shrink, grazing animals follow a diurnal pattern of weight loss and gain. Steer weights declined from 6:00 to 8:00 AM and then increased from 8:00 to 10:00 AM (Whiteman et al. 1954). Lactating cows weighed 11 kg more at mid morning than they did at 7:00 to 7:30 AM (Heitschmidt 1982).

Animals should be weighed with the least possible disturbance and excitement. Excessive use of whip and electric prod and loud shouting should be discouraged. Expeditious routes to the scales should be selected. The order of weighing various lots should be randomized at each weigh day. No particular order is necessary for animals within treatments. Or, all treatment groups can be mixed, and the animals can cross the scales at random. Animals can then be sorted back into treatment groups. The animals should be returned to pasture as soon as possible. It is generally recommended that animals be weighed twice at the beginning and ending of grazing trials, with an overnight stand in all cases, to reduce variation among animals for increased efficiency of the experiment.

Greater uniformity between lots of animals in grazing experiments may be had if consideration is given to body scores. Scores are useful in evaluating condition and growth. Body measurements may be used in conjunction with weights to assess growth more accurately and to obtain an estimate of relative changes in bone, muscle, and fat.

Equipment for measurements used in scoring is relatively simple. A metal bar, calibrated in centimeters and millimeters, with two bars sliding at right angles (with locks) is useful for width and depth measurements and hip height. Built-in levels allow the bar to be held in exactly vertical or horizontal positions. A large metal caliper is useful for taking length and width measurements and can be read by laying it alongside the measuring bar. A flexible steel tape, calibrated in centimeters and millimeters, is convenient for circumference (girth) and over-all length measurements. When inches and pounds are used, they should be recorded to the nearest tenth, rather than to some other fraction.

Measurements obtained from animals in fleece are less accurate than those obtained from sheared animals. Photographic measurements are rather highly correlated with body measurements.

Wool production is difficult to measure accurately for periods of less than a year's growth. Both fineness and length of wool are influenced by environmental conditions. Although amount of clean wool is the best measurement of response to experimental treatment, wool clipped from a measured area has a useful relation to the clean weight. Since small samples have limited accuracy at best, actual shearing should not be ruled out in experiments of four months or less. Staple length alone is a useful measure of wool growth. Also, the wool fiber diameter reflects the health and plane of nutrition in the period when growth was made. Wool fineness or grade generally is obtained by visual inspection in conjunction with standard grade samples. Wool generally is graded in numerical grades or spinning counts which often are grouped into "blood" grades. General agreement concerning these groupings does not prevail.

Equipment for Handling and Weighing Livestock

Good equipment and facilities are essential if errors are to be minimized. Facilities that permit livestock to be quickly handled and weighed are most useful. Procedures and equipment that cause excessive handling contribute to inaccurate results and should be avoided.

Many makes and types of scales are now available. Permanent scale installations in corrals need to be housed to prevent error from wind pressure. Scales accurate to the nearest kilogram are adequate, except for light calves. Accurate, portable scales which can be towed easily or loaded in a pickup and set up for operation at the desired location have an important place in range research projects. Scales that print exact weights are useful for eliminating human errors due to incorrect reading or recording of weights.

Electronic scales utilizing load cells provide an economical and efficient method for obtaining accurate weights. These electronic scales can be linked to computers and provide rapid data entry. Research utilizing these technologies is currently being conducted to develop automatic, unattended identification and weighing of cattle (Anderson et al. 1981).

Convenient cutting or sorting alleys and pens to handle cattle before weighing will help reduce stress from handling. The corral and scale should be located near the center of the range in order to reduce trailing of stock before weighing. However, Whiteman et al. (1954) found that driving during the shrink period had little effect on rate of shrink. Total shrink is primarily a function of length of time removed from water and feed.

An efficient corral system developed at the Ft. Robinson Beef Cattle Research Station, Crawford, Nebraska (Koch 1955) is shown in Fig. 6-1. This

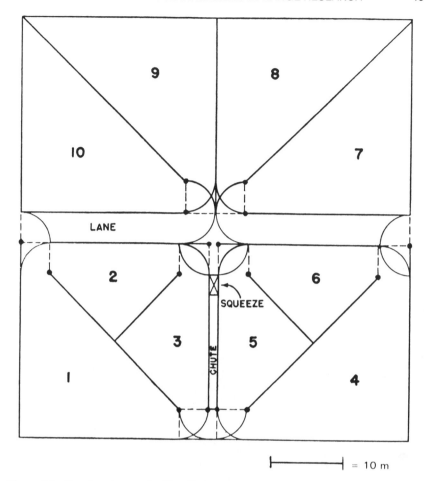

Figure 6-1. Corral system at the Fort Robinson Beef Cattle Research Station, Crawford, Nebraska (Koch 1955).

system could be scaled down if it is too large for experimental setups. Pens 1, 4, 7, 8, 9, and 10 will each hold about 125 cows and calves, and pens 2, 3, 5, and 6, about 62. Pens 1, 2, and 3, plus the chutes and lane, may be adequate for herds of 100 to 125 cows. Several small pens instead of a few large ones will minimize back and forth movement of cattle. Because of the diagonal fences, cattle move through gates much more easily and quickly than in the usual square-corner type of corral. Cattle can be cut 8 to 10 different ways from a single gate. When fewer cuts are required, some division fences may be eliminated. Addition of an 8 to 10 m alley around the pens will facilitate their use in a cell design with paddocks radiating from the center.

Convenient equipment is just as important for sheep and goats. Workable cutting chutes speed the handling and increase the accuracy of results. Sheep will work better in a chute that goes uphill. Portable scales are especially useful for weighing sheep and goats. Often, it is desirable to take scales to the sheep rather than trail them to a central corral with a permanent scale installation. Portable dial scales and a weighing crate for sheep were described by Harris et al. (1952).

In addition to cutting chutes, sheep corrals should be designed with a 1.2 m alley that can be used for individual examination and selection. Such an alley permits a more thorough inspection of animals than when they are moving along a narrow cutting chute. A dog properly trained and supervised is an invaluable aid for working sheep and goats.

Literature Cited

Adams, D.C., and R.J. Kartchner. 1984. Effects of time of supplementation on daily gain, forage intake and behavior of yearling steers grazing fall range. Proc. West. Sect., Amer. Soc. Anim. Sci. p. 158-160.

Anderson, D.M., J.A. Landt, and P.H. Salazar. 1981. Electronic weighing, identification and subdermal body temperature sensing of range livestock, p. 373-382. *In:* J.L. Wheeler and R.D. Mochrie (eds.), Forage evaluation: concepts and techniques. Amer. Forage and Grassland Council, Lexington, Kentucky.

Arnold, G.W., and M.L. Dudzinski. 1978. Ethonology of free-ranging domestic animals. Elsevier Sci. Publ. Co., New York, New York.

Australian Rangeland Society. 1977. The impact of herbivores on arid and semi-arid rangelands. Proc. of 2nd United States/Australia Rangeland Panel, Adelaide, Australia, 1972. Aust. Rangeland Soc., Perth, Western Australia.

Ayuko, L.J. 1978. Management of rangelands in Kenya to increase beef production: Socioeconomic constraints and policies, p. 82-86. *In:* Donald N. Hyder (ed.), Proc. First Int. Rangeland Congr. Soc. Range Manage., Denver, Colorado.

Burns, J.C., R.W. Harvey, and F.G. Giesbrecht. 1983. Methodolgy for determining pasture and animal response differences in unbalanced experiments with intercorrelations among treatments, p. 497-500. *In:* J. Allan Smith and Virgil W. Hays (eds.), Proc. XIV Int. Grassland Cong., Lexington, Kentucky.

Cochran, W.G., and G.M. Cox. 1966. Experimental designs. John Wiley & Sons, New York, New York.

Cook, C.W., J.W. Walker, M.H. Ebberts, L.R. Rittenhouse, E.T. Bartlett, D.A. Cramer, P.T. Fagerlin, and M.C. McKean. 1983. Alternative grass and grain feeding systems for beef production. Bull. 579S. (Revised). Colorado Agr. Exp Sta.

Corbett, J.L. 1978. Measuring animal performance, p. 163-231. *In:* L. 't Mannetje (ed.), Measurement of grassland vegetation and animal production. Bull. 52. Commonwealth Bur. Pastures and Field Crops. Hurley, Berkshire, England.

Dahl, B., J. Burns, M. Vavra, C. Owensby, and F. Bryant. 1982. Animal response to grazing management, p. 32-77. *In:* D.D. Briske and M.M. Kothmann (eds.), Proc. Nat. Conf. Grazing Manage. Tech., Dept., Range Science, Texas A&M Univ., College Station, Texas.

Draper, N.R., and H. Smith. 1966. Applied regression analysis. John Wiley & Sons, New York, New York.

Hacker, J.B. (ed.) 1982. Nutritional limits to animal production from pastures. Proc. Int. Symp., St. Lucia, Queensland, Aust., Commonwealth Agr. Bur., Farnham Royal, England.

Hanley, T.A., and K.A. Hanley. 1982. Food resource partitioning by sympatric ungulates on Great Basin rangelands. J. Range Manage. 35:152-158.

Harrington, G. 1978. The implications of goat, sheep and cattle diet to the management of an Australian semi-arid woodland, p. 447-450. *In:* Donald N. Hyder (ed.), Proc. First Int. Rangeland Congr., Soc. Range Manage., Denver, Colorado.

Harris, L.E., C.W. Cook, and John E. Butcher. 1959. Intake and digestibility techniques and supplemental feeding in range forage evaluation. Agr. J. 51:226-234.

Harris, Lorin E., C. Wayne Cook, and L.A. Stoddart. 1952. Range nutrition techniques. J. Anim. Sci. 11:181-190.

Harvey, W.R. 1975. Least squares analysis of data with unequal subclass numbers. ARS H-4. Data Systems Application Div. USDA-ARS. Washington, D.C.

Heitschmidt, R.K. 1982. Diurnal variation in weight and rates of shrink of range cows and calves. J. Range Manage. 35:717-720.

Henderson, C.R. 1969. Design and analysis of animal science experiments, p. 2-35. *In:* Tech. Procedures in Anim. Sci. Res. Amer. Soc. Anim. Sci., Champaign, Illinois.

Henson, J.B., and J.C. Noel (eds.). 1983. Proceedings: Integrated Range/Livestock Workshop. Consortium for Int. Development, Tucson, Arizona.

Jones, R.J. 1981. Interpreting fixed stocking rate experiments, p. 419-431. *In:* J.L. Wheeler and R.D. Mochrie (eds.), Forage evaluation: Concepts and techniques. Amer. Forage and Grassland Council, Lexington, Kentucky.

Kautz, J.E., and G.M. Van Dyne. 1978. Comparative analyses of diets of bison, cattle, sheep, and pronghorn antelope on shortgrass prairie in northeastern Colorado, USA, p. 438-443. *In:* Donald N. Hyder (ed.), Proc. First Int. Rangeland Congr., Soc. Range Manage., Denver, Colorado.

Koch, R.M. 1955. A new corral plan for big herds. Farm, Ranch, and Home Quarterly. Nebraska Agr. Exp Sta.

Kothmann, M.M. 1980. Nutrition of livestock grazing on range and pasture lands, p. 56-90. *In:* D.C. Church (ed.), Digestive physiology and nutrition of ruminants. Vol. 3, Practical nutrition, O&B Books, Inc., Corvallis, Oregon.

Launchbaugh, J.L., C.E. Owensby, F.L. Schwartz, and L.R. Corah. 1978. Grazing management to meet nutritional and functional needs of livestock, p. 541-546. *In:* Donald N. Hyder (ed.), Proc. First Int. Rangeland Congr., Soc. Range Manage., Denver, Colorado.

Lucas, H.L. 1950. Statistics and research on pasture and grazing. Lecture Ser. 1, No. 3. USDA, Washington, D.C.

McIlvain, E.H., and M.C. Shoop. 1962. Daily versus every third day versus weekly feeding of cottonseed cake to beef steers on winter range. J. Range Manage. 15:143.

Melton, A.A. 1960. Frequency of supplemental feeding for range cattle. Misc. Pub. 450. Texas Agri. Exp. Sta.

Melton, A.A., J.H. Jones, and J.K. Riggs. 1960. Influence of frequency of feeding protein supplement upon development and production of range beef females. J. Animal Sci. 19:1276.

Meyer, J.H., and W.N. Garrett. 1969. Efficiency of feed utilization, p. 166-174. *In:* Tech. and Procedures in Anim. Sci. Res. Amer. Soc. Anim. Sci., Champaign, Illinois.

Michalk, D.L., and J.D. McFarlane. 1978. A low-cost communal grazing design for preliminary evaluation of grazing systems. J. Brit. Grassland Soc. 33:301-306.

Mochrie, R.D. 1981. Survey of techniques used in grazing trials in U.S. from 1975 to 1980, p. 449-459. *In:* J.L. Wheeler, and R.D. Mochrie (eds.), Forage evaluation: Concepts and techniques. Amer. Forage and Grassland Council, Lexington, Kentucky.

Morley, F.H.W. 1978. Animal production studies, p. 103-162. *In:* L. 't Mannetje (ed.), Measurement of grassland vegetation and animal production. Bull. 52, Commonwealth Bur. Pastures and Field Crops, Hurley, Berkshire, England.

Morley, F.H.W. 1981. Grazing animals. Elsevier Sci. Publ. Co, New York, New York.

Morley, F.H.W., and C.R.W. Spedding. 1968. Agricultural systems and grazing experiments. Herbage Abstr. 38:279-287.

Owen, J.B., and O.J. Ridgman. 1968. The design and interpretation of experiments to study animal production from grazed pasture. J. Agr. Sci. Camb. 71:327-335.

Owensby, C.E., and E.F. Smith. 1975. Intensive early stocking of bluestem range. Rep. Prog. 244. Kansas Agr. Exp. Sta.

Pearson, H.A., and L.B. Whitaker. 1972. Thrice weekly supplementation adequate for cows on pine-bluestem range. J. Range Manage. 25:315.

Robards, G.E. 1981a. Factors influencing the design of sheep grazing experiments, p. 433-447. *In:* J.L. Wheeler and R.D. Mochrie (eds.), Forage evaluation: Concepts and techniques. Amer. Forage and Grassland Council, Lexington, Kentucky.

Robards, G.E. 1981b. Techniques used in practice of forage evaluation in Australia, p. 461-472. *In:* J.L. Wheeler and R.D. Mochrie (eds.), Forage evaluation: Concepts and techniques. Amer. Forage and Grassland Council, Lexington, Kentucky.

Scarnecchia, D.L., and M.M. Kothmann. 1982. A dynamic approach to grazing management terminology. J. Range Manage. 35:262-264.

Squires, V.R. 1982. Dietary overlap between sheep, cattle, and goats when grazing in common. J. Range Manage. 35:116-119.

Stouffer, J.R. 1969. Techniques for the estimation of the composition of meat animals, p. 207-219. *In:* Tech. and Procedures in Anim. Sci. Res. Amer. Soc. Anim. Sci., Champaign, Illinois.

Theurer, C.B., A.L. Lesperance, and J.D. Wallace. 1976. Botanical composition of the diet of livestock grazing native ranges. Western Region Coordination Comm. 8. Tech. Bull. 233. Arizona Agr. Exp Sta.

Vavra, M., and F. Sneva. 1978. Seasonal diets of five ungulates grazing the cold desert biome, p. 435-437. *In:* Donald N. Hyder (ed.), Proc. First Int. Rangeland Congr., Soc. Range Manage., Denver, Colorado.

Wheeler, J.L. 1962. Experimentation in grazing experiments. Herbage Abstr. 32:1-7.
Wheeler, J.L., and R.D. Mochrie (eds.). 1981. Forage evaluation: Concepts and techniques. Forage and Grassland Council, Lexington, Kentucky.
Whiteman, J.V., P.F. Loggins, D. Chambers, L.S. Pope, and D.F. Stephens. 1954. Some sources of error in weighing steers off grass. J. Anim. Sci. 13:832-842.

Chapter 7
Methods for Studying Rangeland Hydrology

Introduction

A rancher or range specialist has a vested interest in understanding how grazing animals and grazing systems influence the hydrologic behavior of rangelands. One of the principal objectives of watershed management for rangelands is to manage the soil water balance in such a way that forage production is enhanced and maintained on a sustained yield basis. Managing the range resource to meet this primary objective simultaneously addresses reduction of soil loss and mitigation of frequent flooding. Good watershed management is good range management.

The principal reason for studying the hydrology of rangelands is because the amount and availability of soil water is the fundamental basis for both forage and livestock production. While it is true that forage production also depends on other environmental factors, ultimately, forage production is limited by available soil water.

To manage grazing lands for sustained livestock production, we must understand how grazing influences the hydrology of rangelands to be able to recommend guidelines that are useful for the development or selection of grazing systems and range improvement practices that promote soil water conditions favorable to forage growth. Rangeland hydrology is a complex field of study, and this chapter can only briefly address the methods for studying the hydrologic behavior of rangelands and review techniques that have been used by researchers.

Much of the research in range hydrology has only site-specific applications and cannot be related to other studies because the investigations were carried out: (1) without a commensurable description of grazing levels; (2) without a reference to the spectrum of the climatic variability within which the studies were made; and (3) without an adequate description of the topography and soil properties. These three kinds of information are essential for the comparison and synthesis of studies in rangeland hydrology.

Grazing level or grazing intensity is usually described only as "no grazing", "light", "moderate", or "heavy". Since grazing level is relative, descriptions like these make it difficult to integrate the experimental results into a body of knowledge that can be applied elsewhere.

The spectrum of climatic variability is characterized by the joint variation of precipitation and solar radiation. These two driving variables determine the water/energy balance of the plant environment. Too often, the only description of the climate that is reported is the average annual precipitation and air temperature and, perhaps, the annual or seasonal precipitation for the year(s) in which the research was done. Without knowledge of where the climatic conditions during the experiment fit in the spectrum of the climatic variability for the location, the research results are of limited use in developing guidelines for long term grazing management.

Soil properties, particularly those of the surface horizon, that determine the dynamics of soil water are not adequately described by the information in soil survey reports or from the description of the modal series. Of importance are those soil and surface horizon properties that are subject to change under different levels of grazing and under different management alternatives. Since the extent to which grazing influences the properties of the soil and the surface horizon depends on both the grazing level and the soil itself, the importance of unambiguously describing both grazing levels and the soil properties is obvious.

Those involved in rangeland hydrology research should carefully describe and document the grazing, climate, topography, and soil conditions of the experiment. Results of the investigation can then be related, not only to the range location itself, but to the results of both past and future studies.

Infiltration

Infiltration is the process through which water penetrates the surface and enters the soil. Once within the soil mass, the process of soil water flow distributes the water through the profile.

Infiltration is a surface phenomenon, controlled by conditions in the surface horizon, usually only a few centimeters deep. Movement of the water through the profile depends upon internal controls that are largely independent of those controlling infiltration. Soil water movement within the soil profile is called soil water flow (saturated or unsaturated) to distinguish it from the process of infiltration.

During the course of a storm, changes at the soil surface progressively lower the rate of infiltration. Raindrop impact puddles and seals the surface. Soil colloids swell upon wetting, thereby reducing the size of pores through which the water can percolate. When muddy waters enter the soil, sedimentation of suspended particles obstructs pores and further reduces the infiltration rate.

Rate at which water moves within the soil depends primarily upon the gradient of capillary forces, also called the matrix potential. In many soils, a clay horizon several centimeters, or even a meter, below the surface is considerably less permeable than material above it. Once the pore space above this layer is saturated, both infiltration rate at the surface and rate of soil water flow is limited to the hydraulic conductivity of the least permeable layer.

Infiltration rate after several minutes of rain usually is much less than at the beginning. Usually within an hour, the infiltration rate reaches a minimum which remains essentially constant for the remainder of the storm. As the soil drains and dries, its ability to take in and transmit water is restored. The typical change of the infiltration rate, when the rain rate or snow melt rate at the soil surface constantly exceeds potential infiltration rate, is illustrated in Fig. 7-1.

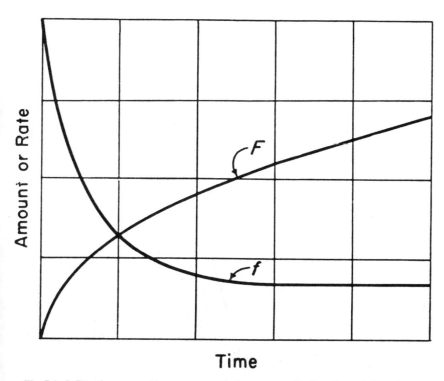

Time

Fig. 7-1. Infiltration curves. F, mass or cumulative amount of infiltration; f, infiltration rate.

Measurements of Infiltration

Ordinarily, infiltration is not measured directly. It is usually deduced from measurements of precipitation and surface runoff. Correct interpretation of these data requires an understanding of the hydrologic processes during a rainstorm. Detailed descriptions of infiltration and runoff have been given by Branson et al. (1981). Measurements of mass infiltration are ordinarily expressed as depth, usually in millimeters of water over the watershed plot or microwatershed. Infiltration rate is expressed in mm/hr. In the following discussion, water artificially applied (simulated rainfall) is spoken of as rainfall or precipitation.

During infiltration, water begins to soak into the soil immediately upon contact. During the early part of the storm, if the potential infiltration rate is high and the amount of rainfall is small, the actual infiltration rate is equal to the rain rate and no overland flow occurs. In Fig. 7-2, this amount of infiltration is referred to as "initial abstraction" (F_i). Potential infiltration rate (f_p) at any moment declines from an initial value (f_o) to a final minimum constant value (f_c), which is the saturated hydraulic conductivity of the

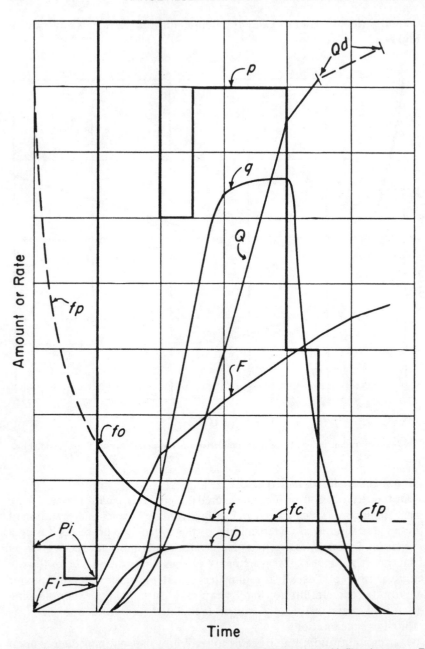

Fig. 7-2. Comparison of hydrograph of a storm with rainfall intensity and infiltration curves. D, surface detention; F, mass infiltration; F_i, initial abstraction, f, infiltration rate; f_p, potential infiltration; f_a, initial infiltration rate; f_c, constant infiltration rate; p, precipitation rate; P_i, initial precipitation, Q, mass runoff; q, runoff rate; Q_d, runoff from surface detention.

surface horizon. An approximate average infiltration rate can be obtained by dividing the mass infiltration (F) by the corresponding time.

Infiltration Terms

Depression Storage

When the rainfall rate exceeds the potential infiltration rate, part of the excess rainfall accumulates in surface depressions and is called "depression storage". After the rain ceases, part of this water infiltrates and part evaporates.

Detention

If depressions fill, water accumulates in excess of depression storage and begins to spill. This detention water is the hydraulic head that drives overland flow. Dynamic detention storage depends upon the extent to which rainfall rate at any moment exceeds the combined infiltration and runoff rates.

Overland Flow

Simultaneously with accumulation of detention, water begins to flow over the ground surface. This runoff leaving the area is called overland flow.

Retention

The sum of all the foregoing except surface runoff is referred to as retention. The difference between precipitation and runoff is retention. On small plots where interception, evapotranspiration, depression storage, and surface detention are negligible, retention may be considered equivalent to infiltration. On large areas (watersheds), the other elements in retention must be accounted for to get reasonable values for infiltration.

Soil Water Storage

Infiltrated water fills the pore space in successive horizons as it moves downward. Water held against the gravity by capillary forces in the soil mass is called unsaturated storage.

Soil Water Flow

Within the soil mass, water moves through the profile in accordance with gradients of soil water potential. If the successive horizons become saturated, the horizon with the least hydraulic conductivity restricts the rate of saturated flow, reducing infiltration and increasing overland flow.

Subsurface Flow

The downward moving soil water may reach impervious layers which divert it laterally to the surface, downslope from its point of entry, or into stream channels.

Groundwater

Infiltrated water that is not held as unsaturated storage and does not reappear as subsurface flow, ultimately, reaches the water table and contributes to groundwater.

Relationships of the principal surface phenomena are illustrated by superimposing a hydrograph (a plotting of rate of runoff against time) onto a similar plotting of rainfall intensities (Fig. 7-2) for a particular storm.

Methods of Field Study

Amounts and rates of infiltration can be determined by two general methods: (1) Plot studies of natural rainfall or artificial applications of water, and associated runoff, by means of infiltrometers, and (2) analysis of rainfall and runoff data from natural watersheds, although other factors are included. A combination of the two methods may also be used.

Plot Studies

Plot studies are especially significant in yielding information on infiltration, soil water storage for plant use, and overland flow. Small plots lend themselves to the comparison of grazing effects on different soil and cover conditions.

The initial part of the infiltration curve (f_o, as shown in Fig. 7-2) is of primary importance to soil water storage and overland flow on rangelands. In much of the rangeland, most rains fall on dry soil and are frequently of high intensity. Application of water on dry plots gives "dry run" information on the infiltration and runoff characteristics to be most often expected under grazing conditions.

For long duration storms, or rain-on-snow, the minimum infiltration rate that prevails after the soil is thoroughly wet is the critical value for initiating overland flow. This critical value is obtained in plot studies by means of the "wet run", a second application of water to the same plot, usually 24 hours after the "dry run" (Rauzi and Smith 1973). Infiltration curves or indices from both runs on the same plot give the most complete picture of infiltration and runoff characteristics of the site being sampled.

Flooded Plots

Flooding methods make use of rings or frames to confine the water on the surface until it soaks into the ground. Water is usually applied at a rate to keep a constant supply or head, on the soil surface. Either mass infiltration or infiltration rate is measured as it is withdrawn from the supply container, either by a recording gauge or by recording the contents remaining in the container, at specified time intervals. Measured intake is plotted against time to give the infiltration curves.

Metal rings or frames can be used on relatively flat areas. They are forced into the soil only far enough to prevent escape of the water from under the ring to the surface outside of the ring. These devices are simple to use, but frequently allow lateral infiltration of the water in the topsoil.

To eliminate the error of lateral infiltration, concentric (double) rings are used (Fig. 7-3). The smaller rings, 15–30 cm in diameter, are placed inside the larger, 45–90 cm in diameter. Water is applied simultaneously in both rings and kept at the same level. Only data from the inner ring are taken as indicating infiltration, assuming that the wetted zone beneath the larger ring serves as a buffer to reduce lateral movement. Standardization equipment and procedures for this method are described by Haise et al. (1956). Cox (1952) described an apparatus using concentric rings with a float-valve control of the water supply and a recording rain gauge to provide automatic continuous record of infiltration.

Early work by Pearse and Bertelson (1937) was conducted through use of 0.09 square m plots (49 cm by 19 cm) enclosed by baffle plates forced into the soil. Water was supplied from a 3.8 liter container through a perforated tube

Fig. 7-3. Concentric-ring type infiltrometer with automatic water supply recording gauge. The rings alone are frequently used with manual application and measurement of water. (USDA, SCS photo, ca. 1950).

which spread it uniformly over the uphill side of the plot. Rate of application was regulated to maintain a constant flooding of the plot with continuous runoff. Runoff was caught below the plot and measured in a tipping bucket. The difference between the amount applied and the amount of runoff was considered infiltration.

Rainfall Simulators

By spraying or sprinkling water on the plots, results more nearly like those occurring in natural rainfall are possible. Since the late 1930's, the Soil Conservation Service and the Forest Service have developed a series of rain simulators. With these devices, water is applied at rates greater than potential infiltration and the runoff is collected and measured. Infiltration is calculated as the difference between application rate and runoff rate. An extensive annotated bibliography on rainfall simulators was prepared by Birk et al. (1979). This bibliography provides information on plot size, portability, and simulated rainfall characteristics. In the same year, a workshop was held on the state-of-the-art of rainfall simulators as a tool for studying erosion, runoff and infiltration (USDA 1979a). A few of the more widely used rainfall simulators are described on the following pages.

Limitations and advantages of rainfall simulators have been discussed by

Mech (1965). Romkens (1979) and Young (1979) briefly discuss interpretation problems associated with rainfall simulator data.

Rocky Mountain Infiltrometer. The Rocky Mountain infiltrometer (Dortignac 1951) may be run using from one to three plots per run (Fig. 7-4).

Fig. 7-4. Rocky Mountain infiltrometer. A. In field use. B. Closeup of apparatus. (U.S. Forest Service photos, ca. 1950).

Individual plots are installed by driving the sharpened edges into the soil surface to a depth of about 7.5 cm with a specially constructed hammer. Type-F nozzles produce a mean drop diameter of about 3.5 mm at intensities between 75 to 100 mm/hr. Kinetic energy of a simulated storm is about 65% (assuming drop diameter of 2.7 mm for natural storm) of a comparable natural storm. Each set of three plots requires about 210 liters of water for a 30 minute run. Use of trough gauges on either side of each plot allows careful monitoring of rainfall application rates on each plot. An adjustable canvas wind shield is used to minimize wind disturbance and raindrop drift. Limitations which have been noted by Gaither and Buckhouse (1979) include steepness of a slope, accessibility of sampling sites, rocky or stony soils, low overstory vegetation (with resultant interceptions of simulated rainfall), and presence of slash or dense litter layers.

Modular-type Infiltrometer. A modular-type infiltrometer originally designed by Meeuwig (1971) and later modified according to Malekuti

Fig. 7-5. Modular-type infiltrometer. (Photo courtesy of G.F. Gifford, Utah State University, Logan, Utah, ca. 1970).

and Gifford (1978) has been used rather extensively for hydrologic studies (Fig. 7-5). The infiltrometer will deliver simulated rainfall at intensities ranging from about 30 to 250 mm/hr over a plot size of 0.34 square m. Raindrop size is approximately 2.9 mm. The water chamber is rotated in a horizontal position to insure equal water pressure on the needles and irregular drop position over the plot. The simulator may be used with or without plot frames. The infiltrometer is portable, well suited to steep slopes and to rocky soils, and requires only about 25 liters of water per 30 minutes at 250 mm/hr.

Mobile Drip Type Rainfall Simulator. Blackburn et al. (1974) described a mobile drip type rainfall simulator. The raindrop-producing module is similar to modified versions of one described by Timko and Skau (1967). The module consists of two, one meter square sheets of 6.25 mm plexiglass spaced 12.5 mm apart. Each module has 2,500 tubes at 2 cm spacing that project 6.25 mm above and 6.25 mm below the lower plexiglass sheet. These tubes are 23-gauge stainless steel. The tubes form simulated raindrops of 2.5 mm in diameter which reach 71% of terminal velocity falling from a height of 2.1 m. Wind shelters are necessary. Rainfall intensities of about 5 mm/hr to 200 mm/hr can be simulated on either a standard plot frame 0.5 m square or a variable size plot frame driven from 2.5 cm to 7.0 cm into the soil.

The rainfall simulator is mounted on a two-wheel trailer. Water is pumped from a 1,100 liter tank to an elevated 200 liter barrel and flows by gravity through filters and flowmeters to the raindrop-producing modules. Modules are suspended 2.1 m above the soil surface on adjustable arms constructed of 10 cm diameter pipe. Supporting arms are adjustable and the modules are raised and lowered by a steel cable and hand winch and must be leveled for uniform raindrop distribution by adjusting turnbuckles on guywires.

Rainfall Simulator-Gamma Probe Infiltrometer. Hamon (1979) describes a modular type rainfall simulator which provides rainfall intensities between 2.5 and 200 mm/hr. The self-contained modules are 0.61 m. by 0.92 m. and utilize a two-compartment system of water and air with water drops formed by capillary needles that project through a main gallery into a nozzle area in the bottom plate. Each module has its own water and air flow measuring systems. The system operates with water being supplied to the needles from the top compartment, forming drops on the end of the needles. Air from the bottom compartment is forced out around the ends of the needles, forming the drop size. Changing air pressure to the bottom compartment allows drop sizes to be varied from a mist to about 2.8 mm. Mean drop size of natural rainfall can be duplicated with the simulator; however, the simulated distribution is much narrower than the natural rainfall distribution. Kinetic energy of the simulated rain is about 83% of the kinetic energy of natural rainfall.

To cover a wide range of intensities, it is necessary to use two sets of modules with two different needle sizes. One set of 0.41 mm diameter needles are used for simulating intensities from 4 to 50 mm/hr, and another set of 0.68 mm diameter needles are used to simulate intensities from 50 to 200 mm/hr.

To monitor the water movement in the soil, a two-probe gamma density gage is used. The density gage is operated remotely by a pulley and drive mechanism on the top of the rainfall simulator. Access tubes, located 30.5 cm apart, extend through the center of the module array downward into the soil. The control system makes it possible to obtain density (water content) measurements and to track the position of the "wetting front" during rainfall simulation.

Portable Adaptation of Colorado State University Design.
Lusby (1977) has described a portable adaptation of equipment described by
Dickinson et al. (1967). Sprinklers are arranged in a staggered grid pattern
and provide a rainfall rate of about 51 mm/hr (Fig. 7-6). Raindrop distribution is similar to natural rainfall and kinetic energy of drops about 55% of a

**Fig. 7-6. Modified Colorado State University sprinkler infiltrometer. (Photo courtesy of G.F.
Gifford, ca. 1975).**

natural storm. Sprinkler grid and spray patterns are arranged so that approximately 325 square m of area can be covered with the desired rainfall intensity.
The sprinklers (Rainjet 78C nozzles) are mounted on 3.1 m riser pipes, and
approximately 37,800 liters are required to simulate a storm of 38 mm in 45
minutes. A grid of storage rain gauges is placed within the study area to
measure rainfall applied. When slope gradients are steep, runoff is collected in
barrels with calibrated orifices. On slopes of moderate gradient, runoff is
measured through the use of a Parshall flume.

Rotating-boom Rainfall Simulator. The rotating-boom rainfall
simulator (Swanson 1979) utilizes application characteristics of the Spraying
Systems Company, Veejet 80100 nozzles, as described by Meyer (1958). The
nozzles, spraying continuously, move in a circular path which is instantane-
ously perpendicular to the long dimension of the nozzle spray pattern (Fig.
7-7). Ten booms, each 7.8 long, support 30 nozzles. Each nozzle is mounted
on a manually-operated globe valve. The nozzles are located on 1.6 m
spacings from the supporting the booms. Intensities of 60 and 120 mm/hr are

Fig. 7-7. Rotating-boom rainfall simulator. (Photo courtesy of G.F. Gifford, ca. 1975).

obtained by operating 15 or 30 nozzles, requiring water supplies of about 270 and 540 liters. Nozzles spray downward from 2.5 m above ground. Each discharges 18 liters at $0.42 \ kg/cm^2$ producing drop-size distributions similar to those of natural rainfall with near-terminal velocities after 2.5 m of free fall. The booms are operated in a level plain to maintain uniform water pressure at all nozzles. A longer (taller) stem has been used on more sloping plots to provide adequate nozzle height upslope. Water is supplied to the booms through the stem to which the booms are attached. Close control of rainfall intensity is obtained by control of the water supply pressure. Plot size is approximately 3.0×10.6 m and two plots are usually run at the same time.

Significance of Plot Data

Plot studies cannot be expected to give results directly applicable to watershed areas. Variations in rainfall rates, soils, and cover which affect infiltration rates preclude this. Data from small plots are most useful in studying the relation of infiltration to selected individual factors, in establishing normal infiltration characteristics of particular soils, and in comparing relative characteristics of different areas.

The soil and topographic characteristics of most grazing lands lend themselves to runoff and erosion plot studies; however, some do not. This is particularly true for heavy clay soils that are subject to intense and deep cracking (50 to 100 cm). The deep cracks intercept and store or divert any overland flow, hence neither runoff nor erosion can be reliably measured.

Under natural conditions, clay swelling eventually closes the cracks. Also, grazing animals definitely hasten their disappearance. Nevertheless, the effect of grazing in such situations cannot be evaluated with plot studies (for plots of any reasonable size) where artificial rainfall or flooding is employed. Small plots (within the uncracked polygons) are simply nonrepresentative. Also, large plots or microwatersheds, studied under natural precipitation for successive years, are subject to sources of variation that preclude clear interpretation of runoff or soil loss under these conditions.

Influence of Method. In interpreting plot data, the effect of the experimental method itself on the results must be kept in mind. For example, flooding-type infiltrometers generally produce higher infiltration rates than rainfall simulators, since with the former, water infiltrates under a constant head and without drop impact. Single-ring infiltrometers generally yield higher values because of the opportunity for lateral movement of water in the soil.

The degree of control over lateral movement of infiltrated water affects the measured results with different equipment. Characteristics of the soil studied and degree to which it offers opportunity for lateral movement, likewise, affect results. For natural rainfall covering a large area, this variable is largely eliminated. Many infiltrometers provide wetted buffer zones around the study plots to reduce this source of error.

In plot studies where lateral movement is not controlled, the plot size affects the magnitude of the measurements. Marshall and Stirk (1950) found that when no buffer zone was used, minimum infiltration rate decreased with plot size. Buffer zones around flooded plots reduce lateral movement somewhat, but results are still subject to some error. Sprayed buffer zones around small plots are generally effective.

Influence of Soil. An early effort to correlate the great mass of data obtained from a wide variety of infiltrometers on many different soils was made by Krimgold and Beenhouwer (1954) by grouping all soils into four categories based on relative infiltration rates. This principle is carried further in developing a "hydrologic grouping" of soils for use in the hydrologic analysis of watersheds. This grouping uses available knowledge of profile characteristics to classify soils first on the basis of similarity of texture and other properties known to influence infiltration. Relative infiltration rates of these groups are then deduced from available data from the groups used in the experiment.

Musgrave (1955) lists the soil factors affecting infiltration rate as: (1) surface condition and amount of protection against the impact of rain; (2) internal characteristics of the soil mass, including pore size, depth or thickness of the permeable portion, degree of swelling of clay and colloids, organic matter content, and degree of aggregation; (3) the soil water content and degree of saturation; and (4) season of the year and temperature of the soil and water.

Influence of Vegetation. Rangeland vegetation greatly affects infiltration. In plot studies, this factor must be measured so its influence on infiltration can be evaluated. Vegetation affects infiltration in two ways; (1) directly, as the canopy and litter cover intercept part of the rain, attenuate the rainfall energy, or detain the water on the soil surface, thereby increasing infiltration opportunity, and (2) indirectly, as the plants have influenced soil aggregation and organic matter.

Soil surface sealing by raindrop impact significantly affects infiltration during the early part of the storm. Total soil cover, including living plants, litter, and rock fragments is more significant than the kinds of plants (Kincaid et al. 1964, Epstein et al. 1966). Soil conditions are profoundly influenced by vegetation. These influences affect the entire range of the infiltration function of the surface soil, including the final (constant) infiltration rate (f_c, as shown in Fig. 7-2) where it is not limited by shallow rock or other impervious material.

Watershed Studies

From records of precipitation and surface runoff from a watershed, infiltration indicies of the area can be determined. The simplest index to infiltration capacity of a watershed is the average rainfall intensity which causes runoff, or the intensity above which all rainfall is runoff. This index is highly variable, changing with topographic features, antecedent and present soil water content, cover, and soil surface features. Infiltration data obtained from watersheds larger than a few hectares are of little value in revealing the influence of grazing, specific soil, or cover conditions on infiltration rates because of the great variability of these factors in any natural area.

However, a combination of small watershed and plot measurements have long been used to good advantage to analyze large complex watersheds (Rowe 1940). This requires subdividing the large watershed into several areas, each homogeneous as to topography, soils, vegetation, and grazing levels. A series of infiltrometer measurements is made within each area to establish characteristic infiltration rates. Infiltration and runoff to be expected of typical rains are calculated for each area from these values, and combined to give a total for the watershed.

Soil Compaction

Information on soil factors (i.e., texture, organic matter, moisture, etc.) influencing watersheds can be found in many sources. Less information is available on compaction. Soil compaction is the packing together of soil particles that causes an increase in bulk density at the surface. The more intensively rangelands are used, the greater the opportunity for soil compaction. Trails, bedding grounds, and water and salt locations are areas of greatest compaction. The effect of compaction increases the bulk density of the soil by reducing pore space (Lull 1959). This reduces infiltration. Overland flow may occur more frequently, which supplies greater energy for erosion. Compaction may also reduce growth of vegetation through its deleterious effects on soil aeration, infiltration, and soil water.

The effect of compaction can be measured directly by comparing the bulk densities of soil under different trampling intensities and noting changes in oven dry weight of the soil per unit volume, or indirectly by comparative measurements of infiltration rates. Since the major effect of compaction is on infiltration, infiltration tests, before and after compaction, may be most revealing.

Bulk density samples are usually obtained with a cylinder of known volume which is driven or pushed into the soil surface at random locations. Samples should be taken when the soil is near field capacity. The oven dry weight of the soil sample, divided by its volume, gives the value of bulk density. Bulk densities of most mineral soils are between 1.00 and 1.50 gm/cm^3.

In stony soils where sampling cylinders cannot be driven into the soil, bulk density may be measured by digging a small hole with a trowel, oven drying and weighing the material removed, measuring the volume of the hole by lining the hole with a plastic film such as Saran-Wrap, and measuring the volume of water required to fill it. Procedures for measuring bulk density have been described by Lutz (1944), Hoover et al. (1954), Broadfoot (1954), and Baver et al. (1972).

Trampling generally compacts only the soil surface. These relatively thin, compacted layers are difficult to sample in the undisturbed state so that indirect measurements of soil compaction by infiltration tests or pore space measurements are more sensitive indicators of its effect.

Relative compaction can be measured with the type of penetrometers that have been used to determine the location and depth of compacted plow layers (Baver et al. 1972). However, stoniness may present a problem by inhibiting penetration of the instrument. Also, variation in soil water content presents problems because penetrability is closely associated with soil wetness.

Compaction also affects soil porosity. Total pore space is reduced with the large pores, the non-capillary portion, most greatly affected. Total pore space may be estimated by dividing the bulk density by 2.65 gm/cm^3 (the specific gravity for sand particles). A soil with a bulk density of greater than 1.325 gm/cm^3 would have, for example, a total pore space of about 50%. Non-capillary pore space can be determined by subtracting the percentage volume of water held in a soil core at 60 cm tension from the volume held at saturation (Hoover et al. 1954). Change in non-capillary pore space provides the most sensitive indicator of compaction effect.

Lull (1959) reviewed soil compaction on forest and rangelands. Bulk densities of the surface horizon of "heavily" grazed areas were reported to be about 1.25 times greater than ungrazed areas. Non-capillary porosity was not as frequently reported, but a study by Read (1957) revealed that bulk density, under "heavy grazing", was increased 1.21 times the bulk density of the ungrazed soil, but total porosity was reduced only 10%. However, non-capillary porosity was reduced by 54%. Although the susceptibility of a soil to compaction varies with clay content, organic matter, and soil water content, other studies support a 30 to 50% reduction in non-capillary porosity under "heavy" grazing.

Compaction can be a transitory effect and may best be measured in the season in which it occurs. This would be particularly necessary where soil surface is loosened or heaved by frost. A soil surface compacted in the fall may, through winter frost action, appear quite porous the following spring. Regulation of stock to obtain a known trampling force over small experimental plots is difficult. To obtain a range of trampling effects on infiltration plots, Packer (1953) pounded the soil with a steel "hoof". Different degrees of trampling were simulated from plot to plot by varying the spacing and number of impacts.

Runoff

Quantity of runoff is usually expressed in depth (mm) over the watershed, or volume delivered at a point in a designated period of time. Streamflow is expressed as a discharge rate (m³/sec).

Streamflow represents a composite of overland flow, subsurface flow, and contributions from groundwater flow. In range studies, most workers have used relatively small areas from which runoff occurs as ephemeral overland flow. Some studies have been made in natural drainage areas sufficiently large to produce sustained streamflow representing all segments of runoff.

A common method of determining runoff in plot experiments is by measuring the volume accumulated in storage tanks from plots or a given area. Usually, runoff is measured after each storm. In some cases where runoff is expected to exceed the storage capacity of the tanks, weirs are installed and equipped with recorders to measure flow. Where experimental watersheds are large enough to produce seasonal or perennial streamflow, standard gauging methods are employed using weirs or flumes to arrive at a rate of discharge (USDA 1979b).

Quantitative information on runoff in range investigations can be obtained from natural watersheds, artificial microwatersheds, or plots. Microwatersheds can be designed to measure the effects of treatments either on surface runoff alone or both surface and subsurface runoff. With natural watersheds it is frequently possible to measure all segments of runoff; surface, subsurface, and contributions from groundwater.

Microwatersheds

Permanent microwatersheds are useful to evaluate changes associated with time. They permit collection of continuous records of the influence of an applied treatment, as well as the effect of associated factors such as seasonal variations in grazing, climate, precipitation, cover, and forage production. Sites are selected to represent an important range type. Microwatersheds are costly and, therefore, the ideal number of samples required to evaluate the variable conditions normally found on the range can seldom be achieved. Offsetting this drawback, permanent microwatersheds provide continuous records of time variation under different treatments or management practices. Statisticians should be consulted before designing this type of research.

Microwatersheds are enclosed by galvanized iron, concrete barriers, or earthen berms to exclude runoff from the plots or runon from outside the plots so that internal runoff can be collected and measured. Natural rainfall supplies the source of runoff in most instances, but in some cases water is applied by artificial means to simulate rainfall.

Natural runoff from plots and microwatersheds is ephemeral. After intense rains, runoff rates rise rapidly to peaks that usually last only a few minutes, and the flow ceases soon after the end of precipitation. Runoff from heavily used ranges may be accompanied by significant amounts of debris and eroded material. Measuring devices must be adapted to such conditions.

If data on rates of runoff are desired, flow from artificial microwatersheds and natural watersheds, as well as low flows from larger ones, are measured by flumes or special weirs developed and calibrated in hydraulic laboratories (USDA 1979b). A continuous record of depth of flow (stage or head) is obtained from water-level recorders (Fig. 7-8). The stage records are con-

Fig. 7-8. Drop-box weir designed to accommodate sediment-laden runoff. (Photo courtesy of C.W. Johnson, Northwest Watershed Research Center, Boise, Idaho, ca. 1966).

verted into rates of flow from rating tables developed for each type of measuring device, or by current-meter calibrations for larger watersheds. Total runoff for any period is calculated by integrating the rates of flow during the period.

If only the total amount of runoff from small microwatersheds is of concern, the entire flow, or an aliquot of it, is collected in a calibrated rank. The same aliquot devices are also used where samples are desired for determining the amount of sediment associated with runoff. These devices are described in the section on Erosion. Similar methods have long been used effectively in determining the influence of grazing on runoff and sediment yield (Croft and Monninger 1953, Dunford 1954).

Data are most useful when related to individual storms causing runoff over a period of years. Runoff can be compared with amounts of precipitation causing it by converting volumes of runoff water to depth over the watershed. Supplemental data on air temperature, wind, evaporation, and soil water often are recorded at these installations.

Watersheds

Natural watersheds or drainage areas have been used in range watershed research, but not as widely as small plots of microwatersheds. The principal reasons are the high cost, long-time nature of watershed experiments, and difficulty of isolating grazing treatments. Also, some technical difficulties are encountered in measuring runoff occurring as ephemeral flow. In the semiarid western ranges, it is difficult to find natural watersheds small enough to provide relatively uniform grazing, vegetation cover, and soil conditions. Changes in runoff behavior resulting from grazing are easily masked by the wide variations in precipitation, soil, and vegetation that usually exist in watersheds larger than 2 to 3 square km.

Despite these difficulties, natural watersheds are valuable research tools. They have been used to test the effect of sheep grazing on surface runoff in the Wasatch Plateau of Utah (Forsling 1931) and cattle grazing in the Northern Great Plains (Allis and Kuhlman 1962; Woohiser et al. 1970).

Experimental Methods of Measuring Runoff

Studies of runoff in range research can fall under two general procedures described by Wilm (1952). The first consists of methods for determining the influence of present and past range practices where the investigator measures variables without a pre-determined experiment. The second is by controlled experimentation in which natural variations are carefully segregated to minimize their effect on evaluation of treatments which the investigator wishes to test.

In using the first of these methods, refinement can be added by segregating the variables involved in the problem into classes, each of which is relatively homogeneous with respect of runoff. For example, Johnson and Niederhof (1941) used simulated rainfall to test runoff rates from three important cover types. Information was obtained for 10 and 40% slopes with simulated rainfall rates of 60 and 100 mm/hr. Similar measurements were made during other early research by Craddock and Pearse (1938) using two rainfall intensities on four range types and two slope gradients. An exemplary study of grazing influences on vegetation, soil properties, infiltration, and soil loss was carried out by Blackburn et al. (1980). These types of experiments enable the investigator to make inferences about the influence of grazing on runoff.

A further refinement can be introduced by supplementary measurements of variables not readily subject to classification. Packer (1951) measured surface runoff and erosion with an infiltrometer on two range cover types and within each sampling plot measured additional site characteristics thought to be associated with surface runoff and erosion. From the data, he was able to statistically test the factors which are correlated with runoff and to make recommendations on range conditions and soil cover needed to control surface runoff.

When making use of the second method, microwatersheds can be used most effectively. It is necessary that microwatersheds be arranged in such a manner that applied treatments are given equal chance to exert their influence without confounding from extraneous variations. An example of such an arrangement is the randomized block design which provides an opportunity to segregate and account for variations such as in soil and slope (see Chapter 10). Several early chapter grazing management experiments were patterned after this design (Johnson 1953, Driscoll 1955, and Sharp et al. 1964). Runoff data may be obtained from each pasture, either from plot measurements or from natural watersheds if entire drainage units can be found within the individual pastures.

Comparison of runoff from pasture is easily obscured by variabilities in soil and cover conditions. For this reason, most tests have been conducted on relatively small and closely spaced runoff plots or watersheds having uniform soil, slope, and cover. Frequently, sets of two or more sample areas are replicated to determine the effect of different soils, slopes, or cover types.

Runoff on rangelands is influenced most by changes which affect the cover and vigor of the vegetation and the porosity of the soil. Controlled experiments may be designed to show the effect of changes in these two basic factors which can be introduced experimentally. Such experiments have been conducted to determine how runoff is affected by various intensities of grazing, prescribed or natural fires, conversion, and range improvement practices. Numerous studies of this kind have been reported (Dortignac and Hickey 1963, Dragoun 1969, Hanson et al. 1970, and Wright et al. 1974).

A general procedure is to compare runoff from treated plots with that of adjacent check plots. If the experiment is carefully designed, provision is usually made for a pre-treatment calibration period before testing treatment effects. Calibration is desirable to determine any pre-treatment variations in runoff indicating inherent differences among plots. If significant variation in runoff is discovered before treatment, these differences need to be taken into account in evaluating post-treatment results.

One notable modification of this general pattern was employed on the Wasatch Plateau in Utah (Forsling 1931). Two adjacent small watersheds began with vegetation densities of 16% (watershed A) and 40% (watershed B) in 1915. For 5 years, these densities were maintained by controlled sheep grazing. During the next 5 years vegetation density on watershed A was raised from 16 to 40% by eliminating all grazing and reseeding where needed. During the third 5-year period, watershed A was again opened to moderate grazing on a deferred system to maintain the 40% density already achieved. These manipulations made it possible to study the influence of fluctuating vegetation densities in one watershed with a second which remained unchanged during a 15-year period.

In another early watershed study, data on runoff were collected from a single drainage (Johnson 1952). Streamflow was measured for a 7-year calibration period before cattle were grazed on the area. The effect of grazing was based on a comparison of streamflow behavior before and after grazing began.

Grazing treatments also have been successfully introduced on small runoff plots. In Colorado, cattle were grazed at moderate and heavy intensities on 0.004 ha surface plots (Dunford 1954). A movable electric fence was used to control cattle movements. In Arizona, sheep were grazed on 0.008 ha natural lysimeters (Martin and Rich 1948).

In general, runoff data from test plots of this type have value as relative indicators of treatment effects rather than as absolute measures of runoff which can be expected from large area of similar grazing land. Of necessity, the treatments on plots must be applied under somewhat artificial conditions. Grazing, for example, has been conducted under confined conditions and for concentrated periods, resulting in somewhat unnatural effects.

Erosion

Methods of Evaluating

Erosion on rangelands can be evaluated by inspection of eroded areas or estimated by measurement of the eroded material itself, either in transit or accumulated at some point. Inspection of eroded areas is the more direct approach because it is done at the point of soil detachment. Quantitative determinations of soil volume removed can be made by comparing surface profiles with known points of reference. Though subjective, extent of erosion can also be classified by terms such as slight, moderate, and severe. These are usually based on erosion indicators which relate in a qualitative way to relative amounts of soil removed. Amounts are expressed in units of depth, volume per unit area, or weight per unit area per unit time.

Soil material in transit as suspended sediment in runoff is expressed in terms of concentration (ppm). Flowing water transports heavier soil particles, gravel, and rock by pushing, rolling, and skipping of the particles along the channel bottom (bed-load).

The most common method of evaluating erosion in transit is by measuring suspended sediment in streamflow. Bed-load and heavier materials are generally measured in small reservoirs such as stock ponds, where the accumulated material can be quantified by weight or volume (USDA 1979b).

Sampling Methods
Displacement or Loss of Soil

A reliable quantitative procedure for rapidly eroding locations is the periodic remeasurement of established transects using fixed reference points or benchmarks to determine successive changes in surface elevations or gully profiles. Fisser (1978) used a point frame to evaluate soil loss over successive time periods. With this technique increased distances to the soil surface connote net soil loss and/or compaction. The general principle of measure ment has been applied on mined lands (Toy 1983).

Sheet erosion cannot be readily detected by periodic remeasurement of surveyed profiles. Collector troughs, graduated erosion pins, or carefully measured distances to the ground surface from a fixed frame or tapeline stretched between two permanently established points can be used. Dunne (1977) describes the methodologies in detail. These methods give only relatively nonexact measures of a change in surface elevation which normally occurs slowly and in minute dimensions. Furthermore, apparent changes may be confounded by factors other than erosion such as frost heaving, colloidal swelling of the soil, disturbance of the pins, or changes in bulk density due to compaction. This latter might be the case on rangeland and especially on brushland soils cleared for soil.

Various indicators of soil displacement have been used qualitatively to gauge the extent of erosion. Ellison et al. (1951) established some useful criteria for judging erosion as a part of a general assessment of range condition and trend. Important indicators were found to be: cover condition, amount of bare soil, observed soil movement, trampling displacement, relics of original soil surface, erosion pavement, lichen lines on rocks, active gullies, wind-scoured depressions, wind and water deposits, and rill-channel ridges formed by grass rows invading old rills and becoming exposed ridges as a result of further erosion.

Measurements of Eroded Material

Methods have been developed for measuring suspended sediment. Determinations of this type are obtained from samples of sediment-carrying streamflow which are obtained simply by dipping a container into a stream at a selected point or by using the DH-48 depth-integrating hand sampler (U.S. Federal Inter-Agency River Basin Committee 1952). Water is collected in a bottle inserted into an aluminum case provided with a small filler inlet. The bottle is filled slowly, allowing the operator time to obtain a representative sample of streamflow at all depths. Adequate spot sampling of suspended sediment is difficult for infrequent ephemeral flow. Many of these difficulties can be overcome by continuous automatic sampling, and several devices are available to meet this need (Edwards et al. 1969, Brown et al. 1970, and USDA 1979b).

Not all eroded material is accounted for in suspended sediment samples. Considerable amounts of the heavier bed-load material are simply moved along the channel bed. This bed-load material can be measured after trapping it in a basin. For small watersheds, debris or sediment catchment basins can be constructed at relatively low cost and provide useful means for measuring accumulations volumetrically. Accumulated bed-load is most commonly measured in natural drainages where runoff is impounded in a stock pond.

Deposited material can be measured in two basic ways, depending on the catchment method and the refinement of measurement needed. Deposits in debris basins can be measured by successively surveying rising elevations of the accumulated material. In most natural watersheds of 4 ha or more, it is difficult to relate deposition of eroded material to individual storms; only seasonal or annual measurements are practical.

Eroded material from plots received in storage tanks is generally measured after each storm or simulated rainfall application. The usual method is to allow suspended matter to settle, and to siphon or decant the clear water. In some instances, a flocculating agent may be used to hasten the settling process (Davis 1937). The residue of eroded material is then measured volumetrically, and samples of known volume are dried before weighing. Erosion is usually expressed in terms of dry weight per unit area (plot or watershed) per time period.

Devices to take proportional samples, or aliquots, of the runoff and its content of eroded material can be used on plots too large for the runoff to be collected. An early development, but still one of the most widely used, is the Geib (1933) multislot divisor. This installation consists of a silt box, where the heavier particles of the runoff settle and the trash is sieved out; a series of divisor boxes, each with an uneven number of identical slots in the discharge end; and a storage tank. Sediment-laden water discharges from the silt box into the first divisor, where the discharge from the center slot is directed into another divisor, and so on until the aliquot is a convenient amount to hold in the storage tank (Harrold and Krimgold 1948).

Fig. 7-9. Coshocton-type runoff sampler. (USDA, ARS Photo, ca. 1950).

The "Coshocton-type" of runoff sampler was developed at the North Appalachian Experimental Watershed at Coshocton, Ohio. The discharge from the measuring flume falls directly upon a water wheel (Fig. 7-9). A sampling head with a narrow opening along its top is mounted on the wheel. With each revolution of the wheel, the slot cuts across the jet from the flume and extracts a small portion of the flow. The sample falls through the sampling head into a collecting pan below the wheel, and thence to the storage tank (Parsons 1954).

On larger plots and microwatersheds, a combination of flume and silt sampler commonly is used. Runoff flows through the flume, where a recording gauge registers the depth and time of flow. The water with its load of eroded material discharges into a silt box, where the heavier particles settle out. The water then flows over a rectangular weir into an outlet ditch. As it passes over the weir, a small amount flows through a slot into a divisor box, and thence into a storage tank.

Long-term sediment yields of watersheds can also be determined by measuring the accumulation of sediment in reservoirs of known age (Gottschalk 1952). Special equipment has been developed to determine the thickness of deposits and volume-weight relationships of the sediment. The volume of sediment is measured by standard hydrographic survey methods. These measurements can be converted to weights on the basis of the volume-weight relationships of the deposits.

Methods for Measuring General Erosion

Erosion studies in range research can be segregated into two general classifications. First are those which the investigator measures and classifies as he finds them. The second are experiments specifically designed to evaluate the results of applied treatments.

A considerable body of knowledge concerning erosion on rangelands has been accumulated from the first of these methods. The most useful has been that which has led to a correlation of erosion severity with associated range use.

A few examples of early research are illustrative. Cooperrider and Hendricks (1937) classified degrees of erosion into normal, moderate, advanced, and excessive. These were found to be associated with low, medium, or high degree of vegetation deterioration. Renner (1936) classified erosion into four classes: none, sheet, shallow-gully, and deep-gully. He then related these classes with observed gradients, aspect, soil-plant types, density of vegetation, rodent infestation, and accessibility to livestock. From these associations, he determined some easily recognizable range characteristics and land-use practices which are susceptible or conducive to erosion.

Investigations of the physical properties of soil have also revealed some usable relationships with erosion and erosion hazards. Croft et al. (1943) used a 3-stage classification based on deviation, moderate, and severe deviation. Soil associated with each class sampled at 0 to 15 cm and 15 to 30 cm depths to determine the relation of erosion severity to content of organic material, moisture equivalent, and total nitrogen. They found that organic matter in the surface horizon is strongly and inversely related to accelerated erosion. Johnson and Niederhof (1941) analyzed soils in simulated rainfall plots to determine percentage of sand, gravel, silt plus clay and colloids. From these percentages, they drew conclusions on the relation of soil texture and porosity to erosion.

Infiltrometer measurements over a wide variety of cover types and soils have demonstrated some useful relations between percentage of bare soil and relative amounts of erosion. Reid and Love (1951) used this type of information to estimate sheet erosion hazard. Packer (1951) used this same type of information to determine the minimum requirements of cover to hold erosion in check. An infiltrometer survey led to the conclusion that a 70 to 75% ground cover was needed for effective control of storm runoff and erosion in areas subject to high rainfall intensities (Marston 1952).

Investigations of this type can aid materially in establishing criteria for classifying erosion hazards and soil protection requirements. However, Wilm (1952) pointed out some of the hazards of interpreting results of these studies in terms of practical land management. The investigator always risks the possibility of bias and the confounding of variables. Controlled experiments offer an alternative when the risk of bias is one the investigator is not willing to take (see Chapters 1, 9, and 10). In making this choice, the investigator adds to the cost of his/her investigation and delays the results.

Treatments used in plot and watershed studies of erosion are designed to alter soil stability and porosity, to change the degree of mechanical protection by vegetation and litter, and to alter the quantity of surface runoff. Treatments have been accomplished in numerous ways: by actual grazing or simulated grazing, by burning (Blaisdell 1953), by revegetating bare and eroding areas, and by mechanically removing vegetation and surface litter.

As presented earlier, Packer (1953) determined what levels of trampling disturbance increase stormflow and erosion beyond safe limits. For this purpose he used a hand-operated steel "hoof". Degree of trampling was controlled by varying the spacing and the number of impacts of the hoof from plot to plot to simulate light, moderate, and heavy trampling.

Conclusions

Research in rangeland hydrology is rapidly converging toward the use of simulation models as the principal tool for synthesizing the body of knowledge of the effects of grazing on hydrologic behavior. This fact makes it all the more important to design hydrologic research on rangelands in such a way that the results can be effectively used for improving our understanding of the effects of grazing systems and range improvements on soil water hydrology and erosion. Only superficial treatment of modeling the hydrologic behavior of rangelands is unwarranted and the reader is referred to the book edited by Hahn et al. (1982).

Models are only "thinking tools" and their integrity and fidelity rest entirely on a thorough understanding of the grazing effects, the individual hydrologic processes, and mutual interactions that determine the hydrologic behavior of rangelands. Branson et al. (1981) and Hewlett (1982) provide the investigator with a comprehensive treatise on rangeland and forest hydrology, respectively. Notwithstanding the rapid advances in modeling, understanding how grazing influences hydrologic behavior remains anchored in the strategic design of experiments, appropriate characterization of the grazing treatment, climatic variation, and soil properties, and the careful interpretation of the results.

Literature Cited

Allis, J.A., and A.R. Khulman. 1962. Runoff and sediment yield studies on rangeland watersheds. J. Soil Water Conserv. 17:68-71.

Baver, L.D., W.H. Gardner, and W.T. Gardner. 1972. Soil Physics. John Wiley and Sons, New York, New York.

Birk, R.D., O.W. Wagoner, and P. Green. 1979. Rainfall simulators. Tech. Note 326. Bur. Land Manage., U.S. Dept. Interior, Washington, D.C.

Blackburn, W.H., R.O. Meeuwig, and C.M. Skau. 1974. A mobile infiltrometer for use on rangeland. J. Range Manage. 27:322-323.

Blackburn, W.H., R.W. Knight, M.K. Wood, and L.B. Merrill. 1980. Watershed parameters as influenced by grazing. pp. 552-569. *In:* Symp. Watershed Manage. Amer. Soc. Civil Eng., New York, New York.

Blaisdell, J.P. 1953. Ecological effects of planned burning of sagebrushgrass range on the upper Snake River plains. Tech. Bull. 1075, USDA, Washington, D.C.

Branson, F.A., G.F. Gifford, K.G. Renard, and R.F. Hadley. 1981. Rangeland hydrology. Society for Range Management, Denver, Colo.

Broadfoot, W.M. 1954. Procedures and equipment for measuring soil bulk density. Occas. Paper 135:2-11. Southeastern Forest Expt. Sta., Forest Service, USDA, Washington, D.C.

Brown, H.E., E.A. Hansen, and N.E. Champagne. 1970. A system for measuring total sediment yield from small watersheds. Water Resources Res. 6:818-826.

Cooperrider, C.K., and B.A. Hendricks. 1937. Soil erosion and stream flow on range and forest lands of the upper Rio Grande watershed in relation to land resources and human welfare. Tech. Bull. 567. USDA, Washington, D.C.

Cox, M.B. 1952. Recording the intake of water into the soil. J. Soil Water Conserv. 7:79-80.

Craddock, G.W., and C.K. Pearse. 1938. Surface runoff and erosion on granitic mountain soils of Idaho as influenced by range cover, soil disturbance, slope, and precipitation intensity. Cir. 482. USDA, Washington, D.C.

Croft, A.R., and L.V. Monninger. 1953. Evapotranspiration and other water losses on some aspen forest types in relation to water available for stream flow. Amer. Geophys. Union Trans. 34:563-574.

Croft, A.R., L. Woodward, and D.A. Anderson. 1943. Measurement of accelerated erosion on range-watershed land. J. Forest. 41:112-116.

Davis, W.E. 1937. A new method for measurement of erosion from experimental plots. Soil Sci. Soc. Amer. Proc. 2:579-583.

Dickinson, W.T., M.E. Holland, and G.L. Smith. 1967. An experimental rainfall-runoff facility. Hydrol. Paper No. 25. Colorado State Univ., Fort Collins, Colorado.

Dortignac, E.J. 1951. Design and operation of Rocky Mountain infiltrometer. Paper 5. Forest Serv., Rocky Mountain Forest and Range Exp. Sta., USDA, Fort Collins, Colorado.

Dortignac, E.J., and W.C. Hickey. 1963. Surface runoff and erosion as affected by soil ripping. Misc. Pub. No. 970:156-165. USDA, Washington, D.C.

Driscoll, Richard S. 1955. A guide to the Starkey Experimental Forest and Range near LaGrande, Ore. U.S. Forest Serv., Pacific Northwest Forest and Range Exp. Sta.

Dragoun, F.J. 1969. Effects of cultivation and grass on surface runoff. Water Resources Res. 5:1078-1083.

Dunford, E.G. 1954. Surface runoff and erosion from pine grasslands of the Colorado Front Range. J. Forest. 52:923-927.

Dunne, T. 1977. Evaluation of erosion trends and conditions. p. 53-84. *In:* Guidelines for watershed management. FAO Conserv. Guide No. 1. Food and Agri. Organ. United Nations, Rome, Italy.

Edwards, W.M., W.W. Bentz, and L.L. Harrold. 1969. Improvements in automatic sampling equipment used to determine extent of pollution in runoff from agricultural watersheds. ARS-41-151. USDA, Washington, D.C.

Ellison, L., A.R. Croft, and R.W. Bailey. 1951. Indicators of condition and trend on high range-watersheds of the Intermountain region. Agr. Handbook 19. USDA, Washington, D.C.

Epstein, E., W.J. Grant, and R.A. Struchtemeyer. 1966. Effects of stones on runoff, erosion, and soil moisture. Soil Sci. Soc. Amer. Proc. 30:638-640.

Fisser, H.G. 1978. Soil Surface movement and relation to vegetation structure. p. 706-716. *In:* M.K. Wali (ed), Ecology and Coal Resource Development. Pergamon Press, Elmsford, New York.

Forsling, C.L. 1931. A study of the influence of herbaceous plant cover on surface runoff and soil erosion in relation to grazing on the Wasatch Plateau in Utah. Tech. Bull. 220. USDA, Washington, D.C.

Gaither, R.E., and J.C. Buckhouse. 1979. Some comparisons of Rocky Mountain infiltrometer capabilities across several vegetation zones. Abstr. of Paper, 32nd Ann. Meeting, Soc. Range Manage.

Gieb, H.V. 1933. A new type of installation for measuring soil and water losses from control plots. J. Amer. Soc. Agron. 24:429-440.

Gottschalk, L.C. 1952. Measurement of sedimentation in small reservoirs. Amer. Soc. Civil Eng. Trans. 117:59-69.

Hahn, C.T., H.P. Johnson, and D.L. Brakensiek. 1982. Hydrologic modeling of small watersheds. Monogr. No. 5. Amer. Soc. Agr. Eng.

Haise, H.R., W.W. Donnan, J.T. Phelan, L.F. Lawhon, and D.G. Shockley. 1956. The use of cylinder infiltrometers to determine the intake characteristics of irrigated soils. ARS 41-7. USDA, Washington, D.C.

Hamon, W.R. 1979. Rainfall simulator-gamma probe infiltrometer. Rainfall Simulator Workshop. SEA, USDA, Washington, D.C.

Hanson, C.L., A.R. Kuhlman, C.J. Erickson, and J.K. Lewis. 1970. Grazing effects on runoff and vegetation on western South Dakota rangeland. J. Range Manage. 23:418-420.

Harrold, L.L., and D.B. Krimgold. 1948. Devices for measuring rates and amount of runoff employed in soil conservation research. TP-51. SCS, USDA, Washington, D.C.

Hewlett, J.D. 1982. Principles of forest hydrology. Univ. Georgia Press, Athens, Georgia.

Hoover, M.D., D.F. Olson, Jr., and L.J. Metz. 1954. Soil sampling for pore space and percolation. Paper 42. Southeastern Forest Exp. Sta., Forest Service, USDA, Washington, D.C.

Johnson, E.A. 1952. Effect of farm woodland grazing on watershed values in the southern Appalachian Mountains. J. Forestry. 50:109-113.

Johnson, W.M. 1953. Effect of grazing intensity upon vegetation and cattle gains on ponderosa pine bunchgrass ranges of the Front Range of Colorado. Cir. 929. USDA, Washington, D.C.

Johnson, W.M., and C.H. Niederhof. 1941. Some relationships of plant cover to runoff, erosion, and infiltration on granitic soils. J. Forest. 39:854-858.

Kincaid, D.R., J.L. Gardner, and H.A. Schreiber. 1964. Soil and vegetation parameters affecting infiltration under semiarid conditions. Pub. No. 65:440-453. Int. Assoc. Sci. Hydrol.

Krimgold, D.B., and O. Beenhouwer. 1954. Estimating infiltration. Agr. Eng. 35:719-725.

Lull, H.W. 1959. Soil compaction on forest and range lands. Misc. Pub. No. 768. USDA, Washington, D.C.

Lusby, G.C. 1977. Determination of runoff and sediment by rainfall simulation. *In:* Erosion: Research Techniques, Erodibility and Sediment Delivery. Geo. Abstr. Ltd., Norwich, England.

Lutz, H.J. 1944. Determination of certain physical properties of forest soils. I. Methods utilizing samples collected in metal cylinders. Soil Sci. 57:475-487. II. Methods of utilizing loose samples collected from pits. Soil Sci. 58:325-333.

Malekuti, A., and G.F. Gifford. 1978. Natural vegetation as a source of diffuse salt within the Colorado River Basin. Water Res. Bull. 14:195-205.

Marshall, T.J., and G.B. Stirk. 1950. The effect of lateral movement of water in soil on infiltration measurements. Aust. J. Agr. Res. 1:253-265.

Marston, R.B. 1952. Ground cover requirements for summer storm runoff control on aspen sites in northern Utah. J. Forest. 50:303-307.

Martin, W.P., and L.R. Rich. 1948. Preliminary hydrologic results, 1935-48, "Base Rock" undisturbed soil lysimeters in the grassland type, Arizona. Soil Sci. Soc. Amer. Proc. 13:561-567.

Mech, S.J. 1965. Limitations of simulated rainfall as a research tool. Trans. Amer. Soc. Agr. Eng. 8:66-67.

Meeuwig, R.O. 1971. Infiltration and water repellency in granitic soils. Paper INT-111. Forest Service, USDA. Washington, D.C.

Meyer, L.D. 1958. An investigation of methods for simulating rainfall on standard runoff plots and a study of the drop size, velocity, and kinetic energy of selected spray nozzles. Special Report No. 81, Soil and Water Conserv. Res. Div. ARS. USDA, Washington, D.C.

Musgrave, G.W. 1955. How much of the rain enters the soil? p. 151-159. *In:* Yearbook of Agriculture. USDA, Washington, D.C.

Packer, P.E. 1951. An approach to watershed protection criteria. J. Forest. 49:639-644.

Packer, P.E. 1953. Effects of trampling disturbance on watershed condition, runoff, and erosion. J. Forest. 51:28-31.

Parsons, D.A. 1954. Coshocton-type runoff samplers. TP-124. SCS, USDA, Washington, D.C.

Pearse, C.K., and F.D. Bertelson. 1937. The construction and operation of an apparatus for the measurement of absorption of surface water by soils. Forest Service. USDA, Washington, D.C.

Rauzi, F.C., and F.M. Smith. 1973. Infiltration rates: three soils with grazing levels in northeastern Colorado. J. Range. Manage. 26:126-129.

Read, R.A. 1957. Effect of livestock concentration on surface soil porosity within shelterbelts. J. Forest. 55:529-530.

Reid, E.H., and L.D. Love. 1951. Range-watershed conditions and recommendations for management, Elk Ridge and lower Elk Ridge cattle allotments, Roosevelt National Forest, Colorado. Forest Service, USDA, Washington, D.C.

Renner, F.G. 1936. Conditions influencing erosion on the Boise River watershed. Tech. Bull. 528. USDA, Washington, D.C.

Romkens, M.J.M. 1979. Interpretation of rainfall simulator data Proc., Rainfall Simulator Workshop. SEA, USDA, Washington, D.C.

Rowe, P.B. 1940. The construction, operation, and use of the North Fork infiltrometer. Misc. Pub. 1. Rainfall Simulator Workshop. USDA, Washington, D.C.

Sharp, A.L., J.J. Bond, J.W. Neuberger, A.R. Kuhlman, and J.K. Lewis. 1964. Runoff as affected by intensity of grazing rangeland. J. Soil Water Conserv. 19:103-106.

Swanson, N.P. 1979. Field plot rainfall simulation (rotating-boom rainfall simulator) Lincoln, Nebraska. Proc. Rainfall Simulator Workshop, ARM-W-10:166-169.

Timko, S.T., and C.M. Skau. 1967. A low intensity rain simulator for long duration rain-on-snow events. *In:* Proc. Third Ann. Amer. Water Resour. Conf., San Francisco, California.

Toy, T.J. 1983. A linear erosion/elevation measuring instrument (LEMI). Earth Surface Processes and Landforms. 8:313-322.

USDA, 1979a. Proceedings of the Rainfall Simulator Workshop. SEA, USDA, Washington, D.C.

USDA, 1979b. Field Manual for Research in Agricultural Hydrology. Agric. Handbook No. 224. ARS, USDA, Washington, D.C.

U.S. Federal Inter-Agency River Basin Committee, Subcommittee on Sedimentation. 1952. A study of methods used in measurement and analysis of sediment loads in streams. The design of improved types of suspended sediment samplers. Rep. 6. St. Anthony Falls Hydraulic Lab., Minneapolis, Minnesota.

Wilm, H.G. 1952. A pattern of scientific inquiry for applied research. J. Forest. 50:120-125.

Woolhiser, D.A., C.L. Hanson, and A.R. Kuhlman. 1970. Overland flow on rangeland watersheds. J. Hydrol. 9:336-356.

Wright, H.A., F.M. Churchill, and W.C. Stevens. 1974. Effect of prescribed burning on sediment, water yield, and water quality from dozed juniper lands in central Texas. Office of Water Res. and Tech. Compl. Report, Texas Tech. Univ., Lubbock, Texas.

Young, R.A. 1979. Interpretation of rainfall simulator data. Proc. Rainfall Simulator Workshop, ARM-W-10:108-112.

Chapter 8
Economic Research in Range Management

Introduction and Purpose

Economic research in range management is concerned with management decisions by people in relation to the goals they desire. Its task is to observe and record facts relevant to decision making, and to organize and analyze these facts so that answers to pertinent questions can be provided by hypotheses tested. Questions usually relate to specific entities, such as an individual ranch, a grazing association, a federal land management agency, or even society as a whole. Usually, the questions are in terms of maximizing net returns or minimizing costs. Questions and decision making are conditioned by the economic and social environment of our society.

Biological research in range management, however, focuses mainly on relationships between or among things—between intensity of grazing and plant composition, root development and rates of plant growth, fertilizers and forage yields, season of grazing and reproduction of certain species, to name only a few. Discovery of these relationships reveals what is possible under conditions defined by the research. Cause and effect relationships permit prediction or extension of results into situations other than those observed in the course of the research.

A distinction commonly made between biological research and economic research is that one asks the question, "will it work?", whereas the other asks, "will it pay?" A more accurate distinction is that one deals with what can be done, whereas the other deals with what people choose to do. To be relevant, economic research must be directed towards questions that will help people decide on a course of action.

"Will it pay to reseed sagebrush range?" is a typical question of this order. The answer is seldom a simple "yes" or "no". It may be "yes" if the cost is low, forage production is increased, livestock can make greater gains or use the range for a longer season, money to pay the costs is available, livestock can be managed so as to make best use of the reseeded range, and/or access to the range itself can be controlled. These and many other factors affect the decision.

Economic decisions are made most frequently by an individual in terms of his/her individual goals. Economists usually assume that the goal of the individual is to maximize net profits over some given time period. Often this is the case, but other goals may exist. For instance, the individual may want to achieve a certain minimum income with the smallest possible labor expenditure.

Two concepts pertinent to understanding of economics and economic research are involved. One is the concept of the firm, and the other is the concept of economic efficiency. As used in economics, a firm is a business entity under a single management. It may be an individual farm or ranch, or it may be a corporation or group that acts as a unit. Decisions are made in terms of the goals desired by the unit. The concept of economic efficiency is basic to economics. Usually, goals of people are expressed in terms of maximizing something—gross returns, net profits per dollar invested, net returns per hour of labor, maximum profits to managerial efforts, net returns per given area of land, or others. Both the concept of the firm and the concept of economic efficiency are used and expanded later.

Theory and Methods

The use of theory in economic research is similar to its use in other disciplines. Whatever the subject to which it relates, theory is used for three separable functions: (1) to help in describing events that occurred in the past, (2) to develop criteria for appraising these events, and (3) to suggest questions or hypotheses which concern predictions about events that may happen in the future. These three functions apply to ecology as well as economics.

Research requires that theory be made specific to particular problems. These problems are set apart by a process of abstraction that makes it possible to investigate one variable while specifying others by means of assumptions, based on the best available estimates. These abstractions are of strategic importance in understanding the function of economic theory in research.

Basic Economic Concepts

In economic research, a ranch is conceived to consist of two entities, a firm and a household. The firm is the business unit, or the group of resources used together about which production decisions are made. The household is the unit that makes decisions relating to the disposition of earnings from the firm. The household decides whether and in what way to spend for current consumption or current production, or to save for future investment in production or future consumption.

Economic theory gives us several basic concepts or principles relating to the firm. The first of these is the principle of diminishing returns. At first, successive units of any factor used in the firm for production will give increased output for each unit added. After a certain point, additional units of input will give added output, but at a decreasing rate. Finally, a point may be reached at which additional inputs actually decrease output. Increasing numbers of livestock added to a given area or range will increase total production up to a point, but continued increases in numbers will decrease total output. This principle gains relevance when prices are associated with the inputs or resources used in production and the resulting outputs. This concept is often called the principle of marginality.

A second important concept is that resources used in production—rangeland, hayland, cattle, labor—may be combined in different ways.

Number of cattle per area of land, amount of labor per unit of livestock, area of hayland per unit of range, and other combinations of inputs to the ranch may be varied one with the other. When costs of the various factors used in production are compared with the volume and value of the product, a most profitable or most desired combination can be determined. Use of an input is jointly determined by its productivity and price. Generally, the less expensive factors per unit of output are used more generously.

Knowing that the product obtained by successive additions of an input will decrease if enough inputs are added and that inputs can be combined in different proportions permits an approximation of the "best" combinations for any given firm. The best may be the combination that results in the greatest net profit for a given period, maximizes returns to some one factor, or maximizes net returns over a period of years. The best solution must be found in terms of the goals held by people who are making decisions.

Economic Behavior of Firms

The term "optimum" is encountered frequently in economics literature. Ordinarily, it describes a solution to a particular type of problem which must be solved as a step toward the ultimate goal set for the firm (for example, maximum net ranch income). In fact, "economics of the firm" consists of little more than specifications for a series of optima, in which the criteria are logically consistent in terms of achieving the goal or goals set by managers of the firm.

The simplest criterion is maximization of net income. While not a universal goal, most managers do prefer more income to less income, other things equal. This is achieved when three optimum conditions are met:

(1) an optimum level of production of each enterprise in the firm,
(2) an optimum proportioning of the resources that can be varied for a given level of production in each enterprise,
(3) an optimum allocation of resources among the various enterprises.

These three optima must be specified for particular time periods. As of a given moment in time nearly all resources are fixed, but the longer the period of time the more resources are variable within respective enterprises and, for that matter, allocable among enterprises. As the time period is lengthened from the "shortrun" to the "longrun", all resources become variable.

Optima solutions in economic research require three types of data: (1) physical or biological data, (2) resource price data, and (3) product price data. For rigorous analysis, the physical or biological data must be in terms of functional relationships, not simply estimates of single points on functions.

Marginality

Maximum net returns. Let us return to the first optimum listed above. For an optimum level of production in each enterprise, the enterprise is expanded until the point is reached at which marginal returns (further increments in returns) are equal to marginal costs (increments in costs). Such a point is reached because of diminishing returns to the individual variable resources.

Table 8-1. Hypothetical production, costs, and returns from steers grazing rangeland.

Variable input (steers)	Fixed input (acres)	Total steer gain (pounds)	Total revenue ($)	Marginal revenue ($)	Total fixed cost ($)	Total variable cost ($)	Total cost ($)	Marginal cost ($)	Net revenue ($)
5	640	400	100		100	50	150		-50
10	640	900	225	.25	100	100	200	.10	25
15	640	1150	288	.25	100	150	250	.20	38
20	640	1360	340	.25	100	200	300	.24	40
25	640	1460	365	.25	100	250	350	.50	15
30	640	1500	375	.25	100	300	400	1.25	-25
35	640	1480	370	.25	100	350	450	-2.50	-80

Table 8-1 shows hypothetical weight gains for steers grazing rangeland at various stocking rates for a two-month season. The effects of diminishing returns are evident. Increased stocking rates bring increased steer gains per section[1], but the increase occurs at an ever decreasing rate. The increase from 5 to 10 steers allows an additional gain of 500 pounds per section, but the next 10 to 15 steer increase results in only 250 added pounds of gain, and so forth. The fact that each successive 5 steer increase yields smaller additions to total steer gain is due to ever increasing competition for forage . Total forage consumption and resulting total steer gain per area both increase but at a decreasing rate. Between 30 and 35 steers per section, forage competition becomes so severe that total steer gain per section declines.

Total steer gain is transformed to total revenue (TR) by simply multiplying pounds of gain by the price per pound ($0.25 in this example for simplicity of calculation). Marginal revenue (MR) is defined as the additional revenue produced by the last unit of output or $MR = \Delta TR / \Delta Y$ where Y is total output (steer gain per section). Thus MR between stocking rates of 5 and 10 steers is [$225 - $100]/[900 - 400]=$0.25. In the purely competitive market for cattle, the rancher can buy or sell all the steers he wants at the going market price and for this reason MR for steer gains in Table 1 remains constant at $0.25 per pound.

Production costs are conventionally separated into fixed costs and variable costs. Fixed costs are those attributable to the fixed factors of production and include both cash costs such as rent, property tax, insurance and non cash costs such as operator and family labor and interest on fixed investment. They do not increase with increased production nor can we avoid paying these costs in the "shortrun" by ceasing our operation. The shortrun is defined as a period of time sufficiently short that at least one production factor, such as land, is fixed. In the example of Table 1, fixed costs are comprised of an annual minimum land charge of $100. This amount, designated Total Fixed Cost (TFC) in Table 1, must be paid no matter how many steers are grazed per section.

Variable costs are those associated with the variable factors of production such as purchased feed. Variable costs increase with increases in output and can be thought of as costs that we can avoid paying by ceasing or reducing the operation. In Table 1, variable costs are composed of grazing fees charged at the rate of $5 per steer month. Total variable cost (TVC) at a stocking rate of 5 steers per section is 5 steers × $5 × 2 months = $50. Total cost (TC) is simply the sum of TVC and TFC. Total cost represents all costs associated with any particular level of output.

Marginal cost (MC) is defined as the additional cost attributable to the last unit of output or $MC = \Delta TVC / \Delta Y$. At a stocking rate of 10 steers per section MC = [$100 - $50]/[900 - 400] = $0.10. Marginal cost increases throughout the range of output shown in Table 1, but due to diminishing returns, the increase occurs at an increasing rate.

[1]Livestock producers commonly use the English units of pounds for weight (1 pound = 0.45 kg) and sections for area (section = 640 acres = 260 ha). Therefore, English units, rather than metric units, will be used in this discussion.

The optimum level of production (optimum stocking rate) is where MC = MR. Thus, the optimum is 20 steers per section, since more net revenue is earned at this stocking rate than at any other. This 20 steer stocking rate can be thought of as the level of production where the last unit of output (total steer gain) adds the same amount to costs as to revenue. The intuitive logic underlying the equating of MR and MC is simple. Up to a stocking rate of 20 steers per section, additional steers contribute more to revenue than to costs (MR>MC), and it pays the stockman to increase the number of steers. Beyond 20 steers per section, additional steers add more to costs than to revenue (MC>MR), and it pays to decrease steer numbers. Only at the optimum (slightly greater than 20 steers per section) is there no incentive to change stocking rate.

Biological vs. economic optima. Concerns have sometimes been expressed by range managers that the profit maximization goal might lead to overstocking and degradation of private rangeland. While ignorance (and optimism) concerning carrying capacity has led to deterioration of much private land, this damage has occurred in spite of the profit motive, and not because of it. The hypothetical livestock gains of Table 1 represent a sustained yield production function such as might be estimated by long-term grazing intensity research (Workman and Lacey 1982). Thus, we can be confident that 30 steers can be grazed year after year on 640 acres for 2 months and an average gain (with wide fluctuations due to weather) of 1,500 pounds per section will result. Given this production function, the stocking rate optimum recommended by the biologist has commonly been to maximize sustained yield or 30 steers per section (Table 8-1). The rationale is that to run fewer than 30 steers would waste forage that could be converted to a product useful to man while more than 30 steers poses a risk of range damage.

But note, again, that the economic optimum (based on the profit motive) is only 20 steers per section. Thus, the profit motive leads to a lower stocking rate than maximum sustained yield and one which poses less risk of range degradation than does the biological optimum. It costs more for the additional steer gain produced by going beyond 20 head than society is willing to pay for it. The economist's recommendation recognizes that scarce operating capital must be spent where it will do the most good (as measured by the value of the product produced) which, at the prices in the example, rules out stocking rates beyond 20 steers per section. It should be noted that, in general, the only market condition under which the economic optimum (maximum profit) would correspond to the biological optimum (maximum sustained yield) would be if marginal cost were zero (that is, if additional steers could be run at zero extra cost).

For simplicity, the above production function example has been presented in tabular form. For detailed examples of more precise marginality applications involving mathematical functions see Workman and Quigley (1974) and Workman and McCormick (1977).

Multiple Inputs and Multiple Products

Let us now expand our marginal analysis to the second optimum. To obtain maximum net ranch income, the cost of resources that can be varied must be at a minimum for each level of production within a given enterprise. As shown in numerous economics textbooks, this is achieved when the marginal rate at which one resource substitutes for the other is equal to the inverse price ratio of the two resources.

In an experiment with commercial fertilizer, Hoglund et al. (1952) have shown forage production (measured in air-dry feed) to be functionally related to inputs of nitrogen (N) and phosphorus (P_2O_5). These data (Table 8-2) suggest that forage output is related to quantities of each fertilizer in diminishing returns and that a given quantity of forage can be produced with several combinations of N and P_2O_5.

Table 8-2. Pounds of air-dry feed per acre of annual range types in California at selected levels of N and P_2O_5 fertilization.[1]

Pounds N per acre	Pounds P_2O_5 per acre			
	0	65	129	172
	—————————yield in pounds/acre—————————			
0	1,601	1,903	1,190	1,799
32	2,757	3,129	3,298	3,256
61	3,837	4,253	4,486	4,494
84	4,500	4,970	4,477	4,952

[1]For the range forage experiment the function fitted was:
log = 3.265 + 0.0577 log N + 0.0136 log P_2O_5 where $\hat{Y}$ is calculated production in air-dry feed per acre, N is pounds of nitrogen and P_2O_5 is pounds of phosphoric acid.

Data in Table 8-2 may be "fitted" or described in a functional relationship so that a quantity of feed can be calculated for each combination of fertilizer ingredients (Heady and Pesek 1954). When this is done, we find, for example, that 3,600 pounds of air-dry feed can be produced with each of the combinations of P_2O_5 and N given in the first two columns of Table 8-3. The marginal rate at which P_2O_5 substitutes for N to maintain the 3,600 pounds of forage is given in the third column of Table 8-3.

Table 8-3. Substitution rates of P_2O_5 for N to produce 3,600 pounds of air-dry feed on an acre of annual range in California.

P_2O_5	N	$\Delta N/\Delta P_2O_5$
—————pounds—————		
0	65	
40	47	−0.450
80	40	−0.175
120	36	−0.100
160	34	−0.050

For example, −0.175 in the third column (Table 8-3) means that as P_2O_5 is increased from 40 to 80 pounds per acre, N may be reduced by an average of 0.175 (7/40) pounds per increased pound of P_2O_5 and still sustain production at 3,600 pounds of air-dry feed per acre. This change entails (1) a reduction in the cost of N and (2) an increase in the cost of P_2O_5. It is clear that if the increased cost of P_2O_5 is less than the decreased cost of N, it would be a profitable change in resource proportions. The optimum proportions are found by equating the marginal rate of substitution (in the example, $\Delta N/\Delta P_2O_5$) with the ratio: — price of $P_2O_5 \div$ price of N.

Although the intervening steps are not shown, the resulting optima are given in Table 8-4. Each fraction in this table represents an "optimum" for the P_2O_5 and N prices given. For example, if N costs 10¢ per pound and P_2O_5 2¢ per pound applied, the optimum quantities to produce 3,600 pounds of feed

Table 8-4. Optimum proportions of P_2O_5 and N to produce 3,600 pounds of air-dry feed on annual range types in California.

Price of P_2O_5	Price of N per pound					
per pound	.10	.12	.14	.16	.18	.20
.02	77/41	84/40	97/38	107/37	114/37	120/36
.04	47/46	57/44	64/43	69/42	73/41	77/41

would be 41 pounds of N and 77 pounds of P_2O_5. This example demonstrates the use of functional relationships in arriving at optimum solutions and the fact that the optimum changes as the price of either resource changes.

Range management often involves multiple use—the production of several products (livestock, forage, water, wildlife, and recreation) from the same piece of land. Determination of the most profitable mix of products is accomplished through the solution of the third optimum above. Application of the marginality concept to the third optimum is similar to the methods already described for the other two optima. For detailed examples, see Hopkin (1954) and Workman (1975).

Problem Formulation as a Step in Research

The above three optima serve at least two useful functions. Firstly, they are logical notions of "constructs" with which to test decisions made by the rancher for consistency with goals affirmed for the use and development of resources within the ranch firm. But secondly, and important from a research viewpoint, they serve as idealized situations or "models" to guide the search for data useful in the solution of economic problems.

The importance of problem formulation as an integral part of the research process is hard to overstate. Without a problem concept, why would the investigator be interested in combining relationships to achieve results such as those given in Table 8-4? A pure search for facts would give, perhaps, (1) only response estimates in range forage product to N or P_2O_5; or (2) a historical series of prices for N or P_2O_5 or both. But when a problem involves optimizing the proportions of N and P_2O_5, it becomes reasonable to relate the two phenomena.

The example of the effects of nitrogen and phosphorus on forage production serves to demonstrate the logic involved in economics research. The "problem" might be stated: ranchers are not making as much net profit from the use of N and P_2O_5 as they believe they should. One hypothesis then becomes: Net profits can be increased by using relatively greater quantities of nitrogen. This latter statement can be verified by observation.

Data Required for Economic Analysis

As already suggested, physical or biological data, input price data, and product price data are crucial for analysis of economic problems. Given the necessary technical input-output relationships, it is possible to derive the solutions necessary for rational economic decisions. Whether obtained from surveys, experiments, or from other sources, the input-output coefficients provide the technical data that apply to the particular set of resources and conditions defined in the hypothesis.

The type and form of data needed for economics research will depend on the hypothesis to be tested. If the need is to establish the effects on aggregate income of following a particular production program, average values for inputs and outputs will serve. But if the need is to determine the effect of a change in resource inputs to a given body of fixed factors, marginal data are usually more appropriate. For example, data relating to only one rate of fertilizer application or one rate of stocking are not adequate. To be most useful for economics research, data on the independent variables should cover a range wide enough to permit establishment of marginal values.

Input data are relatively less difficult for economists to obtain than output data. Acres of land, hours of labor, numbers of livestock, tons of hay, and other factors going into a production process can be quantified. Many of the factors have a price, established in a market, that can be used with confidence. Factors that have no market price, family labor for example, still may be assigned a value based on their worth in some alternative use. If the economic problem under study involves a long-time period, projected prices or values can be based on observable economic trends. The input data required in range economic research can be obtained more easily and used more confidently than output data.

Frequently, the output from rangeland is difficult to measure and may be even more difficult to price or to value. Range forage is one of the main products from rangeland, but frequently it has value only as it is grazed and converted into an economic good such as beef or game. As such, range forage is an intermediate good. The value of range forage then becomes a function of the livestock management systems and practices it supports. The question then arises, how much forage is produced in an economic sense? Furthermore, how is the best way to determine values of, or assign prices to, the range forage produced (North Central Farm Management Committee 1955). Range forage that can be used as a steer pasture may be evaluated readily in terms of the gains in marketable weight by the animals. The same forage used for dry cows kept in a breeding herd does not have a readily identifiable value. This problem of establishing values of range forage is particularly difficult in areas where the feed is usable primarily at a given season. It may have little value unless it is used with other range and feed supplies, when it may become an important part of the annual feed supplies of the ranch.

Range produces products other than forage for domestic livestock, some of which are even more difficult to evaluate. Big game is another rangeland product that has value. But it has no price, in the usual economic sense, because it is not exchanged in a market in which people can express willingness to pay for it (Upchurch 1954, Workman 1975). Many attempts have been made to evaluate game in terms of expenditures by sportsmen. Usually, these attempts were unsuccessful from an economic viewpoint, because their results provide no basis for functional relationships between the costs of producing game and its value.

One way to approach the problem of value of game in economics research is through the value of some other product, such as domestic livestock, which is given up in order to produce the game. For example, if the opportunity to produce 500 sheep is rationally foregone in order to produce 200 deer, then the 200 deer must be worth at least as much as the 500 sheep. Two major difficulties attend this approach. One is the difficulty of establishing the biological relationships between deer and sheep in the use of range forage. The other is the fact that deer and sheep are "produced" by different economic entities or firms—an individual rancher in the one instance and the state in the other. As decisions on economics must be made in the context of a firm, two different levels of decision making are involved. An optimum solution for each individual firm does not always solve the economic problem of allocating range use between deer and sheep.

Often, the firm involved in a range economics study is a livestock ranch operated under a single management. It may be individually owned, a partnership, an estate, a corporation, or other form of business unit. For the firms studied, the researcher needs to know something about their management, organization, size, nature of resources available, which resources are fixed and which are variable, and the tenure or degree of control over resources, especially land. These and other factors help to set the stage for economic analysis and indicate the circumstances within which solutions must be sought. They help to establish and identify management goals of the firm and in this way help the researcher to specify relevant hypotheses required to guide the inquiry.

Sometimes the firm on which economics research is focused is a national forest, a grazing district, a grazing association, a sportsmen's organization, a state, or even the federal government. The only requirement in economic research is that the firm be a management entity through which management decisions are formulated with respect to production of economic goods. Regardless of the nature of the firm, the production factors listed in the preceding paragraph must be known or ascertained in the course of the research. Much economic research could be sharpened and made more meaningful by a clearer definition of the firm or firms to which the research is intended to apply.

Sources of Data

Data used in economics research can be obtained from many different sources. The kinds of data, and to some extent their source, depend on the nature of the hypothesis to be tested.

Records existing in public offices frequently are fruitful sources of data. For example, records in U.S. Forest Service and Bureau of Land Management headquarters contain a wealth of information about rangeland, AUM production, the kind and extent of use, the nature of the firms that use it, and the price for its use. In addition, they may contain data on range improvements, including costs and results, and data from range use studies of many different kinds.

Records in county and other local offices may contain useful data. County tax offices contain data on land ownership, assessed values, and taxes levied. County Agricultural Stabilization and Conservation Service offices often contain useful data on range improvements, including costs of practices eligible for cost sharing under federal conservation programs. Local offices of the Soil Conservation Service may have valuable information on range sites, range condition, production and carrying capacity, and conservation practices. Accurate data concerning prices paid for agricultural inputs and prices received for agricultural products are available from the Statistical Reporting Service (1983). Included are average monthly prices and price indexes for such items as fuel, feed grains, cattle grazing lease rates on private land, and cows, calves, steers, and heifers. Many individual states also provide annual summaries of agricultural statistics. Grazing land prices and real estate market information are available from the Economic Research Service (1981). Particularly helpful in ranch budget and cash flow studies are budgets published periodically by the Economics, Statistics, and Cooperatives Service (1979).

Results of biological research often have direct application to and are highly useful in economics research. This is especially true of experiments dealing with grazing methods and range production practices and their results when such experiments have been made in locations and under conditions relevant to an economic problem under investigation. Usually, however, range experiments are not designed to test an explicit economic hypothesis so use of their results for this purpose is coincidental. Economists rarely have the facilities to carry on controlled grazing experiments of their own. Results of experiments designed by range scientists for other purposes must be used. These experiments may not be adequate for the economic purpose, the range of variation tested may not be appropriate, the variables measured may not be adequate, and the results obtained may not be applicable to real firms or ranches. This in no way reflects on the usefulness of the controlled experiments for the purpose for which they are designed; it merely puts the researcher on guard when using experimental results in economic research. Greater cooperation between range economists and range scientists in selecting, designing, and conducting controlled experiments would be beneficial to the work of both groups.

Many demonstrations of range use and improvement practices have been made. Frequently, they have resulted in data useful for economic investigation. Their limitations are that they may not be "typical" or applicable to an identifiable geographic area; some important variables may not be accounted for or controlled; inputs and products may not be carefully measured or recorded; the range of conditions tested may not be great enough to permit determination of economic optima; and data may be difficult to analyze statistically due to lack of replication. Nevertheless, demonstration plots sometimes provide the only relevant data to be had, and they can be used meaningfully if their limitations are properly recognized.

Analytical Techniques

Analytical techniques in economics research are subject to considerable controversy and continual discussion among economists. Frequently, these discussions arise not because of differences of opinion concerning the worth of the techniques themselves, but because of differences in the task the techniques are supposed to perform. Many of these discussions could be resolved by explicitly stating the hypothesis to be tested and by agreement as to the degree of precision required to accept or reject the hypothesis.

In range economics, as in other research fields, the techniques for collecting and analyzing data must meet the rigorous standards of scientific inquiry. The degree of precision required in the analysis, however, depends on the hypothesis to be tested and on the kind of decisions expected to be made from the results. For example, the hypothesis under scrutiny may be that a reduced rate of stocking would be more profitable than present rates under the same system on a given range site. The inquiry may proceed to a point at which this hypothesis can be accepted. For this purpose, data and analysis may not need to be precise enough to determine the most profitable rate or the exact amount of increased profit. On the basis of this information, a rancher could decide to move in the direction of increased profits without knowing exactly how far he would have to go to achieve the greatest profits. Formulation of other hypotheses, different data, and more precise techniques of analysis would be required for the latter.

Statistical techniques common to other branches of science are widely used in economics research. For example, the problem of fertilizer application on rangeland may be viewed as one of selecting, from among different kinds and quantities of fertilizer, the kind and quantity that would produce the greatest economic return from the land. One hypothesis might be that no significant difference exists in the yields obtained from different quantities of fertilizer. The proper statistical tool for testing this hypothesis would be analysis of variance of mean yields of the different treatments (Snedecor and Cochran 1980).

An example more commonly encountered in economics research involves an estimation of forage production for successive quantities of various combinations of the fertilizer elements (Table 8-2). In this instance, a continuous functional relation is visualized. Experiments designed to estimate successive points on the production surface permit the use of regression analysis with single or simultaneous equations. The standard error of estimate would be used to determine fiducial limits to the regression line or surface, while t-tests would be used to determine whether or not the regression coefficients differed significantly from zero (Kmenta 1971, Chiang 1974).

For problems that involve several independent and dependent variables, a tentative exploration of the relationships by means of tabular analysis or by graphic regression analysis before the more complex task of mathematical regression is undertaken will usually prove to be worthwhile. Some of the possible combinations of variables might be rejected on the basis of this tentative arrangement of data. Furthermore the relations suggested by tabular and graphic analysis usually will suggest the form of mathematical equation to be used in further analysis.

The Single Enterprise

All too frequently, economic relations are measured, analyses made, and conclusions drawn only in terms of cropland, pasture, rangeland, or the livestock on the ranch, each considered as a separate enterprise. Information for the enterprise approach often is obtained from controlled experiments. When this is not possible, information on costs and returns of the particular practices in question can be collected from ranchers who have applied them. If the cost of a practice is less than the increased returns from it (as measured by the expected production increases multiplied by the expected product price), the practice is advocated.

The limitation of the enterprise approach is that it does not consider the ranch as a complex producing unit, that is, a firm for which management decisions are made. Thereby, it ignores alternative uses of the scarce resources that might return more to the rancher if used in some other improvement or practice on the ranch. Also, it ignores many secondary effects that changes in the single enterprise might have on other factors that affect ranch income. For instance, by increasing the carrying capacity of an early spring range, the summer range and winter feed might be used more effectively, or by improving the quality and yield of late summer and fall pasture the calf crop might be increased. Competitive and complementary effects are ignored in the enterprise approach.

The Ranch or Firm

A more accurate appraisal of the economic relationships in range management is obtained when the entire ranch unit or firm is considered. In using this approach, one must decide which ranch unit to study.

The case method. This method is followed frequently in range economics research. A single ranch on which a range improvement, for example, is being applied is selected as representative in some important way of ranches encountering the problem under study. This ranch is then studied in detail. Records of physical inputs and outputs, as well as records of costs and returns, are collected over time. These records show the economic picture before the range improvement practice was applied, the economic situation existing during the transition brought about by the practice, and the situation after the practice was established. From this information, conclusions are drawn concerning the profitability of the practice on the particular ranch. Inferences to other ranch situations are subjective. This approach may include several different cases selected for their similarities or differences with respect to the situation under study.

The advantage of the case method is that it provides a real working environment in which to conduct the research. The sample (one firm) remains intact throughut the study and all forces (anticipated or unanticipated, identified or confounded) operate freely and influence the results. The case approach is useful in appraising cause-effect relations within the firm. Also, it might become an effective demonstration unit in extending the conclusions to other ranchers.

Disadvantages lie in the fact that with only one observation the influence of the manager and of many other unmeasurable factors applicable to that particular firm might influence the results so strongly that erroneous conclusions and inferences might be made. The approach does not result in conclusions that can be generalized, as no estimates can be made of the applicable population.

The survey method. Another procedure followed in range management research is to make an economic survey of the ranchers who, for example, are following a management practice in question. Information relevant to the study is gathered from each of the ranchers or from a random or stratified sample, depending upon the data required. Inventories of resources and production practices, inputs and costs, and production and monetary returns are obtained by means of questionnaires or from ranch records. This information is pooled and some measure of central tendency for each variable is used in "constructing" a ranch that is "representative" of the population or "typical" of a stratum of the population studied. The analysis then proceeds on the firm or ranch approach, using the representative or typical ranch as a basis for the model.

The advantage of this method is that the influence of particular managers tends to "average out" and thus does not exert an undue influence on the conclusions. This can be said also of other unmeasurable and random forces. Consequently, inferences from the model to ranches in the area are usually on safer grounds than when the case method is used.

The disadvantages of the survey method are that the average of any series may not represent any single member in the series and that important characteristics may be obscured because observations within the sample contradict each other. Based strictly on an average of the ranches, odd combinations and sizes of enterprises might occur in the model. These "averages" might yield results that would not be applicable to any particular firm.

This limitation of the survey method can be overcome to some extent by stratifying the ranches by size or type of operation. In other cases the survey averages may be used only as guides to the researcher in setting up a synthetized model of a firm for purposes of analysis. Based on the survey and other information at his disposal, the researcher can construct a working model to represent the ranches to which inferences are to be made. He then proceeds to analyze what might happen to his model when the treatment in question is and is not applied. This approach is similar to the case method except that in this instance the "case" is idealized.

Methods of Analysis

Regardless of the level of aggregation desired (whether the single enterprise, the ranch, or a group of ranches in a particular area), the economic analysis must proceed so that the meaningful hypotheses can be tested. This usually means comparisons of costs and returns of each of the viable alternatives so that the most profitable, or otherwise most desirable, one can be selected.

Budgeting. The procedure often used for this analysis is the partial budget. It is nothing more than a systematic arrangement of the data on resources used, costs, production, and income for each alternative course of action. In partial budgeting, those costs and returns that are the same for each alternative (such as fixed interest charges, taxes and depreciation on buildings and equipment) can be omitted from the tabulations without affecting the conclusions. Thus, changes in the variables can be observed and measured easily. After the most promising alternative has been selected, a complete budget can be prepared to illustrate total costs, total returns, profits, and other characteristics.

The use of the budget as an analytical technique has many advantages, not the least of which is its flexibility. Costs and returns for alternative practices, alternative organizations of the enterprise or firm, or for different time periods may be tabulated in budget form. Each budget for each alternative is independent and each can reflect realistic relations among cost items and between these items and income. A series of budgets may be made to reflect incremental changes in some one factor or group of factors, thus facilitating the search for the most profitable or otherwise most desirable combinations of resources and practices (Black et al. 1947).

For purposes of illustration, summaries for two complete budgets for a Utah cattle ranch are included (Tables 8-5 and 8-6). Table 8-5 describes the ranch before implementation of a range improvement (prescribed burning of 417 acres of native range) and Table 8-6 portrays the same ranch after completion of the improvement.

As shown in the forage balance chart of Table 8-5, cow herd size is constrained prior to improvement by the amounts of forage available during the five summer months (May through September). Prescribed burning of native range provides an additional 125 AUMs of summer forage, which have been evenly distributed among the five summer months (see forage balance chart in Table 8-6), allowing the cow herd to be expanded from 300 to 320 head. As revealed by comparison of the income statements, the 20 head increase in the cow herd causes several important changes in annual costs and returns. Cattle income increases, crops income decreases (more hay is fed on

Table 8-5. Budget summary for 300 head cow-calf-yearling operation, before range improvement (adapted from Workman and Hooper 1971, Workman 1981a).

Feed source	Feed production Quantity	Unit
Native range	1,700	AUMs
Seeded pasture	280	AUMs
Barley	2,000	Bushels
Meadow hay	784	Tons
Crop aftermath	554	AUMS

Stock count and animal class

Month	Cows (1.0 AU) Head	AUMs	Yearling Heifers (.74 AU) Head	AUMs	Calves (.42 AU) Head	AUMs	Bulls (1.29 AU) Head	AUMs	Total Required AUMs
Jan.	300	300			45	18.9	15	19.4	338
Feb.	300	300			45	18.9	15	19.4	338
Mar.	300	300			45	18.9	15	19.4	338
Apr.	300	300	45	33.3	born		15	19.4	353
May	300	300	45	33.3			15	19.4	353
June	300	300	45	33.3			15	19.4	353
July	300	300	45	33.3			15	19.4	353
Aug.	300	300	45	33.3	240	100.8	15	19.4	454
Sept.	300	300	45	33.3	240	100.8	15	19.4	454
Oct.	300	300			240	100.8	15	19.4	454
Nov.	300	300			45	18.9	15	19.4	338
Dec.	300	300			45	18.9	15	19.4	338
Total									4,464

Forage balance

Month	Range	Seeded pasture	Barley	Source of feed Meadow hay	After-math	Total available	Total required
Jan.			25	341		366	338
Feb.			25	341		366	338
Mar.			25	341		366	338
Apr.			25	356		381	353
May	212	140				352	353
June	213	140				353	353
July	355					355	353
Aug.	460					460	454
Sept.	460					460	454
Oct.			30		454	484	454
Nov.			25	240	101	366	338
Dec.			25	341		366	338
Total	1,700	280	180	1,960	555	4,675	4,464

Annual cattle production and revenue

Number and Category	Sale Weight (lb)	Sale Price ($/lb)	Total Revenue ($)
45 cull cows	1000	.17	7,650
5 cull bulls	1300	.20	1,300
75 heifer calves	380	.27	7,695
80 steer calves	400	.29	9,280
40 yearling steers	700	.24	6,720
Total			32,645

Income statement

Annual cash returns		
Cattle	$32,645	
Crops	3,719	
		$36,364
Annual cash costs		
Feed	3,560	
Labor hired	3,200	
Machinery repairs	1,541	
Building repairs	831	
Veterinary	439	
Taxes	2,615	
Crop expenses	4,362	
Bull purchase	2,500	
Other	1,834	
		−20,882
Net cash ranch income		$15,482
Depreciation		
Machinery	5,119	
Buildings	1,508	
		− 6,627
Net ranch income		$ 8,855
Debt service		
Working capital	2,259	
Real estate	4,430	
		− 6,689
Net available for family living		$ 2,166
Land appreciation		13,494
Payment towards mortgage principal		3,549
Gross proceeds to ranch investment		19,209
Value of operator and family labor		−8,000
Net proceeds to owned ranch capital		$11,209
Percent return on $277,341 owned capital		4.04%

the ranch and less sold), and cash costs of veterinary, bull purchase and "other" increase. This results in increases in net cash ranch income, net available for family living, and net proceeds to owned ranch capital. The income statements of Table 8-5 and 8-6 are termed complete budgets because they include fixed costs such as depreciation, real estate debt service, and family labor. For the purpose of determining the economic feasibility of the prescribed burning improvement, partial budgeting would be sufficient. The income statements could stop with the calculation of before and after net cash ranch income and comparison of the $619 increase ($16,101–$15,481) with the investment required for the prescribed burning ($6,118). In this case the 15 year improvement generates an internal rate of return on investment of 5.73% and would be considered economically feasible if (1) investment capital can be

Table 8-6. Budget summary for 320 head Utah cow-calf-yearling operation, after range improvement.

Feed source	Feed production Quantity	Unit
Native range	1,825	AUMs
Seeded pasture	280	AUMs
Barley	2,000	Bushels
Meadow hay	784	Tons
Crop aftermath	554	AUMS

Stock count and animal class

Month	Cows (1.0 AU) Head	AUMs	Yearling Heifers (.74 AU) Head	AUMs	Calves (.42 AU) Head	AUMs	Bulls (1.29 AU) Head	AUMs	Total Required AUMs
Jan.	320	320			48	20.2	16	20.6	361
Feb.	320	320			48	20.2	16	20.6	361
Mar.	320	320				20.2	16	20.6	361
Apr.	320	320	48	35.5	born		16	20.6	376
May	320	320	48	35.5			16	20.6	376
June	320	320	48	35.5			16	20.6	376
July	320	320	48	35.5			16	20.6	376
Aug.	320	320	48	35.5	256	107.5	16	20.6	484
Sept.	320	320	48	35.5	256	107.5	16	20.6	484
Oct.	320	320	48	35.5	256	107.5	16	20.6	484
Nov.	320	320			48	20.2	16	20.6	361
Dec.	320	320			48	20.2	16	20.6	361
Total									4,761

Month	Range	Seeded pasture	Barley	Forage balance Source of feed Meadow hay	After-math	Total available	Total required
Jan.			25	341		366	361
Feb.			25	341		366	361
Mar.			25	341		366	361
Apr.			25	356		381	376
May	238	140				377	376
June	237	140				377	376
July	380					380	376
Aug.	485					485	484
Sept.	485					485	484
Oct.			30		454	484	484
Nov.			25	240	101	366	361
Dec.			25	341		366	361
Total	1,825	280	180	1,960	555	4,799	4,761

Annual cattle production and revenue

Number and Category	Sale Weight (lb)	Sale Price ($/lb)	Total Revenue ($)
45 cull cows	1,000	.17	8,160
5.33 cull bulls	1,300	.20	1,387
80 heifer calves	380	.27	8,208
88 steer calves	400	.29	10,208
40 yearling steers	700	.24	6,720
Total			34,683

Income statement

Annual cash returns		
Cattle	$34,683	
Crops	2,619	
		$37,302
Annual cash costs		
Feed	3,560	
Labor hired	3,200	
Machinery repairs	1,541	
Building repairs	831	
Veterinary	468	
Taxes	2,616	
Crop expenses	4,362	
Bull purchase	2,667	
Other	1,956	
		−21,201
Net cash ranch income		$16,101
Depreciation		
Machinery	5,119	
Buildings	1,508	
		− 6,627
Net ranch income		$ 9,474
Debt service		
Working capital	2,848	
Real estate	4,430	
		− 7,278
Net available for family living		$ 2,196
Land appreciation		13,494
Payment towards mortgage principal		3,832
Gross proceeds to ranch investment		19,522
Value of operator and family labor		−8,000
Net proceeds to owned ranch capital		$11,522
Percent return on $277,341 owned capital		4.15%

borrowed at a rate less than 5.73% and (2) no other available investment promises a higher rate of return (Workman 1981b).

Linear Programming and Other Optimization Techniques

In contrast to partial budgeting, which basically treats only one practice at a time, linear programming seeks the best combination of proposed practices in allocating limited resources (Jameson et al. 1974). Linear programming has been used both to estimate the minimum cost production process for a specific output and also to estimate the short-run maximum profit allocation of limited factors among alternative enterprises. The technique requires that one or more production factors, such as land, labor or capital be limited; the importance of each limiting factor can be determined by sensitivity analysis.

Results are obtained in terms of optimum combinations of resources required to make full use of the limited factors. As commonly used, the programming technique requires the assumption that output is proportionate to input at all levels of production of a given enterprise; profit per animal is the same whether 50 or 100 animals are involved. This characteristic does not invalidate the technique for static solutions within fairly narrow ranges, but it does cast doubt on the accuracy of results in problems that involve optimum scale of enterprises. If scale is a major consideration in a specific application, steps must be performed in the formulation of the linear programs to resolve this problem.

A discussion of the mathematics and computational procedures is available in a number of sources (Kim 1971, Beneke and Winterboer 1973, Jameson et al. 1974). To work through an illustration in this chapter would be too voluminous and it is unnecessary for the purposes here.

Agricultural economics literature, and more recently range science literature, has included illustrations of linear programming application to various types of economic problems. Examples of use by range researchers include Sharp and Boykin (1967), D'Aquino (1974), Bartlett et al. (1974), Leistritz and Qualey (1975), Child and Evans (1976), Hewlett and Workman (1978), and Torell et al. (1982). Modifications of linear programming have been used to investigate various questions in range science. Hunter et al. (1976) examined the optimal stocking level based on uncertain forage production with chance-constrained programming. Bartlett and Clawson (1978) used goal programming to compare the objectives of profit, meat production, and efficient use of energy. The impact of grazing systems on risk and stability of range income was examined by Whitson et al. (1982).

Linear programming has been used to estimate the value of public grazing and the impact of public forage policy on local economies (Olson and Jackson 1975, Cook et al. 1980, Torell et al. 1980, Martin and Snider 1980). Other optimization techniques that are applied to range and natural resource problems include dynamic programming, and optimal control theory (Ritters et al. 1982, Williams 1982). Clark (1976) provides a complete reference on the use of optimal control theory in renewable resources.

Regional or Community Impacts

The above analytical methods are used to measure the "microeconomic" (individual firm) impacts of a particular action or decision. These methods are analogous to conducting an autecological study in biology. However, like a synecological study in biology, some actions involve "macroeconomic" relationships which require the evaluations of community, regional, or national economic impacts. These evaluations are necessary whenever changes in community, regional, or national income, employment, or sales are important to a management decision.

The measurement of these aggregate or macroeconomic impacts follows a three-stage process. The first step involves the measurement of the microeconomic impacts using one of the methods discussed above (e.g., budgeting or

LP). The second step is an aggregation of the microeconomic impacts. The third step involves an estimation of secondary or second-round impacts.

Aggregation. Most estimates of the microeconomic impacts involve either a sample of firms or the simulation of a "typical" firm that is representative of firms in the area. These "average" or "typical" microeconomic estimates must then be summarized to yield an estimate of the total impact on all firms. This aggregation is done with respect to one or more common elements such as size of operations, extent of dependence on federal lands, or type of operations (cattle vs. sheep ranches). Thus, if a particular type of operation suffered a loss of $1,000 due to some action, and there were ten firms of that type in the area, the aggregate microeconomic impact would be a loss of $10,000. This aggregation obviously includes all of the assumptions associated with any estimate that is based on a sample of the affected population. In particular, it is assumed that the impacts of the "sample" or "typical" firms reflect the impact of those firms not included in the sample.

Secondary impacts. A given action may affect a firm or group of firms directly. But other firms in the general area may also be affected because each sector (group of similar firms) buys products and services from and sells products and services to other sectors. Various methods have been developed to evaluate these impacts and each yields an estimation of economic multipliers. Most of the methods used to evaluate regional impacts are derived from either input/output analysis or economic base analysis.

Input/output (I/O) analysis is generally considered the most descriptive method available for estimating regional macroeconomic impacts. The first step in developing an I/O model is the derivation of a transactions table which traces the purchases and sales of various sectors of an economy. This table is derived by either: (1) collecting the primary data from business in the area, or (2) building the model based on a national or state I/O table. Both of these approaches have strengths and weaknesses (Boster and Martin 1972, Richardson 1972, Richardson 1978). The primary data approach generally is accepted as being the most accurate, but the expense associated with the collecting of primary data may prohibit its use. As a result, the second approach is most commonly used and, as Boster and Martin (1972) have shown, the results are generally comparable.

Perhaps the most confusing aspect of regional economics for the inexperienced analyst is the wide range in the magnitude of the multipliers that have been estimated. The primary reason for these differences is that many types of multipliers (e.g., income, employment, output, Type I and Type II) can be estimated. See Meirnyk (1965) for a discussion of the various types of multipliers.

Care should be used in interpreting macroeconomic impacts. A strong tendency exists for some analysts to find and advocate use of the largest multipliers available. A tendency also exists to use the multiplier for an economic sector (such as services and trade) as being representative of an industry (e.g., recreation) that makes up only part of that sector. This violates one of the primary assumptions of I/O analysis. See Dorfman et al. (1958),

Chenery and Clark (1959), Meirnyk (1965), or Richardson (1972) for a review of I/O analysis.

In general, the following guidelines hold concerning the use and magnitude of multiplers:

1. The smaller the region being considered, the smaller will be the region's multipliers because of spending leakages out of the region. Thus, national multipliers will be larger than state, state multipliers will be larger than county, and county multipliers generally will be small.

2. Any income multiplier greater than two should be carefully scrutinized, especially if the region being considered is small (Coppedge and Youmans 1970).

3. Mutipliers from I/O models generally should be used instead of those generated by other methods because I/O allows greater disaggregation of the sectors of an economy.

While it is generally agreed that I/O models provide the most reliable method for estimating regional impacts, I/O models are very expensive to develop (Richardson 1978). Therefore, economic base models have been more commonly used in estimating secondary economic impacts.

Economic base analysis begins with the premise that some sectors of an economy are "basic" to that region. Total employment, income and taxes in the region are then calculated as a multiple of these basic industries. Thus, if total employment in a region were 150,000 people and employment in the basic industries (generally assumed to agriculture, mining and forestry) were 90,000 people, the employment multiplier for the region would be 1.67 (150,000/90,000). Various methods have been developed to estimate these multipliers, but all have some basic conceptual weaknesses (Weiss and Gooding 1968). The problems associated with using these methods have been reviewed by Richardson (1978) and Lewis (1976) and should be recognized when analysts try to estimate the secondary impacts of some action on a region or community by economic base analysis.

National Impacts

Most decisions made by rangeland administrators are not of sufficient magnitude that their effects, from a national perspective, need to be evaluated. When national impacts do occur, the tools that are available for regional analysis may also be used at the national level. The methods discussed below are particularly useful when decision impacts must be evaluated from a national perspective, but they may also be used at the regional and community levels of analysis.

Aggregate supply and demand relationships. If the problem being evaluated is so large that it affects the aggregate supply or demand for a good or service, then the impact on prices must be evaluated. This requires that estimates of the supply and demand functions be obtained and, from these, the change in consumers' and producers' surplus are estimated (Just et al. 1982). For example, Martin et al. (1978) showed that consumers would stand to lose little on a *per capita* basis from reductions in livestock grazing on public lands, but their *total* loss would be substantial. Impacts of rangeland policy changes on aggregate supply and demand are generally larger and even more important in lesser developed countries than in developed nations like the United States.

Benefit-cost analysis. For obvious reasons, economic criteria have long been used for range management and range improvement decisions in the private sector. Public land management agencies have also traditionally used economic feasibility as one criterion in choosing among public investments. However, public agencies (particularly federal agencies) have retained the authority to make investment decisions on other than economic grounds. Government agencies tend to use economic analysis to justify a decision after it has already been made rather than to determine if it is economically feasible. Economic analysis should be done early in the public agency planning process, well ahead of final decision and justification (Workman and Fairfax 1981).

Federal agency benefit-cost analysis is plagued with the problem of comparing market and nonmarket values. Alternative means of resolving this problem are the "cost-effectiveness" approach (an attempt to avoid comparison of market and nonmarket values) and the "nonmarket valuation" approach (an attempt to assign derived values to nonmarket benefits and costs). Cost-effectiveness is simply an attempt to accomplish a stated goal at minimum cost. While the intent is laudable, cost-effectiveness offers little help in answering practical questions of how to best allocate limited budgets and personnel among competing needs. Obviously, this approach makes it possible to economically justify any investment. Efforts to more accurately value nonmarket impacts should continue and the resulting values should be used in decision-making activities, not merely for decision justification (Workman and Fairfax 1981).

A near consensus exists in the literature that the willingness-to-pay procedure (based on estimated demand schedules) is the most appropriate conceptual framework available for nonmarket valuation. Reliable analytical techniques are available for valuation of many nonmarket outputs including wildlife, recreation, and water. However, values for some nonmarket products (e.g. aesthetics, endangered species, and Indian burial grounds) cannot now and perhaps can never be expressed in monetary terms (Workman and Fairfax 1981, Peterson and Randell 1984).

Even when all benefits and costs are expressed in dollars, contradictory project selections are often made by the three standard investment criteria, i.e., benefit-cost ratio, internal rate of return, and net present value. The contradiction problem can be avoided by normalizing alternative projects for differences in life expectancy and required investment or, more simply, by using net present value as the criterion for selecting among alternative investments (Workman 1981b).

Welfare economics and distribution issues. Benefit-cost analysis may represent the analytical tool most widely used by federal land management agencies in the United States. However, one of the most basic assumptions made in B-C analysis is that the benefits to whomsoever they accrue are greater than the costs by whomsoever they are borne. Unfortunately, many decisions, especially those made in the political arena, rest heavily on obtaining benefits that are paid by others. "Any intrusion of government into the domain of public policy is found to cost some and benefit others", for that is the essence of governmental action (White 1979, Gardner, 1983). As a result, some researchers (e.g., Godfrey 1981, Obermiller 1982) have suggested that analytical methods based on the theories of public choice (Mueller 1978) be used to a greater extent. Unfortunately, few natural resource oriented empirical studies of this type have been completed (Martin et al. 1978). Public choice theory shows considerable promise for use by public land administrators to evaluate public input and user group advocation.

Special Problems in Range Economics Research

In the preceding sections, some of the logic and methods of economics research have been discussed. The function of economics research as a tool to help people decide how they will use resources in the production of economic goods has been emphasized. The most common application of this tool is to analyze alternatives available to the manager of a firm or a land management agency so that they may obtain maximum profits or maximum achievement of other rational goals. At times, special problems are encountered in economics research. Some of the problems are discussed briefly in the sections that follow.

Operation of the Firm
Scale of Operations

If all of the factors or inputs used in range production were infinitely divisible, determination of an optimum scale or size of operations would be simple. The same procedure used in arriving at the optimum level of production for an enterprise would apply in arriving at the optimum scale of operation for the firm. Assuming no arbitrary limits on capital or other resources, additional resources would be added until the return for each increment just equaled the cost of the resources. At this point, the most efficient scale of operations is achieved.

In practice, however, many resources are available only in "lumps." Rangeland is added by sections, or parts of sections, and not acre by acre. Usually, an additional worker is employed by the day, month, or year. Ordinarily, the managerial services of the operator are available in units of a full year once the decision to engage in ranching has been made. Once a "bundle" of resources has been committed, the additional cost of using it to capacity over using it at less than capacity is small.

The problem of determining the optimum scale of operations is one of determining the optimum combinations of "lumpy" inputs. In most parts of the range region, labor is one of the most costly input factors and one that is not readily divisible because of scarcity of alternative employment. On most ranches, the minimum efficient scale of operations is that which results in full employment of one person for one year. As many operations cannot be performed by one worker, some seasonal labor is required also. The number of other resources required to provide the worker with full-time employment varies with the type of ranch, location, and other factors.

Once the scale of operation is expanded beyond the size that one person can handle, a new optimum size is established which approaches full employment of two workers. As additional workers are added, a point is reached beyond which profits or other advantages fail to increase with additional labor. This usually results because the managerial ability of the person making the decisions is spread over such a large area that his contribution to the production process becomes the limiting factor to further increases in size.

If managerial ability of the operator ultimately sets the economic limit to increases in scale of operation, it becomes difficult to attempt to establish an optimum scale of operation for all firms within an industry. Actually, an array of optima exist varying with the characteristics of the manager. For detailed examples of methodology and results, see Martin and Goss (1963) and Workman and Hooper (1971).

Survival of the Firm

When persons "outside" the range livestock industry first encounter data concerning costs, returns, and rates of return on investment (such as shown in Tables 8-5 and 8-6), they often ask two important questions: (1) how does the rancher survive in the livestock business? and (2) why would he want to continue ranching? Except for a brief period in the 1880's when rates of return in cattle ranching were from 25 to 40% (Osgood 1929), returns have commonly been in the neighborhood of 2% (Gray 1968, Capps and Workman 1982).

We may begin to answer the first question (how does the rancher survive?) by referring to the entry called "net available for family living" listed in the income statement of Table 8-5. This $2,166 represents the discretionary income left after all ranch bills have been paid. Clearly, a ranch family would have had difficulty surviving on an income of $2,166, even in 1968. However, when combined with several "perquisites" such as utilities and automobile expense already included in cash costs, housing, milk, meat, and garden produce, the $2,166 income looks larger (Workman 1981a). "Off-ranch" sources of income such as part-time (or even full-time) jobs of some members of the ranch family are important for small, part-time ranches. Probably by far the most universal source of off-ranch income is periodic refinancing of ranch real estate, or borrowing back against equity. This source of revenue has been available to the rancher except during severe recessions.

The second question (why would anyone want to continue ranching?) may also be answered by referring to the income statement of Table 8-5 above. To allow calculation of net return on investment, two additional sources of income have been introduced, along with an additional cost component. Firstly, land appreciation has been included as income, calculated at 8.55%, the annual average for grazing lands in the 11 western states 1960–1980 (USDA 1980). High land prices, apparently much higher than justified by crop or livestock production, are perhaps the best proof that expected land appreciation is at least as important to the investor as agricultural income (Workman and King 1982). But, land prices do not always remain high. They commonly decrease during periods of recession.

Secondly, payment to mortgage principal has also been included as income, based on the recognition that a principal payment increases equity and is actually a payment from the borrower to himself. Like land appreciation, principal payment "income" is not available to the borrower until he/she either refinances or sells the land in question. Still, gains in equity (the difference between market value of the land and the amount owed on it) are just as important to the ranch investor as cash livestock income.

Thirdly, the value of operator and family labor is subtracted as a cost. It must be recognized that part of the gross proceeds to ranch investment are due to labor and management. Thus to calculate the income attributable solely to land and livestock ownership, income contributed by labor must be subtracted. Net proceeds to owned ranch capital, $11,209 (considerably higher than the net available for living, $2,166), can now be divided by owned equity, $277,341, resulting in a rate of return on equity of about 4%. This rate of return may be compared directly to rates on other long-term investments and we have a partial answer to the second question (why would anyone want to continue ranching?). While the $11,209 net proceeds is more than five times the $2,166 available for living, it still does not fully explain the rationale underlying continued investment in high priced non-mineral bearing ranches. Another partial explanation involves the substantial federal income tax advantages associated with ranch owernship, primarily the range improvement current cost deduction and capital gains provisions. Also, the much discussed and important "way of life" value of western ranching should be mentioned.

Mix of Enterprises

Most range research as well as most management decisions by ranchers and administrators of public land have assumed that specific rangelands were best suited to one kind of livestock, that is, that a range was either "cattle range" or "sheep range," but not both. Sheep may eat many summer grasses only sparingly, especially as they become stemmy in late season, whereas cattle may prefer the stemmy grasses to the forbs and shrubs. Thus, the most economic use of many ranges may be obtained by some combination of sheep and cattle.

Consider a range on which only cattle are grazed. When the intensity of use is such that none of the grasses is overused, most of the forbs and browse may be underused. If this condition exists, it may be possible to add a substantial number of sheep by removing only a few head of cattle and still leave the range in an unimpaired condition. As long as the added numbers of sheep bring in more profit than is lost by the cattle that are removed, total profits will increase.

The economic problem of determing the combination of sheep and cattle that will maximize revenue or profit turns on two basic relationships that must be estimated: (1) the biological relationships, showing the various combinations of sheep and cattle that will give approximately the same degree of range utilization, and (2) the expected price relationships between sheep and cattle.

The biological relationships required for economic solutions can be derived in two ways. Firstly, they may be obtained from controlled grazing experiments when sufficient combinations of sheep and cattle are observed over time so that a relation may be expressed as a curvilinear regression (Cook 1954, Smith 1965). Obviously, results from grazing experiments of this kind are obtained slowly. When experimental results are not available, production obtained from grazing various combinations of sheep and cattle can be estimated in the same ways as grazing capacity for one type of livestock. Once a biological relation between two different uses of the same resource can be established and expressed as a function, a rational economic decision can be made using the marginality principle illustrated previously for optimum (2) in the fertilizer example. If cattle and sheep use the same range, it is possible to determine the number of each which together would produce maximum net returns (Hopkin 1954, Workman 1975). Maximum net revenue is achieved simply by finding that point on the functional relationship that results in the greatest sum when the quantity of each product is multiplied by its net price.

In addition to decisions concerning kind of livestock, ranchers and public land managers often must decide among other possible enterprises on a particular tract of rangeland. Alternative uses may include dude ranching and the leasing of hunting privileges and rights to mineral exploration on private rangelands. On public lands the list of alternatives may be even longer if the following goods have a market value: watershed protection, water production, wildlife habitat, and a variety of recreational opportunities. In both cases, the principle of marginality can be applied to determine the optimum enterprise mix.

Risk and Uncertainty

Management of a ranch or a public land management district involves deciding on a course of action and putting the plan into operation. Many factors can cause the actual results to deviate from the expected. Due to variability in weather and prices, results of a course of action can seldom be predicted with complete certainty.

In common usage, the term "risk" describes any deviation of the realized results from the expected. However, for purposes of economic analysis, risk can be further divided into "risk" and "uncertainty".

In some instances, the probability of outcome from a large number of events an be established. For example, the number of barns that will burn, the number of automobile accidents that will occur, and the number of farmers who will suffer from hail damage in the United States during the next year can be predicted with a relatively high degree of accuracy. Likewise, a rancher with a large number of cattle and long experience can predict the death loss in his herd with a reasonable degree of accuracy. The term "risk" applies to those events for which the probability of outcome can be established.

In other instances, the probability of outcome cannot be established. For example, in an economy in which prices are free to fluctuate, there is no basis for establishing empirically the probability of realizing a given price from an agricultural product. The term "uncertainty" refers to those events whose outcome cannot be predicted.

Economic research can aid ranch operators and land managers by providing the data required for rational decisions pertaining to assumption of risks or adjustments to uncertainty. Several alternative management strategies have been developed to reduce the impact of risk (Nelson et al. 1978). A number of models are also available for risk evaluation (Walker and Helmers 1983). However, little empirical research has been conducted on the influence of risk and uncertainty on rangeland management decisions. This, therefore, represents a potentially fruitful area of research. For detailed examples of attempts to deal with risk and uncertainty in range management see Whitson (1975) and Banner (1981).

Like flexibility, multiple use can reduce risk and uncertainty. Multiple use is commonly understood to represent the production of two or more products from a given resource base. This concept is widely advocated for management of both private and public lands in the United States. As a result, multiple-use allocations represent an important economic problem. However, formal economic analysis is rarely used to help solve multiple-use problems for several reasons. Firstly, most of the economic work on multiple use has primarily been of a theoretical nature (Gregory 1955, Godfrey 1983) and few studies have empirically evaluated multiple-use tradeoffs. Secondly, the physical or biological relationships between the various uses (e.g., livestock, wildlife, recreation, and watershed) are rarely known or empirically estimated. This represents a problem that must be jointly solved by range ecologists and economists but one that is rarely evaluated simultaneously by both disciplines. Thirdly, a few methods have been developed to start to measure the value of activities such as recreation (Dwyer et al. 1977). But, general agreement does not exist as to their validity (Schuster 1983), and it is generally conceded that they can be easily misused (Godfrey 1983). This suggests that while the theoretical criteria and methodology for solving multiple-use problems may be widely accepted, major problems remain in the application of these methods to the solution of multiple-use allocations.

Conservation and Sustained Yield

Economists generally define conservation somewhat differently and more rigorously than do most popular writers. Conservation decisions, as defined by economists, involve the distribution of resource use over time. Thus, conservation decisions pertain to the "when" of resource use. Conservation and multiple-use decisions are inter-related because which uses receive preference also has an impact on when these uses occur.

In an effort to overcome some of the difficulties of determining the "correct" pattern of use over time, policy makers have often suggested that renewable resources be used on a maximum-sustained yield basis. This criterion does have some merit from a biological point of view, but several authors (Ciriacy-Wantrup 1968, Samuelson 1976, and Dowdle 1981) have shown that this pattern of use cannot be justified from a social perspective except in very special cases.

A growing body of literature is available to help determine the optimal rate of using various resources. Much of this literature is theoretical (e.g., Kamien and Schwartz 1981), but a few studies (e.g., Godfrey 1979) have evaluated how patterns of utilization affect livestock returns from rangelands.

All economic evaluations of the optimal rate of resource use over time are based on a comparison of the benefits obtained and costs incurred through time. The calculated optimum rate of use is usually the one that generates the greatest net present value (NPV) and is, therefore, similar to benefit cost analysis mentioned previously. However, optimal use rate calculations depend upon the discount rate used to calculate NPV. While this is generally not a practical problem for those working for a federal agency because the discount rate is administratively determined, it does inject controversy into conservation decisions because there is wide disagreement in the literature concerning what the "correct" discount rate is (Fisher and Krutilla 1975, Pagoulatos and Walker 1976, Row et al. 1981). The greatest contribution made by economic analysis on conservation decisions is, perhaps, reducing the controversy by identifying the information most critical to the conservation decision.

Computers and Economic Decision Making

The results of economic analysis should be viewed as one input into management decisions rather than as the final decision itself. One of the primary reasons why economic analysis is difficult is the large number of variables upon which an economic answer rests. In the past incorporating a change in one or more of these variables (e.g., product or input prices) into the analysis required hours of additional work. Fortunately, modern computer technology has reduced computational time significantly.

Large mainframe computers have been available to researchers and decision makers for more than two decades. They still represent a major tool needed to help determine solutions to large and complex mathematically expressed problems. The rapid development of personal (micro) computers in the early 1980s has and will continue to change the use of computer technology in ways not yet imagined. Easily programmed spread sheets, flexible data base systems, and word processing programs have made computer power available to nearly everyone. These tools make sensitivity analysis relatively easy and are a must for land administrators. Computer technology has the potential to help decision makers quickly and carefully evaluate complex problems that could have not been solved in the past.

Literature Cited

Banner, R.E. 1981. Economic analysis of long-term management strategies for two sizes of Utah cattle ranches. Ph.D. Diss., Utah State Univ.

Bartlett, E.T., and W.J. Clawson. 1978. Profit, meat production or efficient use of energy in ranching. J. Anim. Sci. 46:812-818.

Bartlett, E.T., G.R. Evans, and R.E. Bement. 1974. A serial optimization model for ranch management. J. Range Manage. 27:233-239.

Beneke, R.R., and R. Winterboer. 1973. Linear programming applications to agriculture. Iowa State Univ. Press, Ames, Iowa.

Black, J.D., M. Clawson, C.R. Sayre, and W.W. Wilcox. 1947. Farm management. Macmillan Publ. Co., New York, New York.

Boster, R.S., and W.E. Martin. 1972. The value of primary versus secondary data in interindustry analysis: a study of the economics of economic models. J. Regional Sci. 6:34-44.

Capps, T.L., and J.P. Workman. 1982. Management, productivity and economic profiles of two sizes of Utah cattle ranches. Res. Rep. 69. Utah Agr. Exp. Sta.

Chenery, H.B., and P.G. Clark. 1959. InterIndustry economics. John Wiley & Sons. New York, New York.

Chiang, A.C. 1974. Fundamental methods of mathematical economics. McGraw-Hill, Inc., New York, New York.

Child, R.D., and G.R. Evans. 1976. COPLAN user's manual. Range Sci. Ser. 19. Colorado State Univ.

Ciriacy-Wantrup, S.V. 1968. Resource conservation: economics and policies. Univ. California Agr. Exp. Sta. Press. Berkeley, California.

Clark, C.W. 1976. Mathematical bioeconomics in the optimal management of renewable resources. John Wiley & Sons, New York, New York.

Cook, C.W. 1954. Common use of summer range by sheep and cattle. J. Range Manage. 7:10-13.

Cook, C.W., G. Taylor, and E.T. Bartlett. 1980. Impacts of federal range forage on ranches and regional economies of Colorado. Bull. 576S. Colorado Agr. Exp. Sta.

D'Aquino, S.A. 1974. A case study for optimal allocation of range resources. J. Range Manage. 27:228-233.

Dorfman, R., P.A. Samuelson, and R. Solow. 1958. Linear programming and economic analysis. McGraw-Hill, Inc., New York, New York.

Dowdle, B. 1981. An institutional dinosaur with an ACE: or, how to piddle away public timber wealth and foul the environment in the process. John Baden and Richard L. Stroup, (Eds.), *In:* Bureaucracy vs. environment: the environmental costs of bureaucratic governance. Univ. Michigan Press, Ann Arbor, Michigan.

Dwyer, J.F., J.R. Kelly, and M.D. Bowes. 1977. Improved procedures for valuation of the contribution of recreation to national economic development. Water Resources Rep. No. 128. Cen. Univ. Illinois.

Econom..ic Research Service. 1981. Farm real estate market developments—outlook and situation. CD-86. USDA, Washington, D.C.

Economics, Statistics, and Cooperatives Service. 1979. Firm enterprise data system, livestock budgets. Commodity Econ. Div., USDA, Washington, D.C.

Fisher, A.C., and J. Krutilla. 1975. Resource conservation, environmental preservation, and the rate of discount. Quart. J. Econ. 89:359-370.

Gardner, B.D. 1983. Market vs. political allocations of natural resources in the 1980's. Proc. Western Agr. Econ. Assoc., Laramie, Wyoming.

Godfrey, E.B. 1979. Utilization practices and the returns from seeding an area to crested wheatgrass. J. Range Manage. 32:171-175.

Godfrey, E.B. 1981. Measuring the economic impact of agency programs on users and local communities. Workshop on applying socioecon. tech. to range manage. decision making, Nat. Res. Council, Boise, Idaho.

Godfrey, E.B. 1983. Economics and multiple use management of federal lands. Gen. Tech. Rep. INT-149, Forest Service, USDA, Salt Lake City, Utah.

Gregory, G.R. 1955. An economic approach to multiple use. Forest Sci. 1:6-13.

Heady, E.O., and J. Pesek. 1954. A fertilizer production surface. J. Farm Econ. 36:466-482.

Hewlett, D.B., and J.P. Workman. 1978. An economic analysis of retention of yearlings on range and potential effects on beef production. J. Range Manage. 31:125-128.

Hoglund, O.K., H.W. Miller, and A.L. Hafenrichter. 1952. Application of fertilizer to aid conservation on annual forage range. J. Range Manage. 5:55-61.

Hopkin, J.A. 1954. Economic criteria for determining optimum use of summer range by cattle and sheep. J. Range Manage. 7:170-175.

Hunter, D.H., E.T. Bartlett, and D.A. Jameson. 1976. Optimum forage allocation through chance-constrained programming. Ecol. Modelling. 2:91-99.

Jameson, D.A., S. D'Aquino, and E.T. Bartlett. 1974. Economics and management planning of range ecosystems. A.A. Balkema. Rotterdam, Netherlands.

Just, R.E., D.L. Heuth, and A. Schmitz. 1982. Applied selfare economics and public policy. Prentice-Hall, Inc. Englewood Cliffs, New Jersey.

Kamien, M.I., and N.L. Schwartz. 1981. Dynamic optimization: the calculus of variations and optimal control in economics and management. North Holland Publ. Co., New York, New York.

Kim, C. 1971. Introduction to linear programming. Holt, Rinehart, and Winston, Inc. New York, New York.

Kmenta, J. 1971. Elements of econometrics. Macmillan Publ. Co., Inc. New York, New York.

Leistritz, L.F., and N.J. Qualey. 1975. Economics of range management alternatives in southwestern North Dakota. J. Range Manage. 28:349-352.

Lewis, W.C. 1976. Export base theory and multiplier estimation: a critique. Ann. Region. Sci. 10:58-70.

Martin, W.E., and W.K. Goss. 1963. Cost-size relationships for southwestern Arizona cattle ranches. Tech Bull. 155. Arizona Agr. Exp. Sta.

Martin, W.E., and G.B. Snider. 1980. The value of forage for grazing cattle in the Salt-Verde Basin of Arizona. Rep. No. 22. Dep. Agr. Econ. Univ. Arizona.

Martin, W.E., J.C. Tinney, and R.L. Gum. 1978. A welfare economic analysis of the potential competition between hunting and cattle ranching. Western J. Agr. Econ. 3:87-97.

Meirnyk, W.K. 1965. The elements of input-output analysis. Random House. New York, New York.

Mueller, D.C. 1978. Public choice: a survey. J. Econ. Lit. 14:395-433.

Nelson, A.G., G.L. Casler, and O.L. Walker. 1978. Making farm decisions in a risky world: a guidebook. Oregon Coop. Ext. Service.

North Central Farm Management Committee. 1955. Economics of forage evaluation. Bull. 623. Indiana Agr. Exp. Sta.

Obermiller, F.W. 1982. Economic efficiency vs. distributive equity: the "Sagebrush Rebellion." Western J. Agr. Econ. 7:253-265.

Olson, C.E., and J.S. Jackson. 1975. Impact of change in federal grazing policies on south-central Wyoming mountain valley cattle ranches. Resource Bull. 96. Wyoming Agr. Exp. Sta.

Osgood, E.S. 1929. The day of the cattleman. Univ. Minnesota Press, Minneapolis, Minnesota.

Pagoulatos, A.C., and L.A. Walker. 1976. On the proper rate of discount for public investment projects in natural resources. Res. Rep. 25. Kentucky Agr. Exp. Sta.

Peterson, G.L. and A. Randall, eds. 1984. Valuation of Wildland Resource benefits. Westview Press, Boulder, Colorado.

Richardson, H.W. 1972. Input-output and regional economics. John Wiley & Sons, New York, New York.

Richardson, H.W. 1978. The state of regional economics: a survey article. Int. Regional Sci. Rev. 3:1-49.

Ritters, K., J.D. Brodie, and D.W. Hann. 1982. Dynamic programming for optimization of timber production and grazing in ponderosa pine. Forest Sci. 28:517-526.

Row, C., H.F. Kaiser, and J. Sessions. 1981. Discount rate for long-term Forest Service investments. J. Forest. 79:367-376.

Samuelson, P.A. 1976. Economics of forestry in an evolving society. Econ. Inquiry 14:466-492.

Sharp, W.W., and C.C. Boykin. 1967. A dynamic programming model for evaluating investments in mesquite control and alternative beef cattle systems. Tech. Monogr. 4. Texas Agr. Exp. Sta.

Schuster, E. 1983. Non-market valued benefits and costs. Gen. Tech. rep. INT-149. USDA Forest Service, Salt Lake City, Utah.

Smith, A.D. 1965. Determining common use grazing capacities by application of the key species concept. J. Range Manage. 18:196-201.

Snedecor, G.W., and W.G. Cochran. 1980. Statistical methods. Iowa State Univ. Press, Ames, Iowa.

Statistical Reporting Service. 1983. Agricultural prices. Crop. Rep. Board, USDA, Washington, D.C.

Torrell, L.A., W.O. Champney, and C.T.K. Ching. 1980. Economic impact of BLM grazing allotment reductions on Humbold County, Nevada. Nevada Div. Agr. Resource Econ.

Torrell, L.A., G.F. Speth, and C.T.K. Ching. 1982. Effect of calf crop on net income of a Nevada range cattle operation. J. Range Manage. 35:519-521.

United States Department of Agriculture. 1980. Farm real estate market developments. CD-85, Econ., Statistics, and Coop. Service, USDA, Washington, D.C.

Upchurch, M.L. 1954. Economic aspects of livestock-big game relationships. J. Range Manage. 7:245-249.

Walker, O.L., and G.A. Helmers. 1983. Risk and risk management in range use. Range Econ. Symp. Proc., Laramie, Wyoming.

Wiess, S.J., and E.C. Gooding. 1968. Estimation of differential employment multipliers in a small regional economy. Land Econ. 44:235-244.

White, S.W. 1979. Public policy and private interest. Nat. Forum 68:2-11.

Whitson, R.E. 1975. Ranch decision-making under uncertainty—an illustration. J. Range Manage. 28:267-270.

Whitson, R.E., R.K. Heitschmidt, M.M. Kothmann, and G.K. Landgren. 1982. The impact of grazing systems on the magnitude and stability of range income in the rolling plains of Texas. J. Range Manage. 35:526-532.

Williams, B.K. 1982. Optimal stochastic control in natural resource management: framework and examples. Ecol. Modelling 16:275-297.

Workman, J.P. 1975. Wildlife and recreation on U.S. rangelands—the economic aspects, p. 131-134. *In:* Arid Shrublands, Proc. Third Workshop of the U.S./Aust. Rangelands Panel. Tucson, Arizona.

Workman, J.P. 1981a. Analyzing range income statements—a modified approach. Rangelands 3:146-148.

Workman, J.P. 1981b. Disagreement among investment criteria—a solution to the problem. J. Range Manage. 34:317-324.

Workman, J.P., and S.K. Fairfax. 1981. Applying socioeconomic techniques to range management decision making. p. 75-88. *In:* Developing Strategies for Rangeland Management. Nat. Res. Council, Washington, D.C.

Workman, J.P., and J. Hooper. 1971. Cost-size relationships of Utah cattle ranches. J. Range Manage. 24:462-465.

Workman, J.P., and K.A. King. 1982. Utah cattle ranch prices. Utah Sci. 43:78-81.

Workman, J.P., and J.R. Lacey. 1982. Base ranching decisions on sound economics. Utah Farmer-Stockman 102:6-8.

Workman, J.P., and P.W. McCormick. 1977. Economics of carry-over response to nitrogen fertilization of rangelands. J. Range Manage. 30:324-327.

Workman, J.P., and T.M. Quigley. 1974. Economics of fertilizer application on range and meadow sites in Utah. J. Range Manage. 17:390-393.

Chapter 9
Sampling Methods with Special Reference to Range Management

Introduction and Basic Requirements

In no field does the research worker encounter a more complex population for estimation than in range investigations. On a single square meter of soil area may be found species representing several families and several genera. Estimates may be required for such characteristics as forage volume or weight, the quantity used or available, cover, species density, distribution, height, or specific growth data.

The intent of this chapter is to provide the researcher with a review of sampling concepts within the context of range research application. The researcher may use this review as a basis for individual planning for a research project and as a basis for communication with a statistician for final project design. A basic knowledge of statistics as background for this chapter may be found in texts such as Snedecor and Cochran (1980), Steel and Torrie (1980), and Iman and Conover (1983). The reader who wishes to delve into the theory of sampling is referred to Cochran (1977).

The discussion in this chapter stresses estimates of population means and totals and the variance and confidence intervals associated with these estimates when samples are collected within specified designs. An understanding of sources of variation when sampling by different designs is essential to efficient sampling and proper interpretation of data. Use of the *t*-distribution to calculate confidence limits is based on the assumption that the population has a normal distribution. The researcher is cautioned to consider the distribution of the population to be studied to determine if confidence intervals should be interpreted only as a general order of magnitude or even if calculation of confidence limits using the *t*-distribution is appropriate.

In a discussion of sampling, we should consider first the basic requirements of a sample if it is to serve the purpose for which it is drawn. Fundamentally, the purpose of a sample is to estimate the result that would have been obtained had every unit of the population been measured. This leads to the basic requirement that the sample represent the population in a known manner. If the selection of the sample is restricted in any way, this must be taken into account in estimates derived from the sample. If changes take place either in the population itself, or in the method or tools of measurement, they must be considered in analyzing the data.

A feature of sampling that is often taken for granted, and often ignored, is the need for a dependable basis for evaluating or appraising the variability associated with estimates derived from the sample (precision). In order that a sample supply the basis for evaluating the precision of the estimate, care must be taken to represent the variability of the sampling units. How well the sample estimates represent the true population parameters (accuracy) usually is unknown, but care in selecting proper statistics, sample design, and measurement techniques to avoid biases helps to assure accurate estimates.

Sampling

General Considerations in Sampling

In identifying the sampling unit and planning the procedure for sampling, the planner must study the population to be sampled: its location; size; accessibility; the nature and extent of variability; costs and accuracy of measurements; features peculiar to the specific population such as sources of possible bias; usable bases for stratification; and correlated variables that may be used for increasing precision of estimates or reducing costs. Before these factors and their effects can be examined, it will be necessary to introduce and discuss the basic concept of statistical variability and its effect on precision of estimates.

Measure of Variability and Central Tendency

Consider a pasture of 32 ha on which the principal forage species is black grama *(Bouteloua eriopoda)*. Let this pasture be subdivided theoretically into square meter plots or sampling units, of which there are 320,000. Thus, N is equal to 320,000. Consider a variable X which is the weight per plot, in grams, of the black grama plants above ground level. We have, then, a population of 320,000 weights. The square meter plots may be given identifying numbers from 1 to 320,000. We have, then, 320,000 separate and distinct values X_i ($i = 1,2,—N$). This population has an arithmetic mean or average[1]

$$\mu = \frac{\sum_{i=1}^{N} X_i}{N} \tag{1}$$

The mean μ characterizes the magnitude of the values of X but gives no idea of how individual values may be dispersed or distributed relative to μ. For this purpose we calculate the population variance

$$\sigma^2 = \frac{\sum_{i=1}^{N} (X_i - \mu)^2}{N} \tag{2}$$

---

[1] Σ is called summation sign and the subscript i is called the index of summation. The $i = 1$ below Σ indicates that the first term in the sum is found by giving i the value of 1. The N above Σ indicates that the last term in the sum is found by giving i the value of N. N is the total number of sampling units in the population.

which is the arithmetic average of the squares of the differences between the X_i valus and their mean μ. The positive square root of σ^2 is the standard deviation of variable X.

Now if we harvest a random sample of n, say 400 units of X_i, we compute the sample arithmetic mean

$$\bar{x} = \frac{\sum\limits_{i=1}^{n} X_i}{n} \tag{3}$$

It can be shown that $\bar{x}$ is an unbiased estimate of μ.
Similarly, we compute the sample variance

$$s^2 = \frac{\sum\limits_{i=1}^{n} (X_i - \bar{x})^2}{n - 1} \tag{4}$$

which can be shown to be an unbiased estimate of population variance σ^2.

Now, it can be shown that, regardless of the form of the original population, means $\bar{x}$ of n observations will have a variance of approximately

$$\sigma_{\bar{x}}^2 = \frac{\sigma^2}{n} \tag{5}$$

These relationships are of importance in statistical tests of significance and in setting confidence limits on estimates. If means of n observations tend to be distributed normally with variance σ^2/n, the probability that a single sample mean $\bar{x}$ will differ from the true mean μ by more than some fixed quantity $"d"$ can be determined directly from a table of the normal distribution. In practice, the sampler does not know σ^2 but makes a sample estimate s^2.

It has been shown that if $t = \dfrac{\bar{x} - \mu}{\sqrt{\dfrac{s^2}{n}}}$, $\tag{6}$

then t follows the well-known Student's $"t"$ distribution when samples are drawn from a normal distribution. This relation remains approximately true when the distribution from which the sample was drawn departs quite widely from the normal. As a consequence, the statement can be made that

$$\mu = \bar{x} \pm t_{.95} s_{\bar{x}}, \tag{7}$$

this is, the true mean μ lies within the interval $\bar{x} - t_{.95} s_{\bar{x}}$ and $\bar{x} + t_{.95} s_{\bar{x}}$, where $t_{.95}$ is the t value corresponding to the 95% limit, and this statement has a probability of 0.95 of being true. In the "t"table, the value given at the 0.05 level of significance is the $t_{.95}$ value as applied here to the confidence interval. The standard error of the mean is calculated by the formula

$$s_{\bar{x}} = \frac{\sqrt{s^2}}{\sqrt{n}}$$

(8)

If it is desired to narrow the confidence interval, with the same number of observations in the sample, a smaller value of t may be used but this reduces the probability that the statement is true. Conversely, if greater probability is desired, it will be necessary to widen the confidence interval. To demonstrate these relations, suppose 31 random observations yield a mean of 100 and a standard error of the mean of 5. We may make the following statements:

(1) The probability is 0.95 or 19:1 ($t_{.95}$ with 30 degrees of freedom = 2.042) that

$$\bar{x} - t_{.95} s_{\bar{x}} \leqslant \mu \leqslant \bar{x} + t_{.95} s_{\bar{x}}$$

or

$$(100 - 10.21) \leqslant \mu \leqslant (100 + 10.21)$$
$$89.79 \leqslant \mu \leqslant 110.21$$

(a range of 20.42)

(2) The probability is 0.50, i.e., a 50-50 chance ($t_{.50}$ with 30 degrees of freedom = 0.683) that

or

$$(100 - 3.42) \leqslant \mu \leqslant (100 + 3.42)$$
$$96.58 \leqslant \mu \leqslant 103.42$$

(a range of 6.83)

(3) The probability is 0.99 or 99:1 ($t_{.99}$ with 30 degrees of freedom = 2.750) that

or

$$(100 - 13.75) \leqslant \mu \leqslant (100 + 13.75)$$
$$86.25 \leqslant \mu \leqslant 113.75$$

(a range of 27.50)

It is assumed in the above that the sample is a small part (less than 2%) of the population. If the sample is a large part, the variance of the mean should be multiplied by a finite population factor

$$f = \left(1 - \frac{n}{N}\right)$$

(9)

which will reduce the variance of the sample mean to the extent of the ratio of the sample to the population size.

Confidence Range or Sampling Error Relative to Magnitude Estimated

It may be desirable to express the sampling error, or range of confidence, in terms of either a percentage of the estimate or in terms of the population total. Thus, we may wish to provide an estimate such as 50 animal months with a confidence range of plus or minus 3 animal months or a sampling error expressed as plus or minus 6%.

The estimate of the total for a population is obtained by multiplying the average value per sampling unit by the total number of such units in the population.

Thus, if there are N square meters in a pasture, the estimated total in the pasture, say $\hat{T}$, is

$$\hat{T} = N(\bar{x}) \tag{10}$$

where $\bar{x}$ is the sample average value of X per square meter. The variance of $\hat{T}$ is

$$\sigma_{\hat{T}}^2 = N^2 \sigma_{\bar{x}}^2 , \tag{11}$$

and the sample estimate is

$$s_{\hat{T}}^2 = N^2 s_{\bar{x}}^2 \tag{12}$$

Consider now the effect of increasing the size of the unit of observation. Let X' be the weight of a 4 m² plot. Obviously, the population average of weights of plots this size should be 4 times as great, and in the population there would be one-fourth as many as when 1 m² areas are used. Now the estimate is T' and

$$T' = \frac{N}{4} \bar{x}' \text{ where } \bar{x}' \text{ is the average of the sample} \tag{13}$$

of 4 m² plots. Now the variance of T' is

$$s_{T'}^2 = \frac{N^2}{16} s_{\bar{x}'}^2 \tag{14}$$

T and T' are, of course, estimates of the same population value; s_T or $s_{T'}$, when multiplied by the value for the probability level selected, show the limit of confidence in either direction or half the confidence range. If the half range is divided by $\hat{T}$ or T' and multiplied by 100, the result is an expression of the confidence limit in terms of a percentage of the estimated total.

Size and Shape of Plot

A comparison of equations 12 and 14 shows that to obtain equal values of the variances of the totals, i.e., s_T or $s_{T'}$, it would be necessary for $s_{\bar{x}}^2$ to be $1/16$ as great as $s_{\bar{x}}^2$. If the 1 m² plots making up the individual 4 m² plots were completely independent, that is, if each could be considered to be a random sample of the entire pasture, the variance of single 4 m² (totals of four 1 m²) plots should be 4 times as great as for 1 m² plots. The m² plots making up 4 m² plots are expected, however, to be less variable than if selected at random over the whole pasture. It is expected, therefore, that the 4 m² totals would be more variable than totals of 4 randomly selected square meters, that is $s_{\bar{x}}^2$ is expected to be more than 16 times as great as $s_{\bar{x}}^2$. To attain the same precision would, therefore, require a greater area to be sampled, i.e., more than one-fourth the number of samples using 4 m² plots than 1 m² plots. To offset the greater sample area requirement, however, the cost of measurement per unit of area should be less for the larger plots because of the reduced travel time and the reduced time to locate sample points. Quite possibly, then, it may cost less to use the larger sample size to obtain the same precision.

The shape of the plot also can be important in the efficiency and cost of the sample. It is usually found that elongated plots which are oriented with the long axis in the direction of greatest variability are more uniform from plot to plot than are square or circular plots of the same area.

To study the importance of plot size and shape, use is made of some field data. An area 30.5 × 48.8 m in size was initially divided into 640 1.52 × 1.52 m plots, and the weight of hawksbeard *(Crepis acuminata)* was obtained for each plot. The plots were combined into 1.52 × 3.04 m plots, 1.52 × 6.08 m plots and 3.04 × 3.04 m plots. The actual variances for these plots are shown in the third column of Table 9-1.

Table 9-1. Shape and size of plots, actual and estimated variance, and efficiency as compared to independent plots.

Shape and size of unit	Number of small plots per unit	Actual variance	Estimated variance*	Efficiency as compared to independent plots
(1)	(2)	(3)	(4)	(5)
1.52 × 1.52 m	1	6,265.66	6,265.66	1.000
1.52 × 3.04 m	2	20,630.39	12,531.32	0.607
1.52 × 6.08 m	4	46,357.23	25,062.64	0.541
3.04 × 3.04 m	4	58,539.30	25,062.64	0.428

*Assuming independence.

The effect of grouping can be seen by comparing these actual plot variances to what would have been obtained by random combination of these plots. The estimated variance of the larger plot is equal to the variance of an individual plot multiplied by the number of plots. The estimated variances are shown in column 4 and were obtained by multiplying the variance of the unit plot, i.e., 6,265.66 by the number of plots shown in the second column.

The effect of plot shape can be seen by comparing the actual variance of plots 1.52 × 6.08 m with plots 3.04 × 3.04 m in size. The long, narrow 1.52 × 6.08 m plot is 58,539.30/46,357.23 − 1.0 = 0.26 or 26% more efficient than the square 3.04 × 3.04 m plots. In other words, 26% more plots of the shape 3.04 × 3.04 m would be required to give the same error as obtained by using 1.52 × 6.08 m plots.

The cost of obtaining kn independent small plots is usually greater than that of obtaining n large plots each having an area equal to k individual plots. For this reason, it is necessary to consider cost when deciding on plot size.

If the cost of obtaining a 1.52 × 3.04 m plot is more than 60.7% of the cost of a pair of independent smaller plots—then the small plots will give smaller error for a given amount of money (Table 9-1). Also, if the cost of obtaining a 1.52 × 6.08 m plot is more than 54.1% of the cost of four random small plots—then the small plots are better. However, if the cost of obtaining a larger plot is less than 54.1% of that of obtaining four small plots—then the larger plots are best.

For instance, if $5,000 is available for a survey, and it costs $10.00 to get a pair of independent 1.52 × 1.52 m plots, the variance of the estimate would be

12,531.32/[($5,000/$10.00)] = 12,531.32/500 = 25.06.

If a larger 1.52 × 3.04 m plot costs $7.00, then the variance of this estimate would be

20,630.39/[($5,000/$7.00)] = 20,630.39/714 = 28.89.

The variance for the larger plots is larger than for the pair of random plots. This is expected, since the cost of the larger plots was more than 60.7% of the cost of a pair of small plots. If the larger plots had cost $5.50 per plot, then the variance of the larger plots would be

20,630.39/[($5,000/$5.50)] = 20,630.39/909 = 22.70.

This is as expected, since the cost of the larger plot $5.50, is less than 60.7% of the cost of a pair of small plots.

Sampling Plans

It will be evident from the discussion of the basic sampling designs that a large number of variants or combinations can be created. In fact, they are limited only by the ingenuity of the sampler and the material available.

Simple Random Sampling

The simplest form of sampling is the random selection of a set of n observations from a population of N. For instance from a total of 640 possible units, 10 are selected with each unit of this total having an equal chance of being selected.

The yield from this random sample of 10 out of a total of 640 plots can now be used to estimate the yield of all plots. The 10 random observations were 60, 0, 40, 75, 115, 95, 150, 190, 75, and 310. The total of the observations is 1,110. The estimate of the mean of the population is 111.0.

The estimate of the population total is

$$\hat{T} = N(\bar{x}) = 640(111.0) = 71,040$$

To determine the precision of this estimate, it is necessary to calculate the standard deviation and the standard error.

The standard deviation is calculated using a rearrangement of Equation 4:

$$s = \sqrt{\frac{\sum\limits_{i=1}^{n} X_i^2 - \dfrac{(\sum\limits_{i=1}^{n} X_i)^2}{n}}{n-1}} = \sqrt{\frac{193,400 - \dfrac{(1110)^2}{10}}{9}}$$

$$= \sqrt{\frac{193,400 - 123,210}{9}} = \sqrt{\frac{70,190}{9}} = \sqrt{7,798.89} = 88.31$$

The standard error

$$s_{\bar{x}} = \frac{s}{\sqrt{n}}\sqrt{1 - \frac{n}{N}} = \frac{88.31}{\sqrt{10}}\sqrt{1 - \frac{10}{640}}$$

$$= \frac{88.31}{3.1623}\sqrt{.9844} = 27.93(.9922) = 27.71$$

In this problem the use of the finite population correction factor $\sqrt{1 - \dfrac{n}{N}}$ has reduced the error by little, i.e, from 27.93 to 27.71.

Since $\hat{T} = N\bar{x}$ the standard error of $\hat{T}$ is

$$s_{\hat{T}} = N(s_{\bar{x}}) = (640)(27.71) = 17,734.40$$

The confidence interval for this estimate of the total is

$$\hat{T} - t_p s_{\hat{T}} \leq T \leq \hat{T} + t_p s_{\hat{T}}$$

If t_p is chosen for a probability level of $p = 0.95$ and 9 degrees of freedom, then $t = 2.26$. The confidence interval is

$$71,040 - (2.26)(17,734.40) \leq T \leq 71,404 + (2.26)(17,734.40)$$
$$71,040 - 40,079.7 \leq T \leq 71,040 + 40,079.7$$
$$30,960.3 \leq T \leq 111,119.7$$

Thus, we are 95% confident that the true population total T is in the range 30,960.3 to 111,119.7.

Since this range is rather large, it may be desirable to obtain a smaller confidence interval by resampling. Therefore, the sample margin of error of 7,000.0 might be selected instead of the value of 40,079.7. The sample size suggested to obtain this accuracy can be obtained from the equation.

$$n = \frac{t^2(N^2s^2)}{(\hat{T} - T)^2 + t^2Ns^2}$$

which is a rearrangement of the expresssion for

$$t = \frac{(\hat{T} - T)}{N(s/\sqrt{n}) (\sqrt{1 - \frac{n}{N}})}$$

The sample supplies the value for s. The value for $(\hat{T} - T)$ in this example is 7,000, the desirable allowable error. The confidence we want to place in the allowable error is measured by the value of t chosen. If we set the confidence interval probability at $P = 0.95$, then from the normal curve of error we find $t = 1.96$ thus

$$n = \frac{(1.96)^2(640)^2(88.31)^2}{(7000)^2 + (1.96)^2(640)(88.31)^2} = \frac{12,271,336,355}{49,000,000 + 19,173,963} = 180$$

If a preliminary sample is not available to supply the estimate of s, then one must use his/her best estimate of s.

Sometimes the research worker wants to collect a sufficient number of samples to give reasonable assurance that the true mean is within a prescribed range of the sample mean. Thus, suppose the confidence interval is to be 10% of the mean or $(0.10) (111) = 11.1$. Therefore, using

$$t_{.95} = \frac{(\bar{x} - \mu)}{s/\sqrt{n}}$$

then

$$n = \frac{t^2s^2}{(\bar{x} - \mu)^2}$$

From the example $n = (1.96)^2 (88.31)^2/(11.1)^2$ or 243. This suggests that if as many as 243 samples are taken, the population mean will not deviate more than 10% from the sample mean with odds of 19 to 1 or a probability of 95%.

Cluster Sampling

Cluster sampling is the simplest of the restricted random sampling plans. It may be thought of in a restricted since as random block sampling. As used here, a cluster location or block will be considered as a relatively small and compact area within which a cluster or subsample of elementary units is confined. For example, a cluster area may be a $1/100$ ha area in which n (for example 2, or 6, or 16) m² plots may be selected for measurement or observation. If cluster sampling, the time or cost of making individual observations within a small area is less than when the plots are scattered at random over the whole area.

For example, returning to the population of 320,000 square meter units in a 32 ha pasture, we may mentally subdivide the pasture into 3,200, 100 m² sub-areas or sampling areas. We may then select 25 of these 3,200 at random and select 16 of the 100 m² units in each of the 25 as subsamples. Alternatively we could select 10, 100 m² areas and at random select 40 subsample units in each. In either event, a sample of 400 square meter plots would be obtained, but the randomization of the selection would have been restricted.

As before, the estimate $\hat{T}$ would be

$$\hat{T} = N\bar{x}$$

where N is 320,000 and $\bar{x}$ the average of the 400 square meter plots. Equivalently we could estimate

$$\hat{T} = \frac{320,000}{400} \sum_{i=1}^{400} X_i$$

which is identical but indicates more apparently that the expansion factor $320,000/400$ is the reciprocal of the sampling fraction.

In order to compute the sampling variance or error of T as estimated from a clustered or block sample, we must consider two sources of sampling error. Consider first the error of the sample estimate if we measured all 100 m² on each of the 25 randomly selected areas. We then should have a simple random sample of 25, 100 m² plots of the 3,200 available. If the true mean of plot "i" is μ_i and the variance of these means σ_b^2, the estimate of the mean for the 25, 100 m² sub-areas would be

$$\bar{x} = \frac{1}{25} \sum_{i=1}^{25} \mu_i$$

and its sample variance would be

$$s_{\bar{x}}^2 = \left(\frac{1}{25}\right) s_b^2 \left(1 - \frac{25}{3200}\right) \tag{15}$$

Since all of the 100 square meter plots are not measured, variance s_b^2 cannot be computed directly by substituting in equation 4, but must be approximated by an analysis of variance computation. The theory of this estimate will be discussed more fully in a later section.

Consider now the second source of sampling error. The value $\bar{x}_i$ as an estimate of μ_i is subject to a sampling variance equal to the variance of square meter samples within 100 m² plots divided by the number of sample square meter units within the 100 m² plot and multiplied by the complement of the sampling ratio. If the variance among square meter plots within 100 m² plots is $\sigma_{w_i}^2$ and its sample estimate is $s_{w_i}^2$, and if there are N sampling units (in this case 100) of which n (in this case 16) are included in the sample, then the sample variance of $\bar{x}_i$, as an estimate of μ_i is

$$s_{\bar{x}_i}^2 = \frac{s_{w_i}^2}{n} \left(1 - \frac{n}{N} \right)$$

(16)

$s_{w_i}^2$ is computed according to formula 4, for a single 100 m² area as

$$s_{w_i}^2 = \frac{\sum\limits_{j=1}^{n} (X_{ij} - \bar{x}_i)^2}{n - 1}$$

(17)

For the entire sample of 25, in this case, 100 m² plots, s_w^2 is computed as the average of the 25 values of $s_{w_i}^2$ by the direct formula

$$s_w^2 = \frac{\sum\limits_{i=1}^{k} \sum\limits_{j=1}^{n} (X_{ij} - \bar{x}_i)^2}{k(n - 1)}$$

(18)

where k is the number of 100 m² plots or clusters sampled (in this case k = 25). Now, the variance of $\bar{x}$ as an estimate of μ is the sum of the two variances, i.e., the variance of $\bar{x}_i$ as an estimate of μ_i and the variance of μ_i as an estimate of μ. If K is the total number of 100 m² plots in the population sampled

$$s_{\bar{x}}^2 = \frac{s_b^2}{k} \left(1 - \frac{k}{K} \right) + \frac{s_w^2}{kn} \left(1 - \frac{n}{N} \right)$$

(19)

If, as in this case, k/K (which is 25/3,200) and n/N (here 16/100) are near zero, the terms in parentheses approach one and may be omitted.

Allocation of Subplots to Clusters

It is evident from the examples given, i.e., drawing 16 square meter samples from each of 25, 100 m² plots, or 40 m² from each of 10, 100 m² plots, that the number of plots and subplots or the number of clusters and observations per cluster are not unique. A specified sampling error $(s_{\bar{x}})$ can often be obtained from a number of combinations of k and n under constant conditions of σ_b^2, σ_w^2 K, and N. Normally the most desirable combination is that which leads to the minimum cost. Let C_b be the cost associated with the cluster. This is principally travel and survey time, and establishing the necessary equipment "on the ground." Let C_w be the cost association with the observation plot. The cost of the sample will then be $C = kC_b + knC_w$. The combination that will lead to the minimum cost will be when

$$n = \sqrt{\frac{s_w^2\, C_b}{s_b^2\, C_w}} \qquad (20)$$

The number of plots per cluster, thus, increases directly as the square root of the ratio of within- to the between-cluster variance and varies inversely as the square root of the observation cost to the cluster cost. The number of plots per cluster must be two or more if the sampling error of the survey is to be self-contained, since if there is only one observation per cluster, neither s_w^2 nor s_b^2 can be computed.

Tabular Computation of s_w^2 and s_b^2

It is customary to compute s_w^2 and s_b^2 by an analysis of variance procedure as typified by the following table.

Table 9-2. Computation of within- and between-cluster variance.

Source of variation	Degrees of freedom	Sums of squares	Components of variance*
Clusters	$k - 1$	$n \sum\limits_{i=1}^{k} (\bar{x}_i - \bar{x})^2$	$\sigma_w^2 + n\sigma_b^2$
Within clusters	$k(n-1)$	$\sum\limits_{i=1}^{k} \sum\limits_{j=1}^{n} (X_{ij} - \bar{x}_i)^2$	σ_w^2
Total	$kn - 1$	$\sum\limits_{i=1}^{k} \sum\limits_{j=1}^{n} (X_{ij} - \bar{x})^2$	

* Components of variance or mean square (M.S.)

$$s_b^2 = \frac{\text{cluster M.S.} - \text{within clusters M.S.}}{n} \doteq \sigma_b^2 \qquad (21)$$

This symbol, $\doteq$, refers to an estimate of some value.

If the sample of k clusters and n plots per cluster is an appreciable part of the population of clusters and plots per cluster, then:

$$\text{Within cluster M.S.} \doteq \sigma_w^2 \left(\frac{N}{N-1}\right)$$

$$\text{Cluster M.S.} \doteq \sigma_w^2 \left(\frac{N-n}{N-1}\right) + n\sigma_b^2 \left(\frac{K}{K-1}\right)$$

The observation for six clusters of three plots each which represent the forage yield in grams of sample plots taken in an experimental pasture are given in Table 9-3.

The mean per plot is

$$\bar{x} = \frac{\sum\limits_{i=1}^{k} \sum\limits_{j=1}^{n} (X_{ij})}{kn} = \frac{2538}{(3)(6)} = 141.00$$

To estimate the error of $\bar{x}$, it is necessary to separate the total variation

Table 9-3. Forage yield in grams per plot for six clusters of three plots each.

Plots							
	1	*2*	*3*	*4*	*5*	*6*	
1	130	139	137	152	151	157	
2	122	155	97	136	111	125	
3	202	171	13	248	199	93	
Total	454	465	247	536	461	375	2,538

into two parts, among clusters and within clusters, and to estimate the variance components.

For calculation, the expression for the sums of squares given in Table 9-2 will be expressed in different forms. Total sum of squares

$$\sum_{i=1}^{k} \sum_{j=1}^{n} (X_{ij} - \bar{x})^2 = \sum_{i=1}^{k} \sum_{j=1}^{n} X_{ij}^2 - \frac{\left(\sum_{i=1}^{k} \sum_{j=1}^{n} X_{ij} \right)^2}{kn}$$

$$= 400,272 - \frac{(2538)^2}{18}$$

$$= 400,272 - 357,858 = 42,414$$

Sum of squares for among clusters

$$n \sum_{i=1}^{k} (\bar{x}_i - \bar{x})^2 = \sum_{i=1}^{k} \frac{\left(\sum_{j=1}^{n} X_{ij} \right)^2}{n} - \frac{\left(\sum_{i=1}^{k} \sum_{j=1}^{n} X_{ij} \right)^2}{kn}$$

$$= \frac{(454)^2 + (465)^2 + (247)^2 + (536)^2 + (461)^2 + (375)^2}{3} - \frac{(2538)^2}{18}$$

$$= 374,597 - 357,858 = 16,739$$

Sum of squares within clusters

$$\sum_{i=1}^{k} \sum_{j=1}^{n} (X_{ij} - \bar{x}_i)^2 = \sum_{i=1}^{k} \sum_{j=1}^{n} X_{ij}^2 - \sum_{i=1}^{k} \frac{\left(\sum_{j=1}^{n} X_{ij} \right)^2}{n}$$

$$= 400,272 - 374,597 = 25,675$$

Table 9-4. Analysis of variance for data shown in Table 9-3.

Source of variation	Degrees of freedom	Sum of squares	Mean square	Components of variance
Among clusters	5	16,739	3,347.8	$\sigma_w^2 + 3\sigma_b^2$
Within clusters	12	25,675	2,139.6	σ_w^2
Total	17	42,414		

Thus $2,139.6 = s_w^2 \doteq \sigma_w^2$

$$\frac{3,347.8 - 2,139.6}{3} = 402.7 = s_b^2 \doteq \sigma_b^2$$

Using these estimates of the variance components, the variance of the mean $\bar{x}$ is

$$s_{\bar{x}}^2 = \frac{402.7}{6} + \frac{2,139.6}{(3)(6)} = 67.1167 + 118.8667 = 185.9834$$

If the population contains 240 clusters each with 15 observations per cluster, then the variance components should be estimated using the equation given below the footnote to Table 9-2.

Thus, $2,139.6 \div \left(\frac{15}{14}\right) \sigma_w^2$ or $1,996.96 \doteq \sigma_w^2$

and $3,347.8 - 1,996.96 \left(\frac{15-3}{14}\right) \doteq 3\sigma_b^2\left(\frac{240}{239}\right)$

$$\frac{3,347.8 - 1,711.7}{3}\left(\frac{240}{239}\right) \doteq \sigma_b^2$$

$$547.65 \doteq \sigma_b^2$$

Block Sampling

A natural extension to the cluster sampling system described under the previous section is to enlarge the blocks from which samples are drawn so that samples are drawn from all blocks. This would be the same as stratified sampling where blocks represent the strata. To see the statistical effect of this extension, equation 19 is copied below:

$$s_{\bar{x}}^2 = \frac{s_b^2}{k}\left(1 - \frac{k}{K}\right) + \frac{s_w^2}{kn}\left(1 - \frac{n}{N}\right)$$

If the size of the blocks in the population or the number of blocks in the sample increases so that n observations are drawn from every block in the population, we find that $k = K$ and hence that $k/K = 1$ and the term $(1 - k/K) = 0$. Thus, if all blocks are represented in the sample in the same manner as in the population sample, any variation s_b^2 among blocks makes no contribution to the sampling error of the survey.

In surveys of areas such as in pasture or range allotment samples, the block type survey has considerable intuitive appeal. Unlike a completely random survey which by the caprices of chance could result in all or the bulk of the observations falling in a quarter or half of the area, block surveys by their very nature insure that all parts of the range are sampled reasonably uniformly. The cost of this insurance is an increase in the size of the t value used in setting the confidence limits. This will usually be slight, however, since the range sampled would normally be divided into no fewer than 25 to 30 blocks. The gain in precision will usually be substantial, since the variation of plots in the same block may be less than the variation in plots over the whole range sampled.

Block and Cluster Sampling

The principles presented in the two previous sections can readily be combined. A range allotment or pasture can be divided first into a number, say H large blocks of 40 ha each. Each of these large blocks can then be subdivided into K (here 400) $1/10$ ha large plots or cluster areas, and these in turn divided into the 1,000 square meter plots. A sample would then consist of k $1/10$ ha plots drawn at random from the K available in each of the H blocks. Within each of the k $1/10$ ha plots, n square meter plots are drawn from the N (here 1,000) available. The estimate of $\bar{x}$ of the population mean μ is now

$$\bar{x} = \frac{1}{H}\sum_{p=1}^{H} \bar{x}_p \qquad (22)$$

where $\bar{x}_p$ = the mean of a block.
The variance of $\bar{x}$ will then be

$$s_{\bar{x}}^2 = \frac{1}{H}\left[\frac{s_b^2}{k}\left(\frac{K-k}{K}\right) + \frac{s_w^2}{kn}\left(\frac{N-n}{N}\right)\right] \qquad (23)$$

With this further extension, it would not have been necessary to have included all H of the large blocks in the sample. Had only h of the blocks been included, a further source of sampling error would have resulted from the variance σ_s^2, say, among the true large block means. The estimate of s_s^2 would have been obtained from an analysis of variance computation similar to that in Table 9-2 where a third line would have been added (Table 9-5).

Table 9-5. Computation of variance among blocks, among clusters within blocks, and within clusters.

Source of variation	Degrees of freedom	Components of variance
Among blocks	$h-1$	$\sigma_w^2 + n\sigma_b^2 + nk\sigma_s^2$
Clusters within blocks	$h(k-)$	$\sigma_w^2 + n\sigma_b^2$
Within clusters	$hk(n-1)$	σ_w^2
Total	$hkn-1$	

To obtain an estimate of the yield from a 100 ha pasture, the pasture was divided into 4 blocks of 25 ha each. Each block was divided into 250, 1/10 ha clusters. Each cluster was divided into 500 sampling units. The sample to estimate mean yield consists of 6 clusters of 3 units in each block. These samples are shown in Table 9-6.

Table 9-6. Forage yield in grams per plot for six clusters of three plots each in four blocks.

			Cluster				
Blocks	1	2	3	4	5	6	Total
1	235	152	191	101	270	85	
	143	194	196	17	279	325	
	241	193	260	182	264	210	
Total	619	539	647	300	813	620	3538
2	163	205	248	215	164	234	
	198	197	124	235	236	196	
	113	221	199	166	188	186	
Total	474	623	571	616	588	616	3488
3	210	50	222	220	190	165	
	285	151	230	327	230	250	
	292	248	282	254	195	154	
Total	787	449	734	801	615	569	3955
4	298	330	161	254	345	280	
	248	143	263	183	264	274	
	225	165	255	305	189	337	
Total	771	638	679	742	798	891	4519

The variation among the 72 unit observations is due to variation among blocks, variation among clusters within blocks, and variation within clusters.

These sources of variation are separated out in an analysis of variance as shown in Table 9-7.

Table 9-7. Block totals, sum of squares of individual observations, and cluster totals for data shown in Table 9-6.

Block	Block total	Sum of squares of individual observations	Sum of squares of cluster totals
	$\sum_{i=1}^{6} \sum_{j=1}^{3} X_{ij}$	$\sum_{i=1}^{6} \sum_{j=1}^{3} X^2_{ij}$	$\sum_{i=1}^{6} (\sum_{j=1}^{3} X_{ij})^2$
1	3,538	795,242	2,227,660
2	3,488	699,408	2,043,502
3	3,955	939,413	2,703,313
4	4,519	1,200,139	3,443,775
Total	15,500	3,634,202	10,418,250

The computations are as follows:
Total sum of squares:

$$\sum_{e=1}^{h} \sum_{i=1}^{k} \sum_{j=1}^{n} X_{eij}^2 - \frac{\left(\sum_{e=1}^{h} \sum_{i=1}^{k} \sum_{j=1}^{n} X_{eij}\right)^2}{(h)(k)(n)}$$

$$3,634,202 - \frac{(15,500)^2}{72} = 3,634,202 - 3,336,806 = 297,396$$

Block—sum of squares

$$\sum_{e=1}^{h} \frac{\left(\sum_{i=1}^{k} \sum_{j=1}^{n} X_{eij}\right)^2}{(k)(n)} - \frac{\left(\sum_{e=1}^{h} \sum_{i=1}^{k} \sum_{j=1}^{n} X_{eij}\right)^2}{(h)(k)(n)}.$$

$$\frac{(3538)^2 + (3488)^2 + (3955)^2 + (4519)^2}{18} - 3,336,806 =$$
$$3,374,832 - 3,336,806 = 38,026$$

Clusters within block—sum of squares

$$\sum_{e=1}^{h} \sum_{i=1}^{k} \frac{\left(\sum_{j=1}^{n} X_{eij}\right)^2}{n} - \sum_{e=1}^{h} \frac{\left(\sum_{i=1}^{k} \sum_{j=1}^{n} X_{eij}\right)^2}{(k)(n)}$$

$$\frac{10,418,250}{3} - 3.374,832 = 3,472,750 - 3,374,832 = 97,918$$

Within cluster—sum of squares

$$\sum_{e=1}^{h} \sum_{i=1}^{k} \sum_{j=1}^{n} X_{eij}^2 - \sum_{e=1}^{h} \sum_{i=1}^{k} \frac{\left(\sum_{j=1}^{n} X_{eij}\right)^2}{n}$$

$$3,634,202 - 3,472,750 = 161,452$$

The basic computations are shown assembled in the analysis of variance in Table 9-8.

Table 9-8. Analysis of variance for data shown in Table 9-6.

Source of variation	Degrees of freedom	Sum of squares	Mean square	Components of variance
Among blocks	3	38,026	12,675	$\sigma_w^2 + 3\sigma_b^2 + (3)(6)\sigma_s^2$
Clusters within	20	97,918	4,896	$\sigma_w^2 + 3\sigma_b^2$
Within clusters	48	161,452	3,364	σ_w^2
Total	71	297,396		

$$3,364 = s_w^2 \doteq \sigma_w^2$$

$$\frac{4,896 - 3,364}{3} = 510.67 = s_b^2 \doteq \sigma_b^2$$

$$\frac{12,675 - 4,896}{18} = 432.17 = s_s^2 \doteq \sigma_s^2$$

The mean yield per plot is

$$\bar{x} = \frac{\sum_{\ell=1}^{h} \sum_{i=1}^{k} \sum_{j=1}^{n} X_{\ell ij}}{(h)(k)(n)} = \frac{15,500}{72} = 215.28$$

Since each of the four blocks is sampled, the variance due to block does not enter into the calculation of the error of the mean. Thus, the variance of this mean is

$$s_{\bar{x}}^2 = \frac{510.67}{(4)(6)} + \frac{3,364}{(4)(6)(3)} = 21.28 + 46.72 = 69.00$$

The process of geographic partitioning and subsampling can, of course, be extended as far as it is profitable to do so, but a hierarchy of more than 3 to 4 levels is rarely desirable or even practicable in most fields.

Stratified Random Sampling

Stratified sampling is a system by which sampling units are drawn from relatively homogeneous classes, groups, types, sites, or conditions which are spoken of in a generic sense as strata. In range vegetation sampling, strata may be mapped or may be homogeneous sampling units within complex mapping units. The number of sampling units selected in each stratum does not have to be equal, since the total or mean value for all strata is computed by adding stratum totals or weighting stratum mean values by the area of the stratum.

If N_h (h = 1,2,---m) is the number of units in stratum h

n_h is the number of sample observations in stratum h

m is the number of strata

$$\bar{x}_h = \frac{\sum_{i=1}^{n_h} X_{hi}}{n_h} \text{ is the sample mean of stratum } h \text{ and}$$

$$s_h^2 = \frac{\sum\limits_{i=1}^{n_h} (X_{hi} - \bar{x}_h)^2}{n_h - 1}$$ is the sample estimate of observations in stratum h,

then

$\hat{T} = \sum\limits_{h=1}^{m} N_h \bar{x}_h$ is the estimated total for the population and its sampling
variance is   (24)

$$s_{\hat{T}}^2 = \sum_{h=1}^{m} N_h^2 s_{\bar{x}_h}^2$$

(25)

If the stratum areas are large so that n_h is an *inconsequential part of* N_h, or if sampling is with replacement, i.e., all sampling units have a chance of being selected at each random draw and the same sampling unit may, therefore, be represented more than once in the sample, then

$$s_{\bar{x}_h}^2 = \frac{s_h^2}{n_h} \qquad \text{and} \qquad (26)$$

$$s_{\hat{T}}^2 = \sum_{h=1}^{m} N_h^2 \frac{s_h^2}{n_h} \qquad (27)$$

If, however, sampling is without replacement and n_h is an *appreciable part of* N_h,

$$s_{\bar{x}_h}^2 = \frac{s_h^2}{n_h} \left(1 - \frac{n_h}{N_h} \right) \qquad \text{and} \qquad (28)$$

$$s_{\hat{T}}^2 = \sum_{h=1}^{m} N_h^2 \frac{s_h^2}{n_h} \left(1 - \frac{n_h}{N_h} \right) \qquad (29)$$

The allocation of sampling units, however, is usually of two types: proportional or optimum (also called Neyman) allocation. These will be discussed in turn.

Stratified Sampling with Proportional Allocation

If the sample measurement locations are selected at random (or even systematically) without regard to stratum boundaries, the sample points, on the average, will be distributed by strata in proportion fo stratum areas. If stratum areas are known and proportional sampling is desired, this can be achieved by restricting the randomization accordingly.

In proportional sampling, the number of observations allocated to stratum h is equal to the total number of observations multiplied by the proportion of the population in stratum h, i.e.,

$$n_h = n\frac{N_h}{N} \tag{30}$$

where

$n = n_1 + n_2 + \text{- - -} + n_m =$ total number of observations in the sample, and

$N = N_1 + N_2 + \text{- - -} + N_m =$ total area or number of observations in the population.

Stratified Sampling with Optimum Allocation

The equation for computation of the sampling variance of the estimate based on stratified sampling (equation 29) is valid regardless of type of allocation. From the components of this sum, it is evident that large values of N_h and s_h, particularly since they appear in the equation as squared terms, will increase $s_{\bar{y}}^2$ and $s_{\bar{y}}^2$ is reduced only by increasing n_h. If the entire cost of the survey is fixed so that only a total number of observations, $n = \sum_{h=1}^{m} n_h$, can be taken, it is often desirable to allocate the observations to the strata in a somewhat disproportionate manner. When such allocations are made, $s_{\bar{y}}^2$ should be kept as small as possible.

It can be shown that if we set

$$n_h = (n)\frac{N_h s_h}{\sum\limits_{h=1}^{m} N_h s_h} \tag{31}$$

this objective will be accomplished. The following examples illustrate that when there are substantial differences in the values of s_h^2, optimum allocation enjoys a substantial advantage over proportional allocation, whereas with reasonably uniform variances the gains are negligible.

The data used in the following example were obtained from three strata: (1) dense timber, (2) open timber, and (3) meadow. From each stratum a sample of 20 random units was drawn and the mean and standard deviation of the units computed. These statistics and the total number of units in each stratum are shown in Table 9-9.

Table 9-9. The mean and standard deviation for three strata of vegetation cover.

Stratum	Number of units in populations	Sample Mean	Sample Standard deviation
Dense timber	246	18.1	20.1
Open timber	322	105.2	69.8
Meadow	72	190.8	130.4

Table 9-10. Calculations for an estimate of the population total and the variance of the estimate for three strata of vegetation cover.

Stratum	N_h	$\bar{x}_h$	s_h	n_h	$N_h(\bar{x}_h)$	$N_h(s_h)$	$\dfrac{N_h^2 s_h^2}{n_h}$	$1 - \dfrac{n_h}{N_h}$	Col. 8 × Col. 9
	(2)	(3)	(4)	(5)	(6)	(7)	(8)	(9)	(10)
Dense timber	246	18.1	20.1	20	4,452.6	4,944.6	1,222,453	.919	1,123,434
Open timber	322	105.2	69.8	20	33,874.4	22,475.6	25,257,630	.938	23,691,657
Meadow	72	190.8	130.4	20	13,737.6	9,388.8	4,407,478	.722	3,182,199
Total	640				52,064.6	36,809.0			27,977,290

Using sample data, an estimate of the population total can be made and its confidence band computed. The estimate of the population total will be made using equation (24) and the variance of this estimate by equation (29). The calculations are shown in Table 9-10.

The estimate of the population total using equation (24) is the sum of column 6 or 52,064.6. The variance of this total is the total of column 10 or 27,997,290. In the computations note that column 8 is column 7 squared and divided by column 5. The error of the estimated total is $\sqrt{27,997,290}$ or 5,291.

Since the strata samples are not small, a t value from the normal curve will be used in determining the confidence band. For a probability of 0.95 the value of t is 1.96. The confidence interval becomes

$$52{,}065 - (5291)(1.96) \leq (T) \leq 52{,}065 + (5291)(1.96)$$
$$52{,}065 - 10{,}370 \leq (T) \leq 52{,}065 + 10{,}370$$
$$41{,}695 \leq (T) \leq 62{,}435$$

If the strata sample sizes had been small, for example, 7, 8, and 5 for the dense timber, open timber, and meadow, respectively, the confidence interval could not be as easily computed, since the degrees of freedom for selecting t are not known.

Using the same means and standard deviations as the data shown in Table 9-10, the error can be recalculated using the smaller sample sizes. The calculation is shown in Table 9-11.

Table 9-11. Calculations for the error of the estimated total for three strata of vegetation cover with seven samples taken from dense timber, eight from the open timber, and five from the meadow.

Stratum	N_h	s_h	n_h	$N_h s_h$	$\dfrac{H_h^2 s_h^2}{n_h}$	$1 - \dfrac{n_h}{N_h}$	Col. 6 × Col. 7
	(2)	(3)	(4)	(5)	(6)	(7)	(8)
Dense timber	246	20.1	7	4,944.6	3,492,724	.972	3,394,928
Open timber	322	69.8	8	22,475.6	63,144,074	.975	61,565,472
Meadow	72	130.4	5	9,388.8	17,629,913	.931	16,413,449
Total	640						81,373,849

Error = $\sqrt{81,373,849} = 9{,}020.7$

In this example the number of degrees of freedom of each class is small, so the normal deviate value of t for large n cannot be used. To choose the appropriate t value, one must have an appropriate number of degrees of freedom. For problems like this, approximation (Cochran and Cox 1966) will be used.

$$n' = \frac{\left\{ \sum_{h=1}^{3} \left[\dfrac{N_h(N_h - n_h)}{n_h} \right] s_h^2 \right\}^2}{\sum_{h=1}^{3} \dfrac{\left\{ \left[\dfrac{N_h(N_h - n_h)}{n_h} \right] s_h^2 \right\}^2}{n_h - 1}}$$

The basic data are obtained from the fourth and the last columns of Table 9-11. The calculation for obtaining n' are shown in Table 9-12.

Table 9-12. Calculations for determining approximate degrees of freedom for the estimated total when unequal sample numbers are among the strata.

Stratum	$\left[\dfrac{N_h(N_h - n_h)}{n_h} s_h^2\right]$	$(n_h - 1)$	$\left[\dfrac{N_h(N_h - n_h)}{n_h} s_h^2\right]^2 \div \ (n_h - 1)$
Dense timber 3,394,928		6	1,920,922,687,531
Open timber............ 61,565,472		7	541,472,477,511,826
Meadow 16,413,449		4	67,350,327,018,900
81,373,849			610,743,727,218,257

$$n' = \frac{(81,373,849)^2}{610,743,727,218,257} = \frac{6,621,703,301,074,801}{610,743,727,218,257} = 10.8 \text{ or } 11.$$

The value of t for 11 degrees of freedom for a probability of 0.95 is 2.201. The confidence interval is $52,065 \pm (2.201)(9,020.7)$ or $52,065 \pm 19,855$.

$$32,210 \le T \le 71,920$$

To determine sample size for a stratified population, it is necessary to specify the type of sampling that will be used as well as the acceptable error and the confidence to be placed in this error.

For the stratified population just discussed, the variance of a total is

$$s_T^2 = \frac{\sum\limits_{h=1}^{m} N_h^2 s_h^2}{n_h}\left[1 - \left(\frac{n_h}{N_h}\right)\right]$$

If the "n_h" are selected by the method called optimum allocation then

$$s_{T_o}^2 = \frac{\left(\sum\limits_{h=1}^{m} N_h s_h\right)^2}{n} - \sum\limits_{h=1}^{m} N_h s_h^2 \tag{32}$$

where

$$n = \sum\limits_{h=1}^{m} n_h$$

If the "n_h" are selected by the method called proportional sampling, then

$$s_{T_p}^2 = \frac{N\left(\sum\limits_{h=1}^{m} N_h s_h^2\right)}{n} - \left(\sum\limits_{h=1}^{m} N_h s_h^2\right) \tag{33}$$

where

$$N = \left(\sum\limits_{h=1}^{m} N_h\right) \quad \text{and} \quad n = \left(\sum\limits_{h=1}^{m} n_h\right)$$

With proportional sampling the total sample size can be obtained from the equation

$$n = \frac{t^2(N)\left(\sum_{h=1}^{m} N_h s_h^2\right)}{(\hat{T} - T)^2 + t^2\left(\sum_{h=1}^{m} N_h s_h^2\right)} \tag{34}$$

With $(\hat{T}- T) = 2{,}000$ and $t = 1.96$ and the estimate of N_h and s_h^2 as used in the last examples, an estimate of total sample size is obtained as shown in Table 9-13.

Table 9-13. Calculations for estimating the total sample size with proportional sampling among the three strata of vegetation cover.

Stratum	N_h	s_h	$N_h s_h^2$	$N_h s_h$
Dense timber	246	20.1	99,386.46	4,944.6
Open timber	322	69.8	1,568,796.88	22,475.6
Meadow	72	130.4	1,224,299.52	9,388.8
Total	640		2,892,482.86	36,809.0

Substituting into equation (34) gives

$$n = \frac{(1.96)^2 (640) (2{,}892{,}483)}{(2000)^2 + (1.96)^2 (2{,}892{,}483)} = \frac{7{,}111{,}528{,}123}{15{,}111{,}763} = 471$$

The distribution among strata will be in proportion to N_h in the strata. Thus, for the dense timber stratum, the number of samples to take is $(471)[(246)/640)]=181$, for the open timber stratum $(471)[(322)/(640)]=237$, for the meadow stratum $(471)[(72)/(640)]=53$.

If optimum allocation were used, the sample size would be obtained from equation (35)

$$n = t^2 \frac{\left(\sum_{h=1}^{m} N_h s_h\right)^2}{(\hat{T} - T)^2 + t^2 \sum_{h=1}^{m} N_h s_h^2} \tag{35}$$

$$= \frac{(1.96)^2 (36{,}809)^2}{(2{,}000)^2 + (1.96)^2 (2{,}892{,}483)} = \frac{5{,}204{,}993{,}371}{15{,}111{,}763} = 344$$

The distribution of these 344 among the strata will be in proportion to $N_h s_h$. Thus, for the dense timber stratum, $n_h = [(344)(4{,}945)]/36{,}809 = 46$, for the open timber stratum $n_h = [(344)(22{,}476)]/36{,}809 = 210$, and for the meadow stratum $n_h = [(344)(9{,}389)]/36{,}809 = 88$.

In the example of sample size under proportional and optimum allocation, it will be noted that as expected fewer samples are needed when optimum allocation is used.

On examining the optimum allocation results, it will be noted that the number of samples computed for the meadow stratum, 88, is larger than the total number in the stratum. This is not a computational error, and when this occurs it means that all observations in the stratum should be taken. Then the number to take in the other strata must be reestimated, assuming optimum allocation in the remaining strata. All of the error is, thus, associated with the remaining strata.

Using equation (35) and noting that now

$$N = 568 \qquad \sum_{h=1}^{m} N_h s_h = 27,420$$

$$\sum_{h=1}^{m} N_h s_h^2 = 1,668,183$$

$$n = \frac{(1.96)^2 \, (27,420)^2}{(2,000)^2 + (1.96)^2 \, (1,668,183)} = \frac{2,888,331,546}{10,408,492} = 277$$

The number of observations to be assigned to the dense timber stratum is

$$\frac{(277) \, (4,945)}{27,420} = 50$$

The number assigned to the open timber stratum is

$$\frac{(277) \, (22,476)}{27,420} = 227$$

The total sample size under optimum allocation is, thus, 72 + 227 + 50 = 349.

It will be noted that the total sample size 349 is a little larger than the original optimum allocation sample size of 344. The reason for this can best be seen by studying the equation for the variance of the total. Thus

$$s_T^2 = \frac{N_1^2 s_1^2}{n_1} \left(1 - \frac{n_1}{N_1} \right) + \frac{N_2^2 s_2^2}{n_2} \left(1 - \frac{n_2}{N_2} \right) + \frac{N_3^2 s_3^2}{n_3} \left(1 - \frac{n_3}{N_3} \right)$$

Whenever $n_i > N_i$ the contribution of that term to the total variance is negative, thus, permitting the other terms to make a larger contribution to the variance of the total, and since those contributions are larger, the sample size is smaller. It is not logical for any term to be less than zero; therefore, the sample size for that stratum is set equal to the stratum total. The sample size in the other strata must be increased to offset the contribution of the negative term because $n_i > N_i$.

To show what is gained by stratification, it is necessary to estimate the standard deviation of individuals if no stratification were used. This is found to be 87.70. The estimated sample size to obtain the same accuracy as stated for the stratified sample is found to be 528. Thus, stratification has enabled the sample size to be reduced from 528 to either 349 or 471, depending on whether the observations are assigned to strata by optimum allocation methods or are assigned in proportion to stratum size.

It is interesting to note that if the confidence limit were set at 5,000 instead of 2,000, the sample size under proportional allocation would be $n = 197$, and under optimum allocation $n = 144$. The latter sample sizes would give a sampling error of less than 10% at the 0.95 confidence level.

To show what is accomplished by stratification, some additional calculations have been made using different stratum means and variances. The stratum means are such that the estimate of the total is unchanged. Three sets of data were used.

(a) Original stratum means but smaller variances.
(b) Original stratum variances but means closer together.
(c) Means used in (b) with variances used in (a).

The data actually used are shown in Table 9-14.

Table 9-14. (a) Original means for the three strata in Table 9-9 with variances smaller, (b) original variances for the three strata with means closer, and (c) means closer and variances smaller.

	(a)		(b)		(c)	
N	$\bar{x}$	s	$\bar{x}$	s	$\bar{x}$	s
246	18.1	16	70	20.1	70	16
322	105.2	50	80	69.8	80	50
72	190.8	100	125	130.4	125	100

Using these data the sample size has been calculated to give the same error assuming stratification with optimum allocation and also assuming no stratification. The sample size for the original data and the three examples are shown in Table 9-15.

Table 9-15. Sample size for stratification with optimum allocation of samples and unstratified vegetation cover for the original data from the three data strata presented in Table 9-9 and the three examples presented in Table 9-14.

	Sample size		Ratio of stratified to
Set of data	No stratification	With stratification	unstratified sample size
Example 1	528	349	0.66
Example a	497	282	0.57
Example b	478	349	0.73
Example c	402	282	0.70

For stratified sampling, the sample size depends only on the variation within strata. However, the gain through stratification depends a great deal on the differences among stratum means. For examples b and c where the stratum means are close together, the size for an unstratified sample is less than for examples 1 and a. However, by stratification a smaller sample of about 70 to 73% of the unstratified sample is needed to give the same error. When the stratum means are further apart, as in examples 1 and a, the sample size for a stratified sample is only 57 to 66% of the unstratified sample.

It should be recognized that optimum allocation is not necessarily more desirable than proportional, or other allocation. In many surveys a number of measurements are taken on a single plot or individual, and in many it is planned to remeasure the plot at intervals. It will usually be the case that the optimum allocation for one of the variables measured may be far from optimum for another, or for measuring changes between remeasurement periods—for example, optimum allocation for studying the use pattern, the encroachment of noxious plants, or the trend of the range condition. It is particularly important in stratified sampling that a thorough evaluation be made, since the allocation of sample observations to the strata, and in fact the formation of the strata, should depend upon the various objectives of the survey and their relative importance.

Multiphase Sampling

It frequently is possible to increase the efficiency or precision of sample estimates by subdividing the work into two or more phases or steps. This technique is, in a sense, an extension of stratified sampling but generally different in that strata are not mapped or otherwise delineated and stratum areas are not known but are estimated in one or more of the phases or steps in the work. The strata and substrata so created, or recognized, may be classes such as range sites, range condition, use zones, or intervals of a continuous variate such as density intervals. A usual feature of such sampling designs is a substantial difference in the unit observation costs of the different steps. In a 2-step sample of the total weight of the forage, or the weight of a single species, the first step might be the classification of a large number of plots into a few (4 to 8) broad weight classes. This could be done rapidly or at a low cost per plot. When sampling a single species, one of the classes might be zero, which would give an estimate of the number of plots (or the percentage of the area) from which the species is absent. In range forage sampling, it may require only two minutes to reach and classify a plot into a broad density or weight class whereas it would require thirty minutes of combined field and laboratory time to reach, clip, transport, and weigh the forage on a plot—a ratio of 15:1.

With this sampling method, the estimating equation is

$$\hat{T} = A \sum_{i=1}^{m} p_i \bar{x}_i \tag{36}$$

where

$\hat{T}$ = total forage in grams.
A = area of pasture in plot units.
p_i = estimated proportion of the pasture in weight class i.
$\bar{x}_i$ = average weight per plot in weight class i.
m = number of classes.

If the p_i were known population values as in ordinary stratified sampling, the variance of T would be

$$s_{\hat{T}}^2 = A^2 \sum_{i=1}^{m} p_i^2 s_{\bar{x}_i}^2 \tag{37}$$

This assumes that p_i is known without error or is small; otherwise, a more elaborate calculation is involved.

In this case, however, the p_i are sample estimates even though based on many (perhaps 1,000) random determinations. The estimate of $\hat{T}$ is now the sum of a series of products of two variables, both subject to sampling error. In addition, the errors of the products are not independent, since evidently the sum of the sample estimates of the proportions in the m classes must be one (unity).

Assume there are D (say 1,000) determinations of weight class, and that there are n_i clipped and weighed plots in class i. Assume further that the samples of both weight class and clipped weight are so small in proportion to the total number of possible observations in the population that the effect of the sample size in the variance of $\hat{T}$ can be ignored. We now have

$$\hat{T} = A \sum_{i=1}^{m} p_i \bar{x}_i = A \bar{x} \tag{38}$$

where

$$\bar{x} = \sum_{i=1}^{m} p_i \bar{x}_i$$

$$s_{\hat{T}}^2 = A^2 s_{\bar{x}}^2$$

Thus, the variance of $\hat{T}$ becomes

$$s_{\hat{T}}^2 = A^2 \left\{ \sum_{i=1}^{m} p_i^2 \frac{s_{x\,i}^2}{n_i} + \sum_{i=1}^{m} \bar{x}_i^2 \frac{p_i(1 - p_i)}{D} - \sum_{i \neq j=1}^{m} \bar{x}_i \bar{x}_j \frac{p_i p_j}{D} \right\}^* \tag{39}$$

which can be written as

$$s_{\hat{T}}^2 = A^2 \left\{ \sum_{i=1}^{m} p_i^2 \frac{s_{x\,i}^2}{n_i} + \frac{1}{D} \left[\sum_{i=1}^{m} p_i \bar{x}_i^2 - \left(\sum_{i=1}^{m} p_i \bar{x}_i \right)^2 \right] \right\} \tag{40}$$

Note that the second term in the square brackets is simply the square of the weighted mean.

As with ordinary stratified sampling, the gain in precision from employing this sampling method is that the variance of measured weights of forage within a stratum or weight class is normally much smaller than that of plots taken at random without regard to weight class.

---

*The term $\sum_{i \neq j=1}^{m} \bar{x}_i \bar{x}_j p_j p_i$ is twice the sum of all products of $p_i \bar{x}_i$ of two weight classes.

In the following example of a forest survey, aerial photographs are used to stratify the area into various strata or classes, such as nonforest, nonstocked forestland, seedling and sapling, pole stands, and sawtimber stands. After classifying a large number of points on aerial photographs, a sample of each class is selected for examination in the field, and for determination of volume. The basic data obtained for such a survey are shown in columns 1 to 5 in Table 9-16. While these data are not from range work, the procedure could be used to estimate forage yield. The points classified on photos could be classed as to (1) meadow, (2) open timber, (3) dense timber; and the field plots could be actual or estimated forage yields on small plots.

Table 9-16. Calculations for estimating the mean volume and its variance from six strata identified from aerial photographs in a forest survey.

Class	N_i	p_i	$\bar{x}_i$	s_i	n_i	$p_i\bar{x}_i$	$p_i\bar{x}_i^2$	p_is_i	$\dfrac{p_i^2s_i^2}{n_i}$
	(1)	(2)	(3)	(4)	(5)	(6)	(7)	(8)	(9)
Nonforest	2642	5403	6	45.4	252	3.24	19.45	24.53	2.39
Large sawtimber	121	.0248	2046	1079.2	16	50.74	103,815.68	26.76	44.76
Small sawtimber	762	.1558	1394	836.5	80	217.19	302,756.17	130.33	212.32
Poles	802	.1640	1025	748.2	65	168.10	172,302.50	122.70	231.62
Seedling-sapling	359	.0734	423	383.8	21	31.05	13,133.39	28.17	37.79
Understocked	204	.0417	77	140.7	15	3.21	247.24	5.87	2.30
Totals	4890	1.0000				473.53	592,274.43	338.36	531.18

The computation of the mean volume and its variance using equations (38) and (41) is shown in columns 6 to 9 of Table 9-16. Correction term (CT) = $(473.53)^2$, therefore, $592,274.43 - 224,230.66 = 368,043.77$. The mean volume is 473.53. Its variance is

$$s_{\bar{x}}^2 = 531.18 + \frac{368,043.77}{4890} = 531.18 + 75.26 = 606.44$$

and its error is

$$s_{\bar{x}} = \sqrt{606.44} = 24.63$$

The confidence interval for a probability of 0.95 is obtained by using $t = 1.96$. Thus, the confidence band or interval is $\pm (1.96)(24.63) = 48.27$.

$$473.53 - 48.27 \leq \mu \leq 473.53 + 48.27$$
$$425.26 \leq \mu \leq 521.80$$

The equation for the variance of $\bar{x}$ is

$$s_{\bar{x}}^2 = \sum_{i=1}^{m} \frac{p_i^2 s_i^2}{n_i} + \frac{1}{D}\left[\sum_{i=1}^{m} p_i\bar{x}_i^2 - \left(\sum_{i=1}^{m} p_i\bar{x}_i \right)^2 \right] \qquad (41)$$

If the estimates of p_i, s_i, and $\bar{x}_i$ are available, then, as for other types of sampling problems, the number of observations needed to give a specified error can be determined. To determine the sample size, one must first decide on the type of sampling to be used to obtain the volume plots. Will the number of plots "n_i" per class be allocated in proportion to "p_i" or will they be obtained by optimum allocation procedures? If the optimum allocation procedures are used, then the equation for the variance of $\bar{x}$ becomes

$$s_{\bar{x}}^2 = \frac{\left(\sum_{i=1}^{m} p_i s_i \right)^2}{n} + \frac{1}{D} \left[\sum_{i=1}^{m} p_i \bar{x}_i^2 - \left(\sum_{i=1}^{m} p_i \bar{x}_i \right)^2 \right]$$

For a given $s_{\bar{x}}^2$, if the value of "n" or of "D" is specified, the equation can then be solved to determine the other value. Such a procedure may not be too efficient as far as the cost of the survey is concerned. If cost is considered, then the relation of D to n is given by the equation

$$D = \frac{\sqrt{\sum_{i=1}^{m} p_i \bar{x}_i^2 - \left(\sum_{i=1}^{m} p_i \bar{x}_i \right)^2}}{\sum_{i=1}^{m} p_i s_i} \left(\frac{\sqrt{C_n}}{\sqrt{C_D}} \right) (n)$$

where

C_n is equal to the cost of a field plot.
C_D is the cost to classify a point on the photos as to an area. To determine "n" the equation is

$$s_{\bar{x}}^2 = \left[\left(\sum_{i=1}^{m} p_i s_i \right)^2 + \sqrt{\sum_{i=1}^{m} p_i \bar{x}_i^2 - \left(\sum_{i=1}^{m} p_i \bar{x}_i \right)^2} \left(\sum_{i=1}^{m} p_i s_i \right) \frac{\sqrt{C_D}}{\sqrt{C_n}} \right] \frac{1}{n}$$

Thus, if $s_{\bar{x}}^2$ is specified and estimates of p_i, $\bar{x}_i$, s_i C_D, and C_n are available, the value of "n" can be estimated. Knowing "n", the value of D can be determined. If the volume plots are assigned to the various strata by proportional allocation, then the only change in these equations is to substitute

$$\sqrt{\sum_{i=1}^{m} p_i s_i^2} \quad \text{for} \quad \sum_{i=1}^{m} p_i s_i$$

Using the data from the example, the sample size will be computed to give a confidence interval of ± 20 for a probability of 0.95. With this probability, the estimate of the variance of $\bar{x}$ would be the square of the ratio of the confidence interval divided by a $t = 1.96$.
Thus

$$s_{\bar{x}}^2 = \frac{(20{:}0)^2}{(1.96)} = (10.2)^2 = 104.04.$$

To obtain an estimate of "n", it is necessary to solve the equation

$$104.04 = \left[(338.36)^2 + \sqrt{368,043.77}\,(338.36)\left(\frac{\sqrt{C_D}}{\sqrt{C_n}}\right)\right]\frac{1}{n}$$

The cost of a field plot C_n for the given locality is about $18 and the cost of a photo determination is about 20¢, thus

$$104.04 = \left[114,487 + (606.67)(338.36)\left(\frac{.4472}{4.2427}\right)\right]\frac{1}{n}$$

$$= \left[114,487 + (205,273)(.1054)\right]\frac{1}{n}$$

$$= (114,487 + 21,636)\frac{1}{n} = \frac{136,123}{n}$$

or

$$n = \frac{136,123}{104.04} = 1,308 \quad \text{and}$$

$$D = \frac{606.67}{338.36}\frac{(4.2427)}{.4472}(n)$$

$$= \frac{2,573.9}{151.3}(n) = 17.01\,(n)$$

$$= 17.01\,(1,308) = 22,249.$$

With proportional sampling $n = 2,633$ and $D = 30,780$. The allocation of "n" to strata is as shown in Table 9-17.

Table 9-17. Calculated number of samples *(n)* per strata shown in Table 9-16 with optimum and proportional allocation.

	Optimum	Proportional
Nonforest	95	1,423
Large sawtimber	103	65
Small sawtimber	504	410
Poles	474	432
Seedling-sapling	109	193
Understocked	23	110
	1,308	2,633

"Double" or Regression Sampling

In many studies it is found that the variable which is to be sampled is difficult or expensive to measure whereas another variable is easy or cheap to measure, and that the values of the two variables for the same individual or plot are related in a significant manner. Range sampling is no exception. Range workers have long recognized the ability of trained range specialists to make ocular estimates of forage density, weight, species composition percentages, and other important variables. These estimates can, of course, be made in a small fraction of the time required to make instrumental measurements of the same variable. The contrast is especially great when measurement requires clipping, bagging, and weighing of the species separately, or the tedious charting and later planimetering of the charts for species cover measurement.

Double sampling requires two separate operations. The first is to obtain observations of the independent and dependent variable (for example, the ocularly estimated and clipped weight of the forage) on a sample of plots. The individuals on which both observations are obtained need not be completely random, that is, the number of observations allotted to ranges of values of the independent variable may be selected arbitrarily, but plots must be selected completely at random within these ranges of the independent variable. These related observations are used to determine the regression line relating the two variables as will be described. The plots for these observations may be selected completely at random and it may be desirable administratively to do so. The second operation (although not necessarily later in time) is to produce a large sample, which must be representative of the whole population and, therefore, preferably random, of the independent variable.

From the first step, the equation of the regression line of the dependent variable (clipped weight) on the independent variable (ocularly estimated weight) is computed by least squares.

$$\hat{Y} = \bar{y}_r + b(X - \bar{x}_r) \tag{42}$$

where

$\hat{Y}$ = regression estimated clipped weight of plot.

$\bar{y}_r$ = average clipped weight of plots in the regression sample.

b = coefficient of regression of Y on X or $\dfrac{\sum\limits_{i=1}^{n}(X_i - \bar{x}_r)(Y_i - \bar{y}_r)}{\sum\limits_{i=1}^{n}(X_i - \bar{x}_r)^2}$

X = ocularly estimated weight of plot.

$\bar{x}_r$ = average of ocularly estimated weights of plots in the regression sample.

To estimate the population mean of the plots if all had been clipped and weighed, it is necessary simply to insert the large sample mean value of the ocularly estimated weights for X in equation (42). Thus

$$\hat{Y}_e = \bar{y}_r + b(\bar{x}_e - \bar{x}_r) \tag{43}$$

where

$\hat{Y}_e$ = estimated mean plot weight of the population.

$\bar{x}_e$ = sample mean of the ocular estimates, based on *"m"* values.

It is assumed here that the regression sample is not a random sample of Y values but was selected so as to provide a good (i.e., small variance) estimate of the population regression coefficient β of which b is an unbiased estimate. The estimate of the population total weight is

$$\hat{T} = N\bar{y}_e$$

where N is the number of plots in the population. Its sampling variance is

$$s_{\hat{T}}^2 = N^2 \left\{ s_{y \cdot x}^2 \left[\frac{1}{n} + \frac{(\bar{x}_e - \bar{x}_r)^2}{\sum\limits_{i=1}^{n} (X_i - \bar{x}_r)^2} \right] + b^2 \frac{s_x^2}{m} \left(1 - \frac{m}{N} \right) \right\} \qquad \textbf{(44)}$$

where

$$s_{y \cdot x}^2 = \frac{\sum\limits_{i=1}^{n} (Y_i - \bar{y}_r)^2 - b^2 \sum\limits_{i=1}^{n} (X_i - \bar{x}_r)^2}{n - 2} \qquad \textbf{(45)}$$

is the sample estimate, based on n - 2 degrees of freedom, of the variance of Y for plots having the same X value. It is assumed that this variance is constant over the range of Y and X values considered.

n = the number of paired regression observations.

Y_i and X_i = the Y and X values for observation $i(i = 1, 2, ---, n)$

and

$$s_x^2 = \frac{\sum\limits_{j=1}^{m} (X_j - \bar{x}_e)^2}{m - 1} \qquad \textbf{(46)}$$

is the estimated variance of X based on the large independent sample of m values of X.

If, even though m is large relative to n, it is insignificant relative to N, the term $(1 - m/n)$ can be ignored. This will normally be true in unimproved pasture or range allotment sampling.

The variance of $s_{\hat{T}}^2$ can be reduced by making either n or m or both larger. The most profitable distribution of the sampling effort between the regression sample and the sample of the independent variable depends upon the relative cost of Y and X observations and on the ratio of the variance of Y for a specific value of X and the variance of a random sample of Y, ignoring X. The procedure for computing the appropriate allocation of effort is somewhat cumbersome and will not be outlined here. It is suggested, particularly in new fields of application, that equation (44) be solved, for a selected value of $s_{\hat{T}}^2$ for a series of values of n, and the corresponding values of m, using guessed values for the costs, variances, and correlation of Y and X. These computations will lead rapidly to efficient combinations. If the specifications of linearity of regression and uniformity of variance are not met, small biases will be introduced but these usually will not be serious. If the correlation of Y and X is high and the cost of Y observation is high relative to that of an X observation, substantial economies can result.

The concept of double sampling can be extended readily to stratified sampling. Here, separate regression estimates are made for the total weight T_h of each stratum. If there are m strata, the estimate becomes

$$\hat{T} = \sum_{h=1}^{m} \hat{T}_h \tag{47}$$

and its variance is

$$s_{\hat{T}}^2 = \sum_{h=1}^{m} s_{\hat{T}_h}^2$$

where $s_{\hat{T}}^2$ is the variance of the regression estimate of the total weight of forage in stratum h.

Ratio Estimates

If the regression of Y and X can be expected to pass through the point $Y = 0$, $X = 0$, the ratio estimate is available. This method finds its greatest advantage in situations where the population value is known for independent variable X. In many cases the value of X is the value of the variable being estimated but measured at a previous date. An example may be a recent estimate of the volume of records in National Forest Service files based on a complete canvass in a base year and a random sample of forest records in the current year. More often the independent variable is a different but related variable.

If we designate by Y the variable to be estimated and by X the related variable for which the population value, say T_x, is known, the ratio, or regression, estimate is

$$T_y = rT_x$$

where r is the sample estimate of the ratio $R = \dfrac{T_y}{T_x}$.

If a random sample of n observations is taken from the N available in the population, then r is computed as

$$r = \frac{\sum\limits_{i=1}^{n} Y_i}{\sum\limits_{i=1}^{n} X_i}$$

It can be shown that if the regression of Y on X passes through $Y = 0$, $X = 0$, and if the variance of Y values for constant values of X is proportional to X, then r is an unbiased estimate of R. In fact, it is the value of the regression coefficient when a line is fitted by the method of least squares taking into account that the weights of Y observations are inversely proportional to their variance, in this case to $1/X$. When these conditions are not met, r is a biased estimate of R, the population ratio. The bias decreases as n increases and as the correlation of Y with X for individual sample observations increases. In general, in cases where the ratio estimate would be profitable, the bias is small in relation to the sampling error of r and can be neglected.

The variance of T'_y is

$$s^2_{T'_y} = T^2_x s^2_r,$$

however, the variance of the estimate of T'_y is best expressed as the relative error squared, in which case

$$\frac{s^2_{T'_y}}{(T'_y)^2} = \frac{s^2_r}{r^2} = \left(\frac{N-n}{N}\right)\frac{1}{n}\left[\frac{s^2_y}{\bar{y}^2} + \frac{s^2_x}{\bar{x}^2} - 2r_{xy}\frac{s_x}{\bar{x}}\frac{s_y}{\bar{y}}\right]$$

In this equation r_{xy} is the coefficient of correlation of Y and X i.e.,

$$r_{xy} = \frac{\Sigma(X-\bar{x})(Y-\bar{y})}{\sqrt{\Sigma(X-\bar{x})^2\,\Sigma(Y-\bar{y})^2}}$$

The factor $N-n/N$ is the finite population sampling factor and may be omitted if n is small relative to N.

A useful alternative form of the variance is

$$s^2_{T'_y} = N^2\bar{x}^2 r^2 \left(\frac{N-n}{N}\right)\frac{1}{n}\left[\frac{s^2_y}{\bar{y}^2} + \frac{s^2_x}{\bar{x}^2} - 2r_{xy}\frac{s_x}{\bar{x}}\frac{s_y}{\bar{y}}\right]$$

which may be expanded readily to accommodate ratio sampling of stratified populations.

Systematic sampling

Systematic sampling usually means a plan of selecting sample observations such that a description of the system of selection plus the selection, at random or otherwise, of the initial observation predetermines the selection of all other observations in the sample. If n observations are to be taken, the population is divided into k equal parts of size n, and one observation is selected at random, usually in the end or corner segment. With this as a starting point, every k^{th} successive observation is selected. Systematic sampling is easily planned and controlled and in some tests, with areally dispersed natural populations, has been found to be efficient.

If the systematic sample has a random starting point as described above, the entire sample can be recognized to be a single random observation and as such provides an unbiased estimate of the population mean or total. Since, however, it is but a single observation, it contains no measure of dispersion to which such observations are subject. Examples in which the variance among randomly selected systematic grids or clusters could be evaluated have shown that the application of random sampling error formulas to systematically selected values may lead to estimates of precision that are far divergent from those measured.

The advantages of convenience, control, and efficiency are so great that attempts have been made to assess the accuracy of systematic samples through a study of relationships among the observations making up the cluster or grid. These generally have approached the problem through fitting a curve or surface to the specially related observations and use of the variation around the curve or surface as the basis of estimating the precision of the observation grid as a whole (Osborne 1942, DeLury 1950). Generally, it cannot be said categorically that systematic samples lead to more, or less, accurate estimates than random samples of the same intensity or cost. This depends upon the specific system adopted and the distribution in space or time of the variable measured as well as on the knowledge of strata, trends, and other factors available before the sampling is begun.

It should be kept in mind that controversies regarding systematic and random sampling arise almost only in those instances when the computation of a sampling error is required. In sampling a pasture, for instance, the sample may consist of 50 randomly selected 1/10 ha plots. On the plots, the forage measurement may consist of three mechanically spaced transects 25 m long on each of which are located three 1 X 2.25 m plots which are clipped and weighed. In this case, the variance of the pasture estimate is based upon the variation among the 50, 1/10 ha values. The variance is inflated by an unassessable amount from that which would have been obtained if the 1/10 ha plots had been completely clipped and weighed, because the results from the clipped 2.25 m plots, when expanded to the 1/10 ha plots, do not equal exactly the 1/10 ha values. Variation among the 2.25 m plot values do not enter the computation of the variance of the pasture mean or total explicitly.

Literature Cited

Cochran, W.G. 1977. Sampling techniques. John Wiley and Sons, New York, New York.

Cochran, W.G., and G.M. Cox. 1966. Experimental designs. John Wiley and Sons, New York, New York.

Delury, D.B. 1950. Values and intergals of the orthoginal polynomials up to n = 26. Univ. Toronto Press, Toronto, Canada.

Iman, R.L., and W.J. Conover. 1983. A modern approach to statistics. John Wiley and Sons, New York, New York.

Osborne, J.G. 1942. Sampling errors of systematic and random surveys of cover-type areas. Amer. Statistical Ass. 37:256-264.

Snedecor, G.W., and W.G. Cochran. 1980. Statistical methods. Iowa State Univ. Press, Ames, Iowa.

Steel, R.G.D, and J.H. Torrie. 1980. Principals and procedures of statistics. McGraw-Hill Book Co., New York, New York.

Chapter 10
Experimental Designs

Introduction

The primary reason for experimental design is to provide accurate estimates of treatment effects and the variation associated with treatments, and likewise the variation associated with experimental error (see Chapters 1 and 9). Design provides an effective and simple method of obtaining valid estimates of means and isolating and testing variation in the process of making statistical inferences. Otherwise, laborious sampling procedure, complicated mathematical formulae, and elaborate computer programs might be required for arriving at the same conclusions (Anderson and McLean 1974).

Natural biological systems that characterize rangelands differ materially from agronomic systems and, therefore, may need ingenuity and modification from most standard agronomic research designs. Green (1979) presents a refreshing approach to experimental designs, statistical analyses and interpretation of results as they relate to natural ecosystems and their management.

Steps in Designing

Three important steps should be followed in designing an experimental study. First, the objectives of the study must be clearly stated, and each objective must be given an appropriate priority. This will lead to statements of the hypotheses to be tested. A hypothesis is a statement about the parameters of the populations being studied (see Chapter 1). In biological research, the population being studied usually does not exist in its present concept, but the experiment is designed to establish something about a conceived population if it did exist. A null hypothesis generally, but not necessarily, states that no difference occurs between the parameters involved.

The second step involves a description of the experimental material, an outline of the treatments to be made, and conditions under which the treatments will be compared. Experimental material may be homogeneous or highly variable, and the proposed treatments must be selected on the basis of the contribution they will make to the objectives (see Chapter 1). Likewise, the conditions under which the treatments are to be applied and measured will influence the choice of design. Such factors as soil fertility variation, climatic conditions, season of the year, harvesting procedures, and method of treatment application are examples of conditions that may affect type of design.

The third step in selecting a design should be a description of the measurements to be made, the precision desired, and the type of conclusions to be drawn. All of these are informative and contribute to the ultimate selection of the design. To a large degree, the application of results is determined by the design of the experiment.

These steps should be well outlined so that the experimental design can be carefully planned in advance. Too often the objectives of the study and interpretations and application of the data are conjured after the study has been made.

Systematic and Randomized Designs

All designs fall into two general categories: (1) the systematic design and (2) the randomized design. In the systematic design, treatments within the study area are assigned according to a predetermined pattern so that, generally, the position of each treatment is chosen and not left to chance. For instance, the experimenter may restrict his/her treatments within each of three replications in any number of combinations, such as:

Replication I			Replication II			Replication III		
A	B	C	A	B	C	A	B	C

Replication I			Replication II			Replication III		
A	C	B	B	C	A	C	A	B

Replication I	A	B	C
Replication II	C	A	B
Replication III	B	C	A

A systematic design may be valuable in a demonstrational area. However, in systematic sampling, no valid estimate of error exists for testing differences. The adjacent effect of treatments may be accentuated, since the same individual treatments may always appear together. Also, danger may occur of confounding treatment effect with soil and environmental variation differences within the experimental area. This especially might be the case if the systematic design placed all three replications in one segment of the experimental area.

A	A	A	B	B	B	C	C	C

The randomized design may be completely randomized whereby treatments and replications are randomly located over the entire experimental area. Randomization may also be restricted. Randomization is done to obtain unbiased estimate of experimental error and treatment means.

Methods for Reducing Errors in Research

When one or more treatments are applied to experimental material, the results are affected not only by the nature of the treatments, but also by extraneous variations or by variations that cannot be explained (see Chapter

1). Carefully planned research attempts to measure these two kinds of variation accurately. Inferences can then be made concerning the real treatment effects expected under the conditions observed. The magnitude of treatment effects may be influenced by a bias inherent in the method of measurement of the results. This can only be removed by refinement of technique. The decision as to how far one should go in this direction must be based upon the cost involved and consideration of the magnitude of the bias removed as related to the size of the extraneous variation. If one is interested primarily in treatment difference, a bias may not be serious, since, presumably, it affects all treatments alike.

Failure to standardize the application of treatments and measurement of results will affect both the treatment effects and the extraneous variation. The effort and resources expended in this direction must be consistent with the result achieved, as measured by the reduction in this source of variation. One frequently finds that the small reduction achieved by refining experimental technique is not worth the cost involved when the magnitude of other sources of extraneous variation is considered.

Application of an appropriate design is important in obtaining an unbiased estimate of experimental error. Extraneous sources of variation, however, may inflate the estimate of experimental error. Regardless of the sources or causes of extraneous variation, their effect on this estimate may be reduced to any desired point by increasing the size of the experiment in terms of increased replications, more treatments, or a combination of both. This is based on the assumption that increased size will not require the use of more variable material. Increased replication of a simple design should always be considered in terms of costs and results to be achieved when compared with fewer replications of a more complicated design. Often a limited amount of experimental material may make this choice impossible.

It is also possible to reduce the estimate of experimental error by various methods of handling the experimental material. In the first place, one might select or develop more uniform experimental material upon which to apply the treatment. This is often effective, but is fraught with danger, since it may seriously limit the breadth of application of the results. Often, it is possible to reduce the effect of extraneous variation by making additional measurements on the experimental material, using the statistical technique known as the "analysis of covariance" to reduce the magnitude of the experimental errors involved in testing differences between treatments. There are some disadvantages to this method, since the summary, presentation, and interpretation of results with respect to the normal population may become complicated. Frequently, however, precision can be increased considerably at small cost when additional measurements can be easily made, and when a high degree of correlation exists between them and the extraneous variation of the experimental units. Cochran and Cox (1966), Snedecor and Cochran (1980), and Steel and Torrie (1980) explain analysis of covariance procedures.

Great advances have been made in controlling the effect of undesirable variation in experiments by careful grouping of the experimental units to which the treatments are applied. Many arrangements exist from which one may chose. Before deciding upon a given design, one should be familiar with the methods of randomization to be used and the analysis of the results. If an analysis of variance is to be made, the degrees of freedom should be partitioned and the appropriate formulae for arriving at the standard error of a mean difference should be available. It is also worthwhile to become familiar with the advantages and disadvantages of various designs. In comparatively new fields of research, it is desirable to test the relative efficiency of simple designs compared to more complicated ones, so that the benefits of each will be known for future planning.

Efficiency in Experimental Design

If it is desired to compare two designs, one with mean square per units of s_1^2, and the other with the mean square per unit of s_2^2, the relative efficiency of design 1 to design 2 is the inverse ratio of s_1^2 to s_2^2. However, if the degrees of freedom are different for the two designs, the relative efficiency of design 1 to design 2 is measured by the formula (Cochran and Cox 1966)

$$\frac{(n_2 + 1)(n_1 + 3)\, s_1^2}{(n_1 + 1)(n_2 + 3)\, s_2^2} = \text{Relative efficiency}$$

where n_1 represents the error degrees of freedom for design 1 and n_2 represents the error degrees of freedom for design 2.

In many cases the researcher in the selection of the experimental design will need to consider costs as well as the ratio of the comparative magnitude of the mean squares per unit. In this case, use is made of the formula (Federer 1955)

$$\frac{(r_2 c_2)}{(s_1^2)}\frac{(df_1 + 1)}{(df_1 + 3)} \left/ \frac{(r_1 c_1)}{(s_2^2)}\frac{(df_2 + 1)}{(df_2 + 3)} \right. = \text{Relative efficiency,}$$

where s^2 is error variance per unit, r the number of replications, c the cost per replicate, df the error degrees of freedom, and the subscripts the first and second design.

Size and Scope of Experiment

One of the first questions encountered in designing an experiment concerns its size or the number of replications required for attaining a given degree of precision. In order to answer this question, the researcher must specify the degree of precision required, have an estimate of the standard error per experimental unit, and decide the risk he/she is willing to run of being wrong. The precision desired may be specified as the size of the true difference the experiment is to detect by a test of significance or by stating the width of the confidence interval desired for the true difference. For routine applications of this method, the reader is referred to Cochran and Cox (1966). It is important to consider this problem in designing every experiment to make sure that the limitations of the results will be known before the experiment is started.

Interpretation of Results

Experimental results frequently are variable and drawing conclusions may be extremely difficult. For this reason, experimental design, statistical estimation, and hypothesis testing are used to make definite statements which have a specified probability of being correct. From these statements, accurate application of the results can be made.

Statements from experimental results frequently are made with reference to confidence limits with certain probabilities. For instance, it is possible to calculate an upper and lower limit within which the true value or the true difference will lie with a given probability of being correct (see Chapter 9).

After an experiment is completed, it is the responsibility of the researcher to summarize and present the results in a concise form and to give his/her interpretation of their meaning. This is usually done by computing a test of significance of the treatment variation compared with the appropriate experimental error. If the treatment variation is not significant, the conclusion is that any real treatment effects were too small to be detected by the experiment conducted. If, however, the test is significant, further analysis may be necessary to separate the significant treatment differences.

Often the residual mean square in an analysis of variance is written as the mean square for error. The researcher is cautioned, however, that this may not be the appropriate error term for specific F tests of interest. The appropriate error term for each F test in an analysis of variance may be determined by writing out the expected mean squares for the factors included in the experiment.

Expected mean squares are different for fixed factors and random factors included in experiments. Factors are said to be fixed if the levels of the factor included in the experiment are considered the population to which the data are to be extrapolated. Factors are random if the factors are random samples from a population to which the data are to be extrapolated. Snedecor and Cochran (1980) and Steel and Torrie (1980) provide excellent discussions of expected mean squares for fixed and random models for factorial experiments.

It frequently is desirable and necessary to divide the treatments into as many sub-groups as they will naturally fall, making a test of significance for the treatments within each group. A well-planned analysis should include planned comparisons among treatment means using the appropriate mean separation or multiple comparison techniques (Steel and Torrie 1980). When selecting comparisons after significance is found at the probability level chosen, the research worker should use appropriate methods for making comparisons among the individual means. The reader is referred to Steel and Torrie (1980) for discussion and the use of appropriate methods for testing significance among means.

A routine analysis of variance in all of its aspects, including tests of significance and the use of confidence limits, is based upon three assumptions which may or may not be true in actual practice. First, it is assumed that all treatment and block effects are additive. This is to say that each treatment or block has the constant effect of increasing or decreasing the response of any experimental unit by a constant amount. Second, the residual or extraneous variations are assumed to be independent from one experimental unit to another, and third, to be normally distributed with the same variance. When these basic assumptions are not met, it may be desirable to transform the scale of measurement to bring the data into agreement with any one of the assumptions. If deviation exists in more than one of the assumptions, it is difficult to find a transformation which will correct all of them. For a detailed description of this subject see assumptions made in model (Cochran and Cox 1966), or transformation of data (Federer 1955). Alternatively, an appropriate nonparametric statistical analysis may be useful (Conover 1980 and Conover and Inman 1981).

The assumption that effects of factors included an experiment must be additive is illustrated by the mathematical model for a two-way classification of data as
$x_{ij} = \mu + \alpha_i + \beta_j + \epsilon_{ij}$ where
μ = the overall mean
α_i = fixed treatment effects
β_j = replication effects
ϵ_{ij} = independent random variables which are normally distributed with mean 0 and variance σ^2

Snedecor and Cochran (1980) provide a numerical example for this model which may help the researcher understand the concept of the linear model and the assumptions associated with the analysis of variance. A mathematical model may be written for each experimental design.

Complete Block Designs

Completely Randomized Design

This design is flexible and simple and frequently is applied to conditions in which all treatments and replications are allocated to plots within one large area entirely by chance or, in a similar manner, a group of animals are allocated to various treatments at random. Randomization is not restricted to insure treatment application to similar or uniform units or plots within a separate block or replication. The replications, or repeated treatments, are completely randomized within the experiment. Therefore, the entire variation among plots enters into the experimental error term and contributes to the experimental error variance. In this sense, precision may be improved by other designs. The completely randomized design should be used when experimental units are considered homogeneous.

By the use of completely randomized designs, the degrees of freedom are greater for error as compared to other designs (Table 10-1). In this way, the completely randomized design is considered more sensitive than other designs if experimental units are homogeneous. The error term, by including all variation other than that accounted for by treatments, is the best estimate of experimental error. It is only when the experimental units are not alike that the error term in the completely randomized design includes something more than experimental error. An illustration using three species (A, B, and C) and

Table 10-1. Analysis of variance for the completely randomized design using three species and four replications.

Source	D.F.	Sum of squares	Mean square
Species	2	211	105.5
Error (among plots within species)	9	66	7.3
Total	11	277	

four replications, showing actual response per plant for a completely randomized design follows:

Completely Randomized Design

Spec.	Spec.	Spec.	Spec.	Spec.	Spec.	Spec.	Spec.	Spec.	Spec.	Spec.	Spec.
A	A	C	A	B	C	C	B	A	C	B	B
10	12	18	8	6	16	18	6	14	10	5	4

Randomized Blocks

The randomized block may be more efficient in field research than the completely randomized design when the block variable identifies an extraneous source of variation that inflates the estimate of experimental error. Reduction in experimental error variance may more than compensate for the increased error degrees of freedom obtained by the completely randomized design. The design consists of the application of treatments randomly within several blocks or locations. The use of blocks is sometimes referred to as replication of the experiment. Blocks generally increase the precision of comparing treatment means, because differences among blocks are kept free from sources of experimental error. Normally, uncontrolled variation is kept to a minimum within blocks, but it is allowed to vary among blocks. In fact, variation among blocks is introduced frequently to test the responses of the treatments to highly variable conditions. The data have application only to the population for which variability is included among replications. For this reason, replications are sometimes widely separated and include distinct contrast. If topography, fertility, or other variability is present, blocks should be placed to separate such differences among them and yet retain as much uniformity within blocks as possible.

It must be remembered in selecting locations for replications, differences between blocks can become so great that it would be better to set up separate experiments in each of the different sites or strata. If the yield in the best block exceeds the yield in the poorest by more than 5 to 10 times, effects may be nonadditive and mean squares heterogeneous. Therefore, there is no way of obtaining suitable error terms for testing treatment differences statistically.

In randomized block experiments, uncontrolled variation or normal variation to be included is kept to a maximum between blocks and to a minimum within blocks. Plots within blocks should be made as nearly alike as possible.

Randomized Block Experiment

Block I			Block II			Block III			Block IV		
Spec. A	Spec. C	Spec. B	Spec. C	Spec. A	Spec. B	Spec. A	Spec. B	Spec. C	Spec. B	Spec. A	Spec. C
10	16	5	18	12	6	14	6	18	4	8	10

Table 10-2. Analysis of variance for the randomized block experiment using three species and four replications.

Source	D.F.	Sum of squares	Mean square
Species	2	211	105.5
Blocks	3	51	17.0
Error (spec. × blks.)	6	15	2.5
Total	11	277	

The randomized block experiment can be used with any number of treatments and replications. At least two replications are required to establish an experimental error for testing significance among treatments. However, unless differences among treatments are comparatively large, two replications are generally insufficient. When differences among treatment means are expected to be small, it is advantageous to add replications in order to provide a better estimate of experimental error to test relatively small differences. If, for instance, the standard error among treatments is 15% of the mean for all treatments in four replications, the estimate of standard error of a treatment mean $s/\sqrt{n}$ pecentage-wise is then $15/\sqrt{4} = 7.5\%$, the standard error of a mean difference is $\sqrt{(2)}(15)^2/4 = 10.61\%$. The previous example for a randomized block experiment dealing with three species and four replications yielded a standard error $\sqrt{2.5}$ or 1.58 and a mean value of 10.58. The standard error (1.58) divided by the mean of all treatments (10.58) equals 15%. Thus, the $T_{.05}$ value (2.45) at 6 degrees of freedom multiplied by the standard error of a mean difference (10.61%) would yield a difference of about 26.0%. This is the approximate difference necessary between treatment means for significance at the 5% level. Similar calculations for the 1% significance level gives a mean difference of about 39.3%. If the required difference appears too great, the replications might be increased to 6, whereby the estimate of standard error of a treatment mean percentage-wise would be $15/\sqrt{6}$ or 6.12%. A difference of about 19.05% between treatment means would be significant at the 5% level. The calculation is $2.2\sqrt{(2)(15)^2/6}=19.05$ ($T_{.05}$ at 10 degrees of freedom = 2.2). By the same calculation using $T_{.01}$ value 3.1, a difference of about 26.85% at the 1% level would be required for significance. Degrees of freedom for error mean are now 10 because there are now replications and three species. The number of replications to be used will depend largely upon available resources, probable size of mean differences to be measured, and desired accuracy of testing the mean differences. Since the randomized block design is popular, nearly all textbooks on experimental design or research methods present many and varied examples of its use.

Latin Squares

This design is well adapted where relatively few treatments are involved and the experiment is to be carried out in the laboratory or in the field where heterogeneity is suspected but is not evident from physical observations or variation is evident in two directions. Number of replications must be the same as number of treatments; therefore, it is less flexible than the randomized block. In the field, the Latin square is usually laid out in an area with four equal sides. The square is divided into rectangular strips called rows, and subdivided into strips perpendicular or at right angles to the rows. These latter strips are referred to as columns. There are an equal number of columns and rows and as many of each as there are treatments. The Latin square design is usually used so that field variability is controlled in both directions; however, the field design may be laid out with all plots in one continuous line instead of a square.

Random assignment of the treatments is made to the plot with the restriction that each treatment must occur only once in each row and each column. An illustration using five treatments, A, B, C, D, and E, in a square area and a rectangular area appears as follows:

Columns

B	E	A	C	D
D	A	E	B	C
E	B	C	D	A
A	C	D	E	B
C	D	B	A	E

Rows

or

Columns

	I	II	III	IV	V
	B 12	E 8	A 10	C 14	D 6
	D 14	A 12	E 4	B 16	C 30
Rows	E 6	B 12	C 20	D 10	A 18
	A 10	C 30	D 10	E 6	B 16
	C 20	D 16	B 14	A 14	E 10

The Latin square may offer greater precision than the randomized block, since it eliminates field variation in two ways. The error has increased from a mean square of 13.5 for the Latin square (Table 10-3) to 15.7 for the randomized block (Table 10-4). However, the additional degrees of freedom for the

Table 10-3. Analysis of variance for the Latin square using 5 treatments.

Source	D.F.	Sum of squares	Mean square
Rows.................................	4	88.6	22.2
Columns............................	4	88.6	22.2
Treatments.........................	4	687.0	171.8
Error................................	12	162.0	13.5
Total................................	24	1026.2	

Table 10-4 Analysis of variance as a randomized block for data shown in Table 10-3.

Source	D.F.	Sum of squares	Mean square
Reps. (columns).....................	4	88.6	22.2
Treatments........................	4	687.0	171.7
Error (reps. × treat.)...............	16	250.6	15.7
Total............................	24	1026.2	

randomized block design must be considered. To make allowances for this advantage of increased degrees of freedom from 12 for the Latin square (design 1) to 16 for the randomized block (design 2), we use the formula to calculate relative efficiency as discussed previously in this chapter: [(12 + 1) (16 + 3)(15.7)/(16 + 1)(12 + 3)(13.5) = 1.126] (Cochran and Cox 1966). Thus, in this case there was an increased efficiency of about 12.6% by use of the Latin square. If the field variation is slight or it can be controlled by blocks in one direction, there would be no advantage of the Latin square over the randomized block.

Graeco-Latin and Hyper-Graeco-Latin Squares

Graeco-Latin square and Hyper-Graeco-Latin square designs are seldom used because units cannot be conveniently balanced into the appropriate number of groupings. However, when there are more than two sources of extraneous variation to control, the use of these designs may prove advantageous. For details of the designs and analysis of data see Federer (1955), Cochran and Cox (1966), and Fisher (1951).

Simple Factorial Experiments

In a factorial experiment, the effects of a number of factors are tested in all combinations. An example of a factorial experiment is one in which different treatment levels may be applied to different varieties or to a given variety at different times. Then each combination of variety and treatment is included in the test. Such a factorial arrangement of treatments could be used with any design. In a randomized block design, for example, each combination would be represented in each block.

The effect of such treatment-variety combination consists of the sum of varietal effect plus treatment effect plus interaction of variety and treatment. Treatment might refer to the amount of fertilizer, different combinations of fertilizer, different amounts of herbicide, or different intensity of seeding as it might concern different species. The interaction between treatment and species measures the degree to which treatment effects vary with species. The interaction term is an important term in these tests, since the object is to find the optimum treatment combination.

Should it happen in a factorial experiment that the interaction is not significant, no information is lost because treatment and species is replicated. Therefore, effects can be tested over a wider range of situations than would be the case without the factorial.

Experiments studying many factors simultaneously and in all combinations are analyzed in factorial arrangements. For example, we might want to test the effect of four intensities of seeding (1, 2, 3, and 4), four drill-row spacings (I, II, III, and IV) with four species of grass (A, B, C, and D) at two seasons (fall and spring) with three replications. For randomized complete block design, each of the following 128 treatment combinations is randomly assigned to one of the 128 plots in each block. Treatments should be randomized for each block.

	Fall			
Species A				
Spacing	I	II	III	IV
Intensity	1,2,3,4	1,2,3,4	1,2,3,4	1,2,3,4
Species B				
Spacing	I	II	III	IV
Intensity	1,2,3,4	1,2,3,4	1,2,3,4	1,2,3,4
Species C				
Spacing	I	II	III	IV
Intensity	1,2,3,4	1,2,3,4	1,2,3,4	1,2,3,4
Species D				
Spacing	I	II	III	IV
Intensity	1,2,3,4	1,2,3,4	1,2,3,4	1,2,3,4
	Spring			
Species A				
Spacing	I	II	III	IV
Intensity	1,2,3,4	1,2,3,4	1,2,3,4	1,2,3,4
Species B				
Spacing	I	II	III	IV
Intensity	1,2,3,4	1,2,3,4	1,2,3,4	1,2,3,4
Species C				
Spacing	I	II	III	IV
Intensity	1,2,3,4	1,2,3,4	1,2,3,4	1,2,3,4
Species D				
Spacing	I	II	III	IV
Intensity	1,2,3,4	1,2,3,4	1,2,3,4	1,2,3,4

In the factorial experiment, the effect of each factor can be compared separately and in all combinations with the other factors. For example, the effect of intensity (3 degrees of freedom) can be evaluated and also the effect of intensity with season, intensity with spacing, intensity with species, intensity with season and spacing, intensity with spacing and species, intensity with season and species, and intensity with all three factors (Table 10-5). Each

Table 10-5. Treatments and degrees of freedom for a randomized block factorial experiment using three replications, four species, four drill row spacings, and four seeding intensities during the fall and spring.

Source	D.F.
Species	3
Spacings	3
Intensity	3
Season	1
Replication	2
Spec. × spa.	9
Spec. × int.	9
Spec. × sea.	3
Spa. × int.	9
Spa. × sea.	3
Int. × sea.	3
Spe. × spa. × int.	27
Spe. × spa. × sea.	9
Spe. × int. × sea.	9
Spa. × int. × sea.	9
Spe. × spa. × int. × sea.	27
Error	254
Total	383

factor can be separated into its various effects singly or in combination with other factors.

In analyzing factorial experiments, it often is useful to segregate the sums of squares for individual degrees of freedom. In cases where successive levels of treatment are applied, it is then possible to determine whether the effect is linear, quadratic, or cubic. The procedures for response curve analysis are described by Cochran and Cox (1966), Snedecor and Cochran (1980), and Steel and Torrie (1980).

In a factorial experiment, factors frequently are applied at various levels or in increasing increments of equal value. For example, intensity of seeding could be made at 1, 2, 3, and 4 kg/ha, and spacing at 15, 30, 45, and 60 cm. The effects of levels or increasing increments are important in the interpretation of data and should not be overlooked in the analysis. In many factorial experiments, various levels or increasing increments of the factors make up the entire treatment effects and are, therefore, designed to determine the effects of increasing levels. Such an examination of effects of increased intensity of seeding would consider each degree of freedom as shown in Table 10-6.

The measure of intensity (3 degrees of freedom) is a measure of intensity as a main effect as compared with the experimental error (254 degrees of freedom). If intensity is significant, then it is of interest to know whether the effect is linear, cubic, or quadratic, or a combination of these effects.

If the factors being tested are independent, a factorial experiment measures the main effects with the same precision as when the whole experiment is devoted to each of the factors individually. However, it does not measure the specified effect of each factor acting entirely alone unless such comparisons are incorporated into the experiment.

Table 10-6. A separation of degrees of freedom to determine the linear, quadratic, and cubic relationship in a factorial experiment dealing with increasing increments as treatments.

Source	D.F.	
Intensity	(3)	
Int. linear		1
Int. quadratic		1
Int. cubic		1
Int. × species	(9)	
Int. L spe. L		1
Int. L spe. Q		1
Int. L spe. C		1
Int. Q spe. L		1
Int. Q spe. Q		1
Int. Q spe. C		1
Int. C spe. L		1
Int. C spe. Q		1
Int. C spe. C		1
Int. × season	(3)	
Int. L × S.L.		1
Int. Q × S.L.		1
Int. C × S.L.		1
etc.		
Error	254	
Total	383	

Another example of use of the factorial experiment is in a range feeding trial studying supplemental feeding of livestock with various nutrients at different levels. For example, 10 animals in each of 27 groups could be used as follows:

$Protein_0$
$Phos._0$ $Phos._1$ $Phos._2$
$E_0E_1E_2$ $E_0E_1E_2$ $E_0E_1E_2$

$Protein_1$
$Phos._0$ $Phos._1$ $Phos._2$
$E_0E_1E_2$ $E_0E_1E_2$ $E_0E_1E_2$

$Protein_2$
$Phos._0$ $Phos._1$ $Phos._2$
$E_0E_1E_2$ $E_0E_1E_2$ $E_0E_1E_2$

Table 10-7. Source of variation and degrees of freedom for a factorial experiment in a completely randomized design using three nutrients with three levels of feeding in each of twenty-seven treatment groups.

Source	D.F.
Treatment	(26)
Protein (Pr)	2
Phosphorus (P)	2
Energy (E)	2
Pr × P	4
Pr × E	4
P × E	4
Pr × P × E	8
Error	243
Total	269

The objective in a factorial experiment is to obtain a broad picture of the effects of the various factors being studied, their main effects, and their effects in combination with other factors. The measure of interaction is a measure of independence. A significant interaction indicates dependence; thus, the factors are interdependent and function together in some way to cause a significant effect upon the responses being measured. If the effects of the various factors are independent, then each factor could have been studied in separate experiments just as effectively. However, unless they are studied in a factorial experiment, their interdependence and relative effects cannot be determined. For example, suppose wool yield is to be maximized from supplements including three variables such as protein, phosphorus, and energy. The researcher desires the optimum combination of these three constituents in order to obtain the maximum wool yield. In like manner, it might be desirable to determine the optimum level for each constituent to obtain maximum yield consistent with cost per unit of the various constituents. These can be determined from an experiment such as the example of supplemental feeding. However, to accomplish this, special formulae are required depending upon the results and manipulation of cost and return relationships (Cochran and Cox 1966).

The factorial experiment is ideally suited to determine the effects of each of a number of factors over a specified range of increased or decreased magnitudes. The factorial experiment lends itself to testing many factors suspected of being interdependent that could not be determined under individual studies dealing only with individual factors. In addition, results lead to recommendations that have broad scope and apply over a wide range of conditions.

It should be remembered that all main effects and interactions are really measurements of the additive effect of these factors on all others and, therefore, are not actual measurements of the specific effects of the various factors operating alone. If interactions are significant, treatment means at the interaction level are the appropriate level for discussion (main effects are meaningless without considering individual factors and interaction effects). The supplementary feeding example contains 27 treatments, and to measure the specific effect of any one level of protein alone, without the superimposed effect of other factors, the results would be based on only 10 animals in each group. This small number may be inadequate to predict the expected returns from feeding any one supplemental factor alone. However, when measuring the additive effect of the various levels of protein in all other treatments, 90 animals are contained in each of the three levels (protein, two degrees of freedom).

If specific returns in saleable produce from individual supplemental factors are important evaluations, the factorial arrangement of treatments is frequently inadequate and must be followed or preceded with designs to measure the individual factors separately without additive effects from other factors. When several factors at several levels are used, the factorial design may become unwieldy. Inclusion of several factors at several levels in field trials may require the blocks to be so large that experimental error cannot be efficiently controlled, since it is desired to maintain uniformity within blocks and let the variability occur among the blocks.

Confounding in Experimental Design

Confounding is usually described by referring to non-orthogonality among treatments with replication. Orthogonality in designing is the most direct and simple method whereby each block or replication contains the same kind and number of treatments and is referred to as a balanced design. Nonorthogonality or confounding occurs when each block does not contain all of the treatments. In this case, special methods of calculation are required to separate the treatment and block effects because treatment effects are confounded with block effects.

The purpose of confounding is to increase the accuracy of measuring the more important effects by sacrificing accuracy of comparisons of less important effects. Other advantages may include the reduction of plots or animals required for treatment combinations and a reduction in labor requirement. Cochran and Cox (1966) provide detailed procedures and analyses for confounding in experimental designs.

The method of confounding can be illustrated by use of a simple design involving three fertilizers (nitrogen, phosphorus, and sulfur) at two levels along with a control. This presents a total of eight treatments (check, N, P, S, NP, NS, PS, and NPS). If we choose to use eight replications, confounding could be used in a 8 × 8 Latin square. However, if we choose fewer replications, it would ordinarily be arranged into a randomized block design. A field plan and data for three replications in a randomized block design without confounding would be as follows:

Replication I			Replication II			Replication III		
N	7	NS 7	S	5	NSP 14	P	4	NP 7
NP 5	(1)	2	(1) 2	P	3	PS	6	(1) 1
P	5	PS 5	NP 6	PS	5	NPS 16	N	6
S	6	NPS 15	N	6	NS 10	S	5	NS 8

Actual signs and methods of calculating sum of squares are shown in Table 10-8.

Table 10-8. Calculations of sum of squares for a simple randomized block experiment using three fertilizers singly and in combination.

Factorial effect	Treatment combinations								Comparisons	Sum of squares
	(1) 5	N 19	P 12	S 16	NP 18	NS 25	PS 16	NPS 45		
N	−	+	−	−	+	+	−	+	$(58)^2/24$	140.17
P	−	−	+	−	+	−	+	+	$(26)^2/24$	28.17
S	−	−	−	+	−	+	+	+	$(48)^2/24$	96.00
NP	+	−	−	+	+	−	−	+	$(12)^2/24$	6.00
NS	+	−	+	−	−	+	−	+	$(18)^2/24$	13.50
PS	+	+	−	−	−	−	+	+	$(14)^2/24$	8.17
NPS	−	+	+	+	−	−	−	+	$(28)^2/24$	32.67

In a simple experiment of this kind, the three-factor interaction NPS would generally be considered of least importance; therefore, it may be confounded with blocks. This interaction effect is estimated by data comparison (NPS) + (N) + (P) + (S) –(NP) –NS) –(PS) –(check). Therefore, if three replications are used and NPS is confounded with block, each replication would be split into two blocks making a total of six with the (+) effects in one block of each replication and the (–) effects in the other block as follows:

Replication I		Replication II		Replication III	
1	2	3	4	5	6
NPS 15	NP 5	NPS 14	NS 10	(1) 1	P 4
N 7	NS 7	P 3	NP 6	NP 7	N 6
P 5	PS 5	N 6	PS 5	NS 8	S 5
S 6	(1) 2	S 5	(1) 2	PS 6	NPS 16

The total from blocks 1, 3, and 6 subtracted from blocks 2, 4, and 5 represents the NPS interaction total. This NPS effect is also a block effect and is said to be completely confounded with blocks. However, the remaining effects are not confounded and are orthogonal with blocks. In each of the 6 blocks there are 2 treatments containing each of the fertilizers and 2 that do not.

The analysis of variance for both the confounded design and the ordinary randomized block for this simple illustration are shown in Tables 10-9 and 10-10.

Table 10-9. Analysis of variance for a randomized block with the treatment (NPS) confounded.

Source	D.F.	Sum of squares	Mean square
Main effects (N, P, S)	3	264.34	88.11
1st order interaction (NP, NS, PS)	3	27.67	9.22
Blocks	5	38.00	7.60
Error	12	7.99	0.67
Total	23	338.00	

Table 10-10. Analysis of variance for the same treatments shown in Table 10-9 without confounding in an ordinary randomized block design.

Source	D.F.	Sum of squares	Mean square
Main effects (N, P, S)	3	264.34	88.11
1st order interaction (NP, NS, PS)	3	27.67	9.22
2nd order interaction (NPS)	1	32.67	32.67
Replications	2	0.25	.12
Error	14	13.07	0.93
Total	23	338.00	

In the confounded randomized block design, 5 degrees of freedom among blocks have been used for error control among blocks, compared to only 2 degrees of freedom in the ordinary randomized block design. Thus, by isolating heterogeneity among blocks by increasing the degrees of freedom from 2 to 5, the error term (12 degrees of freedom) is proportionally smaller with the confounded design and, thus, gives a more precise estimate of the remaining effect than the error term with 14 degrees of freedom in an ordinary randomized block design. If the variation within blocks is slight or it is difficult to group the confounded effects in order to control extraneous variation, little can be gained by confounding.

In the illustration, the confounded randomized block had a mean square error of 0.67 and the ordinary randomized block had a mean square error of 0.93. However, the additional degrees of freedom for the mean square value of 0.93 must be considered in evaluating relative efficiency by confounding. This can be accomplished by the formula $(n_1 + 1)(n_2 + 3)\sigma_2^2/(n_2 + 1)(n_1 + 3)\sigma_1^2$ = relative efficiency. Thus, $(12 + 1)(14 + 3)(0.93)/(14 + 1)(12 + 3)(0.67) = 1.36$. Thus, this illustration shows that the efficiency was increased about 36% by confounding, compared to the ordinary randomized block experiment. The illustration is somewhat exaggerated to demonstrate the gain in efficiency when extreme variability within replications exists compared to only slight variability among replications. Actual experiments of this size would seldom be confounded.

This example of confounding was of the simplest type; however, any of the many factorial effects may be confounded in his manner. Frequently, the more complicated and difficult to interpret interactions are confounded so that more accurate evaluations of the remaining effects can be obtained.

In complete confounding, all information on the confounded effect is lost. Therefore, designs frequently employ partial confounding with only a partial loss of information for the confounded effects. In partial confounding, different effects are confounded only in part of the replications. In this manner, it is possible to obtain a part of the information from the confounded effects.

Suppose NPS, NP, and SP are partially confounded. As before, NP is estimated by the comparisons (check) + (NP) + (S) + (NPS) – (N) – (P) – (NS) – (PS) – and PS by the comparisons (check) + (PS) + (N) + (NPS) – (P) – (S) – (NP) – (NS). The design would be in the following form:

Replication I		Replication II		Replication III	
1	2	3	4	5	6
NPS 15	NP 5	(1) 2	N 6	(1) 1	P 4
N 7	NS 7	NP 6	P 3	PS 6	S 5
P 5	PS 5	S 5	NS 10	N 6	NP 7
S 6	(1) 2	NPS 14	PS 5	NPS 16	NS 8

In replication I, the interaction effect NPS is confounded, but in the other two replications this effect is orthogonal with blocks. Thus, the NPS effect within replications II and III can be determined. Similarly, NP effect is confounded with blocks in replication II, but estimates of the effects can be made from replications I and III and, in like manner, PS effect which is confounded with blocks in replication III can be estimated from replications I and II (Table 10-11).

Table 10-11. Calculations of sum of squares for partially confounded effects NPS, NP and PS.

	Totals from Treatment Combinations in Replications II and III								
	(1) 3	N 12	P 7	S 10	NP 13	NS 18	PS 11	NPS 30	Comparisons	Sum of squares
NPS	−	+	+	+	−	−	−	+	$(14)^2/16$	12.25
	Totals from Treatment Combinations in Replications I and III								
	(1) 3	N 13	P 9	S 11	NP 12	NS 15	PS 11	NPS 31	Comparisons	Sum of squares
NP	+	−	−	+	+	−	−	+	$(9)^2/16$	5.06
	Totals from Treatment Combinations in Replications I and II								
	(1) 4	N 13	P 8	S 11	NP 11	NS 17	PS 10	NPS 29	Comparisons	Sum of squares
PS	+	+	−	−	−	−	+	+	$(9)^2/16$	5.06

The factorial effect in an analysis of variance for the partially confounded experiment is shown in Table 10-12.

Table 10-12. Analysis of variance for a randomized block where NP, PS, and NPS are partially confounded.

Source	D.F.	Sum of squares	Mean square
Main effects N, P, S	3	264.34	88.11
NS	1	13.50	13.50
NP_{pc} (partially confounded)	1_{pc}	5.06	5.06
PS_{pc}.................................	1_{pc}	5.06	5.06
NPS_{pc}	1_{pc}	12.25	12.25
Replications	5	29.00	5.80
Error	11	8.79	0.80
Total	23	338.00	

Since information on each confounded effect was recovered from 2 of the 3 replications, the ratio of 2/3 is a measure of the extent of confounding and, likewise, an index to the percentage of recovery of information. In the analysis of variance, the sum of squares for blocks and for unconfounded effects is found in the usual way. Thus, in partial confounding only part of the information was lost and, as with complete confounding, the accuracy of determining the effects of the more important factors was increased.

Treatments in a Latin square, as in the randomized block, can be confounded. Such designs are sometimes referred to as quasi-Latin square, half-plaid Latin square, plaid-Latin square, and the magic-Latin square. If the variation within rows and columns is small, little is to be gained from confounding the effects in a Latin square.

Split Plot Designs

The split plot normally described in literature refers to an additional factor or factors that are applied to a portion of each plot in each of the blocks. This technique is often used where a treatment has been added after the original experiment has been under way for some time. An illustration is the application of an herbicide to one half of each plot in a block that was seeded to grass at 5 intensities in 3 replications to determine the effects of released annual weed competition on grass establishment (see Split Plot Design, Example 1). Note that the one-half of each plot to be sprayed was randomly selected for each treatment within each block.

Split Plot Design, Example 1

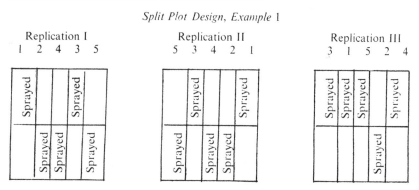

Replication I
1   2   4   3   5

Replication II
5   3   4   2   1

Replication III
3   1   5   2   4

Table 10-13. Source of variation and degrees of freedom for a split plot design using five intensities of seeding in three replications with an herbicide applied on one half of each plot.

Source	D.F.
Intensity	4
Replication...................	2
Rep. × int. (Error a)...........	8
Spray vs. unsprayed	1
Int. × spray	4
Error b	10
Total	29

This same experiment could have included spraying at the outset of the experiment and could have been arranged in a randomized block. This, of course, implies that the application of the herbicide was anticipated at the time the design was laid out in the field and all treatment combinations were randomized within blocks. In this case there would be 3 blocks with 10 treatments and the analysis of variance would be as shown in Table 10-14.

In the randomized block design, all treatment effects are measured with the same degree of precision. However, in a design where plots are split, the

Table 10-14. Source of variation and degrees of freedom for five intensities of seeding with and without herbicide in three replications as randomized block experiment.

Source	D.F.
Replications...................	2
Treatments....................	(9)
Spray	1
Intensity....................	4
Spray × intensity	4
Error........................	18
Rep. × spray	(2)
Rep. × intensity	(8)
Rep. × spray × intensity	(8)
Total........................	29

split-plot or subplot treatments and interactions are measured more precisely than the main plot treatments (Table 10-13).

Sometimes in field work it is necessary to use a split plot design or modification of it in order to make use of large machinery, aerial application, or treatments not suited to small plots, such as drilling, prescribed burning, and plowing. In this case, the blocks are randomly divided into large treatment strips and the second treatments applied to randomly placed strips across each large strip (Example 2) or to plots randomly selected within each large treatment strip (Example 3). An illustration consisting of strips fertilized before seeding and unfertilized strips, seeded to grass, legumes, and a mixture in four replications follows (Example 2):

Split Plot Design, Example 2

Replication 1		Replication 2		Replication 3		Replication 4	
Fert.	Unfert.	Fert.	Unfert.	Unfert.	Fert.	Fert.	Unfert.
grass		mixture		legume		grass	
legume		legume		grass		legume	
mixture		grass		mixture		mixture	

Where the blocks are split (Example 2) and the treatments applied in strips, the fertilizer effect (with 1 degree of freedom) is tested with error a (3 degrees of freedom). The main effect of seeding (with 2 degrees of freedom) is tested with error b (6 degrees of freedom), and the interaction between fertilizer treatment and seeding is tested with error c (6 degrees of freedom) (Table 10-15). If in the foregoing example the seeding treatments had been randomized within the 6 plots in each block in the randomized split plot design instead of seeded across the entire block, the seeding effect (2 degrees of freedom) would be tested with an error with 12 degrees of freedom (Example 3) and (Table 10-16).

If application of treatments can be adapted to the design, the randomized

Split Plot Design, Example 3

Replication 1	Replication 2	Replication 3	Replication 4
Fert. Unfert.	Fert. Unfert.	Unfert. Fert.	Unfert. Fert.

grass	legume	mixture	grass	legume	mixture	mixture	grass
mixture	grass	mixture	legume	grass	mixture	legume	legume
legume	mixture	legume	grass	legume	grass	grass	mixture

Table 10-15. Source of variation and degrees of freedom for a modified split plot design where fertilizer was applied first, followed by seeding a grass, legume, and a mixture.

Source	D.F.
Fertilizer	1
Replications	3
Fert. × rep. (error a)	3
Seeding	2
Reps. × seeding (error b)	6
Fert. × seeding	2
Reps. × fert. (error c)	6
Total	23

Table 10-16. Source of variation and degree of freedom for a modified split plot where the fertilizer was applied to one half of each of four replications but the seeded grass, legume and mixture was randomized within each of the fertilized and unfertilized plots.

Source	D.F.
Fertilizer	1
Replications	3
Fert. × reps. (error a)	3
Seeding	2
Fert. × seeding	2
Error b	12
Reps. × seeding	(6)
Reps. × seeding × fert	(6)
Total	23

block experiment could be used. In this case fertilizer, 1 degree of freedom, and seeding, 2 degrees of freedom, are both tested with error, 15 degrees of freedom as shown by the following example of a plot layout. The analysis of variance is shown in Table 10-17.

Replication 1	Replication 2	Replication 3	Replication 4
grass fert.	legume unfert.		
mixture unfert.	grass unfert.		
legume fert.	mixture fert.		

Table 10-17. Source of variation and degrees of freedom for a randomized block where both fertilized and unfertilized grass, legume and mixture were placed at random in each of four replications.

Source		D.F.
Treatments		5
Fertilizer	(1)	
Seeding	(2)	
Fertilizer × seeding	(2)	
Replication		3
Replication × treatment (error)		15
Total		23

Sometimes the split plot is applied to the Latin square when equipment and treatments require relatively large plots. An illustration testing the effects of an herbicide under dry and moist conditions on eradication of six noxious plants, applied in strips and at random in split plots in a Latin square design is as follows:

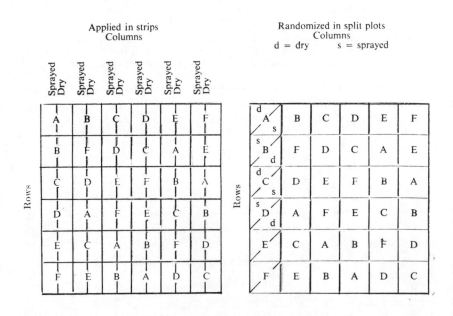

Applied in strips
Columns

Randomized in split plots
Columns
d = dry   s = sprayed

Incomplete Block Designs

An increase in the number of treatments in a randomized block design is usually accompanied by an increase in the experimental error, since it becomes more difficult to get uniformity within large groups of experimental material required for one complete replication. This effect is frequently

Table 10-18. Source of variation and degrees of freedom for a modified split plot where herbicide was applied as a spray and dry in strips on six noxious plants previously planted in a Latin square and for a standard split plot where each half of each plot was randomly assigned and treated separately with the wet or dry application of the herbicide.

Analysis when applied in strips		Analysis when applied at random in each plot	
Source	D.F.	Source	D.F.
Plants	5	Plants	5
Rows.	5	Rows.	5
Columns	5	Columns	5
Error (a)	20	Error (a)	20
Application (dry and moist) . .	1	Application (dry and moist) . .	1
Error (b)	10	Plants × application	5
Row × application	(5)	Row × application	5
Column × application	(5)	Column × application	5
Plants × application	5	Error (b)	20
Error (c)	20	Total	71
Total	71		

alleviated by reducing the block size through confounding less important degrees of freedom, as previously shown in a factorial experiment. When the treatments are not factorial in nature, the same effect can be gained by using one of many incomplete block designs (Cochran and Cox 1966). For example, one might wish to evaluate the adaptability of a large number (25 or more) of species or varieties of forage plants. In this case, one of the many incomplete block designs might be used to control environmental variations within replications.

An incomplete block design is one where the individual blocks contain only part of the treatments. The variation among blocks is removed in a similar but more complicated way than the error control automatically afforded by the complete blocks in a randomized block design. If a large number of varieties or treatments are to be compared and all comparisons are of equal importance, then balanced incomplete blocks can be formed which provide for every variety or treatment to occur with every other variety or treatment the same number of times in a block. Balanced designs are greatly restricted as to number of units per block and number of replications. In some designs the blocks may be arranged to form complete replications. This is desirable whenever possible, because the design cannot then be appreciably less efficient than a randomized block experiment.

Only a few of the more popular incomplete block designs most likely to be useful to the range researcher will be reviewed here. If this type of design is to be used, it is suggested that the basic layout, the method of randomization, and method of analysis be obtained from one of the texts listed in the references.

One group of incomplete block designs which has been widely used in agricultural experiments is known as lattice designs. With the exception of the rectangular and cubic lattices to be described later, these designs are limited to a number of treatments which form a perfect square, e.g., 16, 25, or 49. The number of units in a block is the square root of the number of treatments. For purposes of illustration a 3 × 3 lattice design with nine treatments will be used. In practice an experiment of this size would usually not be considered large enough to warrant the use of a lattice design.

Simple Lattice

If the key numbers for the treatment are written in the form of a square, then for a simple lattice the treatments in the rows form one set of blocks and those in columns the second set. A minimum of two replications is required and these may be repeated to provide an even number of replicates. This may be illustrated as follows:

Basic square

1	2	3
4	5	6
7	8	9

Rep.	Block	Treatments	Rep.	Block	Treatments
1	1	1, 2, 3	2	4	1, 4, 7
	2	4, 5, 6		5	2, 5, 8
	3	7, 8, 9		6	3, 6, 9

Triple Lattice

For a triple lattice there are three groups of different incomplete blocks. The first two are identical with those of the simple lattice, and the third is obtained from the diagonals of the square as follows:

Rep.	Block	Treatments
3	7	1, 5, 9
	8	2, 6, 7
	9	3, 4, 8

A minimum of three replications is required and these may be repeated to provide any multiple of three replications.

Quadruple and Other Partially Balanced Lattice Designs

The required grouping of treatments into incomplete blocks can be obtained for any square to form simple and triple lattices. One group takes the rows of treatments, a second the columns, and the third the diagonals as indicated previously. As one considers quadruple or higher lattice designs, obtaining the groupings of incomplete blocks becomes more difficult. The problem has been studied extensively by statisticians, and rules can be given for writing the blocks, but they vary square to square. For example, for all squares where p, the square root of the number of treatments, is prime or a power of a prime number, it is possible to write out $p + 1$ different groups of blocks, the last completing a balanced set of replicates giving a balanced lattice design. A balanced set does not exist for the 6 × 6 square and the 10 × 10 has not been carried beyond 3 groups, nor the 12 × 12 beyond 4. The most useful arrangements that exist have been given by Cochran and Cox (1966). Where the groups exist, any number of replicates for a partially balanced lattice may be used for the balanced design with p + 1 replicates. It is best to use the most nearly balanced design where a choice exists. For example, a quadruple lattice design is generally superior to a simple lattice with 4 replications where the 2 groups are repeated.

Balanced Lattice Designs

If sufficient replications can be employed to balance a lattice design, it has several advantages over the partially balanced design, the most important of which are greater ease in summarizing the results and every treatment comparison is made with the same degree of precision. The most serious limitation is the requirement of $\rho + 1$ replications which for the larger squares may be excessive.

For a balanced 3×3 lattice, the fourth group to be added to the 3 for the triple lattice design outlined previously is as follows:

Rep.	Block	Treatments
4	10	3, 5, 7
	11	2, 4, 9
	12	1, 6, 8

If one reviews the 4 replications ($\rho + 1$) of the 3×3 square used to illustrate the principle of lattice designs, he/she will find that treatment 1 occurs with 2 in block 1, 3 in block 1, 4 in block 4, 5 in block 7, 6 in block 12, 7 in block 4, 8 in block 12, and finally with treatment 9 in block 7. Treatment 1 never occurs with any treatment more than once in the same block. This is an important property of all balanced incomplete blocks, namely, that every treatment occurs an equal number of times with every other treatment in a block. In the example given each treatment occurred once with every other treatment. With other balanced incomplete block designs, the integer might be 2, or 3, etc., although the number of replications is likely to be excessive.

Rectangular Lattice Designs

Another group of designs which adds to the assortment of designs available for testing a large number of treatments is the rectangular lattice. With the ordinary lattice designs discussed previously, the number of treatments must form a perfect square, whereas with the rectangular lattice the number of treatments must be the product of 2 adjacent integers $\rho(\rho + 1)$, e.g. $5 \times 6, 6 \times 7$, 7×8. A simple rectangular lattice may be used with 2 replications or a triple rectangular lattice with 3 replications. Each of the basic designs may be repeated for greater replication.

The rectangular lattices are handled in about the same way as other lattice designs. The summary of results is somewhat more complicated. The reader is referred to Cochran and Cox (1966) for a complete description on methods of analysis for these designs.

Cubic Lattice Designs

When the number of treatments, varieties, or species to be evaluated becomes extemely large, or where blocks of uniform experimental material are small, a cubic lattice may prove advantageous. In this design, the number of treatments must form a perfect cube and the size of the incomplete block is the cube root of the total number of treatments. Suppose that one wishes to compare the effect of 27 chemical compounds on the leaves of a plant and that only 3 comparable leaves are available on each plant. In this case one might use a cubic lattice with 9 plants of 3 leaves each to evaluate the 27 compounds. The cubic lattices must have 3 or some multiple of 3 replications. For a description and method of analysis of these designs see Cochran and Cox (1966).

Other Designs

The incomplete block designs reviewed here are comparable to randomized complete block designs in that they control variation in one direction or from one source only. A great many incomplete block designs exist which, like the Latin square, will control two sources of variation. These are known as lattice squares and incomplete Latin squares. The reader is again referred to Cochran and Cox (1966) for a review of these designs.

Literature Cited

Anderson, V.L., and R.A. McLean. 1974. Design of experiments. Marcel Dekker, Inc. New York, New York.

Cochran, W.G., and G.M. Cox. 1966. Experimental designs. John Wiley and Sons, New York, New York.

Conover, W.J. 1980. Practical nonparametric statistics. John Wiley and Sons, New York, New York.

Conover, W.J., and R.L. Inman. 1981. Rank transformations as a bridge between parametrics and nonparametric statics. Amer. Statistician 35:124-133.

Federer, W.T. 1955. Experimental design. Macmillan Co. New York, New York.

Fisher, R.A. 1951. The design of experiments. Hafner Publishing Co., New York, New York.

Green, R.H. 1979. Sampling design and statistical methods for environmental biologists. John Wiley and Sons, New York, New York.

Snedecor, G.W., and W.G. Cochran. 1980. Statistical methods. Iowa State College Press, Ames, Iowa.

Steel, R.G.D., and J.H. Torrie. 1980. Principles and procedures of statistics. McGraw-Hill Book Co., New York, New York.

Chapter 11
Problems Involved in the Application of Research Techniques in Range Management

Introduction

This chapter discusses some of the problems and variables the investigator encounters in conducting each of several phases of range research: range seeding, fertilization, brush and weed control, experimental grazing, and use of fire as a range improvement measure. Of the many methods, statistical techniques, and concepts described in the preceding chapters, some are more suited to certain problems than are others. Also, variables exist which are not readily apparent to one unfamiliar with some of the problems encountered when conducting research. Proper evaluation of these at the start is essential to the research program.

Range Seeding Research

Research in range seeding is intended to solve problems encountered when revegetating rangeland on a large scale by seeding to grass, legumes, shrubs, and/or other plants. Such seeding may be for the purpose of reestablishing vegetation on depleted rangeland that cannot be improved through management alone, reestablishing certain kinds of plants, or introducing new species to fill a certain need. Increasing quantity or quality of forage, increasing browse on game ranges, and erosion control are examples of reasons for seeding.

Techniques used in range seeding research include those used in both ecological and agronomic research. However, variability of stand and yield resulting from geologic, climatic, and biotic influences on rangelands usually exceeds that encountered on more mesic arable land. Remnants of original cover are usually present. These make necessary the use of larger plots or more replications than are generally employed in agronomic research.

The main biological problems of range seeding are (1) evaluating range sites as to potential for and need for seeding; (2) finding species and varieties that establish readily and yield a satisfactory quantity and quality of herbage on available sites over a long period and are adapted to needed uses; (3) preparing land for seeding; (4) assuring good quality seed; (5) planting proper amounts of seed, at appropriate depths, and at the optimum season; (6) establishing uniform stands of optimum density; and (7) managing seeded stands for maximum, dependable production (Plummer et al. 1955, Hull and Johnson 1955, Cornelius and Talbot 1955, Lavin and Springfield 1955, Vallentine 1980).

Adaptation to Site and Use

Considerable research has been conducted in the last 40 years on the adaptation of plants to different range sites. Time spent in libraries reviewing previous research will save time and effort. Duplicate research can also be avoided by contacting other researchers who are familiar with the area and who may have knowledge of previous research on revegetation trials which were never published.

After completing the library research, the researcher will be able to eliminate numerous species and will be able to concentrate his/her efforts on a smaller number of species. Often as much variation occurs within species as between species for traits desirable for rangeland improvement. For many range species, varieties are available that have been developed by state experiment stations or federal agencies. However, for other range species, varieties are not available, and it will be necessary to evaluate ecotypes or even seed lots from native harvests. Some varieties, ecotypes, or native collections can be eliminated by considering their origin. For example, switchgrass *(Panicum virgatum)* strains native to southern Oklahoma or Texas will often winter kill in Nebraska while strains from North Dakota will mature rather early in Nebraska but will not be as productive as strains native to Kansas or Nebraska.

Small field trials can then be used to evaluate the strains that the researcher believes have the possibility of surviving on the revegetation site (Figs. 11-1 and 11-2). Replicated small plots, usually about 10 m² per plot, are often used in these studies. It is important to obtain seed that is not more than two to three years old and which still has good germination to be used in these studies. Germination tests need to be conducted prior to seeding. Aged seed lots often have poor seedling vigor and negatively bias stand establishment evaluations. Once these plots are seeded, the researcher will need to evaluate traits such as stand, forage yield and quality, persistence, and any disease and insect problems. These studies need to be conducted for a minimum of three to five years in order to be able to properly evaluate persistence. Better strains can then be seeded in larger fields or pastures where their palatability to livestock and persistence to grazing under various management systems can be evaluated.

Land Preparation

The purpose of land preparation is usually to eliminate competition from existing plants and develop a suitable seedbed. Characteristics of the soil and plant cover will govern the choice of tools for land preparation. Soils may be rough or rocky, precluding use of ordinary farm tillage equipment. Specialized equipment adapted to range conditions has been developed (U.S. Forest Service 1957) (Fig. 11-3). Unwanted species such a big sagebrush *(Artemisia tridentata), rabbitbrushes (Chrysothamnus* spp.), downy brome *(Bromus tectorum),* or tarweeds *(Madia* spp.) may be present and must be killed to remove competition before seeding (Pechanec et al. 1954, Vallentine 1980). Sandy soils should not be exposed to wind erosion, nor steep slopes to erosion by runoff water. Control burning, treatment with herbicides, beating, drag-

Figure 11-1. Row trials to determine adaptability of grass and legume plants to climatic zone. In these trials each species was planted in three rows and on different sites. The center of the three rows is the only one observed since the two outside rows are subjected to interspecies competition. (U.S. Forest Service photo.)

Figure 11-2. Field trials where several species can be tested, using project scale equipment, and allowed to compete with native vegetation. On this site, each species was planted in two plots each 4 m wide (width of the drill) and 20 m long. (U.S. Forest Service photo).

Figure 11-3. Four kinds of equipment commonly used on rough rangelands: A, heavy offset disc; B, brushland plow especially adapted to brushy and rocky terrain; C, beater used for reducing short stiff brush; and D, rail used to remove sagebrush. (A, B, and D, U.S. Forest Service, and C, courtesy of the Caterpillar Tractor Company.)

ging, or various methods of tillage may be used. For example, beating, dragging, and fire are usually ineffective against crown-sprouting species of rabbitbrushes, oak (*Quercus* spp.), and horsebrushes (*Tetradymia* spp.). On the other hand, such methods may serve well to reduce nonsprouting species and provide excellent land preparation under certain conditions. Many annual forbs may be reduced by early spring tillage (Stevenson 1950) or through the use of herbicides (Vallentine 1980). Herbicides may also be used to suppress competing vegetation in conjunction with normal seeding or sod seeding (Samson and Moser 1982, Martin et al. 1982). The first step in many situations will involve experiments dealing with methods of eliminating these undesirable plants. Information on designing such experiments is presented in this chapter under the heading of "Control of Brush and Weeds."

Land preparation for erosion control is aimed at retaining water and increasing infiltration. Terraces may be necessary on steep slopes, whereas contour furrows may suffice on moderate slopes. Range pitting is a method used to retain water where it falls and is often used to improve native vegetation as well as in connection with seeding (Rauzi and Lang 1956, Branson et al. 1966, Rauzi 1968).

Seed Quality

An adequate, uniform stand that quickly establishes with the minimum rate of seeding is desirable. Seeds of native shrubs, forbs, and some grasses present troublesome seeding peculiarities such as size, dormancy, and appendages. Certain species that germinate well in the spring after fall planting may not germinate for a full year after spring planting. Others with high viability soon after harvest are known to lose viability rapidly in dry storage. Still others are unable to germinate when fresh but improve gradually over a year or more, sometimes up to a period of ten years. Seeds of native plants which fail to germinate after several days in the germinator probably require some type of treatment to induce germination, such as chilling, chemical or mechanical scarification, or leaching (U.S. Forest Service 1948, U.S. Production and Marketing Administration 1952, Frischknecht 1959, Mayer and Poljakoff-Mayber 1975).

Seeds of species known to have none of these peculiarities should germinate well when fresh. Should it be necessary to use older seed with low viability, the percentage germination should be determined shortly before planting and used to calculate the adjusted rate of seeding to plant the desired amount of viable seed, or pure live seed (PLS) (Table 11-1).

Seeds of many species deteriorate gradually in the soil from time of planting until temperature and moisture conditions are right for germination. The time and rate of such decline in viability may be studied by placing seed in porous bags in the soil at usual seeding depths. Bags are removed at intervals for examination and germination tests.

The need for treating seed to prevent damping-off or other diseases and for inoculating legumes should not be overlooked. Stubbendieck and McCully (1972) reported that three-times as many plants were established from grass seeds treated with a pathogenicide than from untreated seeds.

In research, it is important to know the source and genetics of the seed. Mounted specimens should be deposited in a permanent collection to provide identification reference.

Seeding Process

It is important in research projects to be able to plant known quantities of seed at rather precise depths. Rangeland drills can be used, but they may be difficult to accurately calibrate. Special drills for experimental plots have been developed (Barker et al. 1976). Rangeland drills can also be converted to experimental plot seeders (Vogel 1978).

Evaluation of Stand Establishment

Measurement of stand establishment of perennial plants seeded on semi-arid range should be started near the end of the second growing season. Only tentative data can be obtained the first season, because the seedlings have not been subjected to the stresses of winter. Seedling numbers commonly decline from the first to the second growing season (Stubbendieck et al. 1973). Strong, hardy grass seedlings sometimes go into dormancy, induced by inadequate moisture during the first summer after planting and appear to be dead.

Relative establishment on different sites; or by different species or varieties; or at different fertility levels, planting dates, planting depths; or seed treatments may be studied individually, or together in a larger experiment. Where information on the combined influence of several factors upon establishment is needed, a factorial design may be more desirable than two or three simpler experiments dealing with the principal factors separately. Consultation with a statistician is necessary to determine the most desirable experimental design. Physical limitations inherent in certain methods may restrict the free assignment of treatment combinations. For example, the relation of normal rodent or insect populations to stand establishment may require study. Methods of rodent exclusion or use of insecticides are not as applicable to subplots as are planting dates or fertility levels.

Establishment on row plots is often expressed as number of plants per meter of row. Survival as a percentage of emerged seedlings, and emergence as a percentage of live seed planted are useful expressions. However, these percentages should be accompanied by information on causes of mortality. Seedlings, as they emerge, may be marked to show the period of appearance. Painted wire pins have been used with a different color for each emergence date. Others have planted seeds in small containers and placed them in the seeded rows (Stubbendieck and McCully 1972). Subsequent weekly observations until the dormant period will help reveal the relative importance of insects, erosion, birds, inadequate moisture, pathogens, rodents, or other causes of mortality.

Stand evaluation on large areas may be done on either permanent or temporary plots. Results are expressible in either plants per unit of area or percentage frequency. Either will provide comparative data if adequate numbers of the same size plot are used on all areas. Frequency increases with

Table 11-1. Conversion factors for determining number of kg of sack-run seed to sow per ha (Pechanec 1950).

Purity	% germination										
%	50	55	60	65	70	75	80	85	90	95	100
50	4.00	3.64	3.33	3.07	2.86	2.66	2.50	2.35	2.22	2.10	2.00
55	3.64	3.30	3.03	2.80	2.59	2.43	2.27	2.14	2.02	1.92	1.82
60	3.33	3.03	2.78	2.56	2.38	2.22	2.08	1.96	1.85	1.76	1.67
65	3.07	2.80	2.57	2.37	2.20	2.05	1.93	1.81	1.71	1.63	1.54
70	2.86	2.59	2.38	2.20	2.04	1.90	1.79	1.68	1.59	1.50	1.43
75	2.66	2.43	2.22	2.05	1.90	1.78	1.67	1.57	1.49	1.40	1.33
80	2.50	2.27	2.08	1.93	1.79	1.67	1.56	1.47	1.39	1.32	1.25
85	2.35	2.14	1.96	1.81	1.68	1.57	1.47	1.38	1.31	1.24	1.18
90	2.22	2.02	1.85	1.71	1.59	1.49	1.39	1.31	1.23	1.17	1.11
95	2.10	1.92	1.76	1.63	1.50	1.40	1.32	1.24	1.17	1.11	1.05
100	2.00	1.82	1.67	1.54	1.43	1.33	1.25	1.18	1.11	1.05	1.00

increased plot size. Belt transects 0.1 m wide and long enough across the drill rows to include 100 plants can be read rapidly because one can count the plants, then pace back to the starting point. With reasonable care in counting and pacing, the number of plants per 0.1 m² can be estimated reliably. Statistical analysis of the data may cause some difficulty because of uneven plot size.

Two additional difficulties arise in use of the plant count method in studying bunchgrasses. Plants in drilled rows tend to merge by the second or third year, making the identification of individual plants difficult. Crowns of bunchgrasses will eventually break into small remnants, and plant counts will have little meaning. The stem count method may be best for erect, sod-forming grasses which have begun to propagate vegetatively. Stoloniferous sod-forming grasses may be measured as percentage cover. Cover becomes more useful as a measure as the percentage increases.

Estimates of relative success can be used to compare seeded stands of different grasses. Such estimates are unavoidably subjective but are guided by consideration of (1) plant numbers per unit area, (2) distribution of individuals, (3) knowledge of potential requirements of demands upon the habitat by each species, and (4) apparent vigor (Hull 1954). The success ratings may be made on a 5- or 10-point scale and are less reliable for rating seedlings than for older stands. A maximum rating should indicate that the seeded species is fully monopolizing the immediate habitat to the exclusion of other plants, or that it shows every promise of doing so (Vallentine 1980).

Site Evaluation

Much has yet to be learned about classifying range sites with respect to their potential for seeding. Owing to the relatively small number of weather stations, site classification sometimes must proceed without the benefit of complete climatic data, i.e., on the basis of topographic, geologic, and biotic measurements. These measurements may be applied in either of two ways in approaching the problems of site evaluation.

One approach is to find numerous good stands of the seeded species throughout a certain environmental range. Such a range might correspond to that of a major dominant or indicator species. Average yields of the seeded species at each location would be correlated with aspect, soil, and cover measurements. Soil depth, organic matter content of the topsoil, elevation, latitude, cover density, height of plants, and the presence of certain species are examples of site characteristics whose variability may be found by correlation analysis to be associated with variations in yield of the seeded species (Miller 1956). Magnitudes of the standard partial regression coefficients will indicate the relative importance of each site characteristic in estimating the capabilities of ranges (Major 1951, Snedecor and Cochran 1967).

A more general approach is to prepare a range site-type classification based upon expression of soil, topography and native vegetation. The same geologic and biotic features are described, but not necessarily quantitatively. These features are used as key characters in distinguishing site-types. Average yields of good stands of seeded species on the various classified site-types are determined. Similar yields of the same seeded species may be expected on the same site-types wherever they occur. Likewise, success of establishment should be similar. In problem areas, seeding experiments should be accompanied by tests of species, fertilizers, soil conditioners, mulches, contours, and mechanical treatments until the best combination of practices is found for the particular site.

Range Fertilization

Techniques and designs for determining the effects of applying fertilizers on rangelands are similar in many respects to agronomic principles applicable for evaluating crop responses to fertilization, particularly of nonirrigated perennial forages (Rehm 1984). Studies on rangeland usually must be of longer duration because of frequently greater variation in precipitation and other environmental factors.

Fertilizers may be expected to increase herbage yield, nutrient yield, forage quality, palatability, and plant vigor. Vegetation composition also may be altered. Ultimate effects might be expected to influence the grazing capacity, yield of animal products, the capacity of the plant cover to resist erosion, and the profitableness of a ranching enterprise (Rogler and Lorenz 1974, Stubbendieck 1977, Schultz and Stubbendieck 1982 and 1983).

Artificial rehabilitation of ranges may include fertilization along with seeding. In this case, it would be desirable to determine the influence of various fertilizer treatments—kinds, rates, dates of application, and placement—upon the estabishment of seeded species compared to the increase of resident plants on the same area.

In all fertilization trials, it is important to evaluate the effects of various levels of an applied nutrient as fertilizer. Therefore, it may be necessary to use a rather wide range of application rates to determine optimum or maximum responses consistent with expected or determined economic returns.

Most fertilizer investigations commence with the suspicion or recognition of a need for the addition of fertilizers or soil amendments. A knowledge of soils or geological formations may indicate inherent deficiencies. Cropping experience on particular soil types may suggest a need for fertilizers.

Before expensive field trials are undertaken, greenhouse tests may be conducted to determine which fertilizer constituents might produce plant responses on a particular soil. Such tests may indicate various levels of the fertilizers that would be most appropriate in the field trials. Many soils can be tested with several fertilizers in the greenhouse in a relatively short period of time, thereby pointing out the fertilizers and rates of each which should be tested in the field.

Pilot trials may also be employed to explore the need for testing certain fertilizers in more intensive field plot investigations. Such trials may first be made by using single fertilizers at various levels. It is advisable to choose fertilizers which will supply a single nutrient to avoid complementary or other effects which might be incorrectly interpreted in planning more intensive future studies.

Since some fertilizer constituents are complementary to others when added in certain proportions, it is essential to determine the proper combination of constituents and the appropriate level of each. Therefore, a factorial design is generally used.

If, for example, it were suspected that if nitrogen and phosphorus would increase the yields and quality of forage, and it was desired to study these influences and determine the proper levels of each when applied together, a simple factorial design would be appropriate. In this case, three levels, of each nutrient might be used such as: phosphorus at 0, 40, and 80 kg/ha, and nitrogen at 0, 30, and 60 kg/ha. If these were to be applied in a factorial design, the total of nine treatments would be as follows:

P_0	P_{40}	P_{80}
$N_0N_{30}N_{60}$	$N_0N_{30}N_{60}$	$N_0N_{30}N_{60}$

These nine treatments could be applied in a randomized block including any appropriate number of replications on any number of sites or locations. This particular example is comparatively simple but could be expanded to include more levels and more fertilizer nutrients.

Season, soil type, soil moisture, and carryover of the fertilizer treatment from year to year may be as important as the fertilizers. They should be included in the study as main effects, or evaluated in a suitable manner appropriate to determine their influence upon range fertilization responses and economics. In semiarid rangelands, the residual effects of an initial fertilization may last two or three years, and the cost of the application may be so great that it may be feasible only to apply fertilizers every third year instead of annually. Methods of applying fertilizers and the placement of nutrients where they may be readily available are problems deserving critical study.

On all areas, but especially on slopes, care must be taken to leave an adequate untreated buffer strip between plots which receive fertilizer treatments. This is necessary to avoid contaminating effects of runoff water. Protective border ridges or dikes may be essential where plots are irrigated or are subject to overland flow.

Control of Brush and Weeds

Research on brush and weed control involves many problems common to other types of range research, but some are quite different. Since weeds and brush involved in range research may be natural stands, their location and prevailing conditions impose limitations on the size and design of experiments. Selection of suitable areas or plant populations to fill the requirements of the experiment may be difficult but is of prime importance. Often the experiment will need to be planned or revised to fit the stand of brush or weeds available and existing conditions.

Many studies in brush and weed control involve use of herbicides. This introduces a number of problems in designing experiments, in equipment and techniques to provide controlled rates of application under highly variable conditions, and for minimizing herbicide drift (Scifres 1980).

Relation of Objectives to Experimental Design

Many factors affect the size and design of brush and weed control experiments. Usually the variables of species, herbicides, application rates, and dates of application are involved. Others may be carriers, volumes, and spray droplet size. It is easy to include too many variables in one experiment. Since one usually cannot reasonably study the effects of all variables in one experiment, he/she must clearly define the objectives, pinpointing the variables of primary interest. Experiments designed to answer a multitude of questions usually yield limited information on any specific point.

The researcher must first decide how small a difference he/she is interested in and how many replications will be necessary to measure this difference. If the study is merely exploratory and the expected differences large, a completely randomized design with two or three repetitions of each treatment usually will be sufficient (Bohmont 1952, Hurd 1955, Snedecor and Cochran 1967). If several factors such a chemicals, rates, and dates of application are studied in all combinations in one experiment, a much larger experiment must be designed and a randomized complete block or an incomplete block design probably would be the most suitable (Hyder 1953, Klingman and McCarty 1958, Snedecor and Cochran 1967). If a factorial combination is included in the experiment, the main effects of each factor can be separated and the interactions studied. Factorial combinations should be included if it is known, suspected, or even questioned that the action of the variables may be interdependent (Hyder and Sneva 1955). However, if it is known that the interaction of two variables is of no importance, an incomplete factorial with respect to these two factors may be considered to reduce the number of treatments (Alley et al. 1956, Robocker et al. 1958). Usually, it is best not to include more than three variables in one experiment. If more are involved, companion experiments should be used to test them in groups of two or three (Hyder and Sneva 1955). Multivariate statistical methods should be considered (Wilson and Stubbendieck 1981, Stroup and Stubbendieck 1983). A statistician should be consulted before designing any experiment (see Chapters 1, 9, and 10 for a more complete discussion of design).

When determining the objectives of an experiment, the researcher should consider the type of inference which is to be made from the results or the area where the information will be applied. If the results are to have general applicability, for example, the optimum date for applying 2,4-D on sagebrush (*Artemisia* spp.) in Wyoming, then the different altitudes, moisture situations, seasons, and other aspects must be sampled. These environments may be represented by experiments conducted in different years, experiments conducted at different locations, altitudes, sites, or a combination of these. For such experiments, two or three replications per experimental site or year may be sufficient.

On the other hand, if it is desired to make a critical evaluation of one or two factors at two or more levels, such as the optimum rates of one or two promising herbicides, extreme care is necessary in designing and locating the experiment. A more uniform stand of brush or weeds, more replications, and more refined techniques are required to measure small differences for treatment effect.

In many instances, weed or brush control is only one facet of an overall range study. The effect of various management practices upon revegetation following weed control is of primary importance. Where such a program is planned, it may be possible to compare all variables in a randomized complete block design, but often it may be more convenient to use a split-plot design where use of large equipment, differential grazing practices, or some other consideration requires large plots (Alley 1956, Klingman and McCarty 1958). Where possible, the main effects of the study should involve the factor on which the most information is known or which is expected to yield the largest differences, while the subplots should involve those factors about which little information is available or upon which a more critical evaluation is needed.

Effect of Plant Factors

The nature and size of the infestation often will limit or dictate the size and design of the experiment. In the study of some herbaceous perennial range weeds such as low larkspur *(Delphinium bicolor)*, tailcup lupine *(Lupinus caudatus)*, and deathcamas *(Zigadenus venenosus)*, infestations usually are small, spotted, and limited to areas where moisture and soil conditions are favorable. In such situations, several distinct locations may be used as blocks with each block containing all treatments. It may be desirable to include several untreated checks in each block and use an incomplete block design. This is especially desirable where all treatments are to be compared with untreated observations. Small stands are best suited to small plots and hand methods or small-scale chemical or mechanical treatments with motorized equipment, rather than airplane or large-scale ground-rig applications.

Infestations of annual range weeds may be on either small or large areas and in either relatively pure stands or interspersed among brush and other perennial range vegetation. Considerable variation may be found from year to year in density of stand, plant vigor, and other characteristics. These factors should be considered in planning experiments and interpreting data on annual weed infestations. Repeated experiments in successive or different years may be necessary to measure the effects of varying seasonal conditions.

Brush infestations such as sagebrushes (*Artemisia* spp.), honey mesquite *(Prosopis glandulosa)*, or oaks (*Quercus* spp.) usually are extensive but frequently are highly variable in density or stand, age, and size of plants. In brush control experiments involving large areas treated by airplane or ground-rig equipment, individual plots should be large enough to provide for efficient operation of the equipment and inclusion of variation in stands. On the other hand, they should be small enough to avoid introducing other undesired variables such as other species of brush and differences in topograpy or soil. The number of variables that can be compared and the number of replications that can be included without exceeding the area of uniform plant population and growth conditions available are limited. In large plots, the variations in size, density of stand, and/or age of plant can be controlled by basing the measurements on individual plants within each plot selected for uniformity in the desired characteristics or by stratifying the population.

When working with brush or tree species in exploratory experiments or in critical experiments involving a large number of treatments, it may be best to treat individual plants over an area with conditions as uniform as possible (Tschirley 1956, Cable 1957, Leonard 1957). This may be true of either basal or foliar chemical applications, if the individual plants are sufficiently far apart to prevent the treated plants or untreated check plants from being affected by another treatment. It may be best to consider each plant as a treatment replication and to select the plants for each treatment at random within each of the replicate areas or blocks. For exploratory studies, five to ten individual plants in replications of each treatment may be sufficient, but for critical studies intended to measure small differences, 30 or more plants in ten or more replicated plots may be necessary. Again, it is important to consult with a statistician while designing the experiment.

Effect of Site Factors

The high degree of variation in soils and topography of rangeland has a definite influence on brush and weed control experiments. Either of two approaches may be adopted. One would be to limit the size and scope of the experiment to include only one environment, such as a south facing slope or a shallow soil. Another would be to sample a large number of environments so that a generalized conclusion might be drawn.

Effects of Size of the Experiment on the Design

The researcher should choose the simplest design which will efficiently control variability and still yield the information desired. If only two treatments are involved, such as two rates of herbicide, a simple comparison of paired plots may suffice. In experiments that have only three to six treatments involving several levels of only one factor, a Latin square design may be best if a two-way classification of variability is present such that a significant reduction in the magnitude of experimental error can be attributed to both the row and column restrictions. However, the Latin square design should not be used if a simple randomized block design will adequately control the variability. Where an experiment includes 7 to 25 treatments and a study of one to three variables at several levels, a randomized complete block design usually is best. Where a large number of treatments or large plots make it impossible to maintain suitable homogeneity of stand and age of weeds, soil type, slope, or topography within each replicate block, an incomplete block design will give better control of variability (Hyder et al. 1958, Snedecor and Cochran 1967).

When studying two or more variabiles at two or more levels in an experiment, for example, three different chemicals, each at three rates, in three different volumes, the selection of treatments based on the factorial principle yields highly desirable information since it is possible to separate the effects of the variables and to study the interactions between the variables. However, the number of treatments and amount of land required for a complete factorial are often prohibitive in experiments on range weeds, especially brush species. Where this situation prevails, a simpler experiment should be designed in which each factor is varied at an optimum level of the remaining factors. For example, the factorial experiment referred to above could be reduced from 27 treatments to 15 by omitting the volume comparison to two of the rates of all three chemicals or at all rates for two chemicals. These possibilities are shown in the following three designs:

	2,4-D ester			2,4,5-T ester			2,4-D amine		
	Volume of spray, l per ha			Volume of spray, l per ha			Volume of spray, l per ha		
Rate kg per ha	30	50	70	30	50	70	30	50	70
A. Complete factorial—permitting study of factors and interactions									
1	3	5	7	3	5	7	3	5	7
2	3	5	7	3	5	7	3	5	7
3	3	5	7	3	5	7	3	5	7
B. Nonfactorial—permitting study of factors only									
1		5			5			5	
2	3	5	7	3	5	7	3	5	7
3		5			5			5	
C. Nonfactorial—permitting study of factors only									
1	3	5	7		5			5	
2	3	5	7		5			5	
3	3	5	7		5			5	

An example of a reduction in number of treatments and size of an experiment from the tentative plan to the treatments of greatest interest due to unsuitable topography and the restricted area of suitable sagebrush available is shown in Fig. 11-4 (Alley 1956). Both the size and layout of the experiment were adjusted to fit the range conditions which prevailed. In Fig. 11-5, the area was limited, which required the omission of some treatments, but no topographical difficulties were encountered.

Plot Size and Shape

For a given experiment the size and shape of plots will necessarily be controlled by (1) the size of the overall infestation where the experiment will

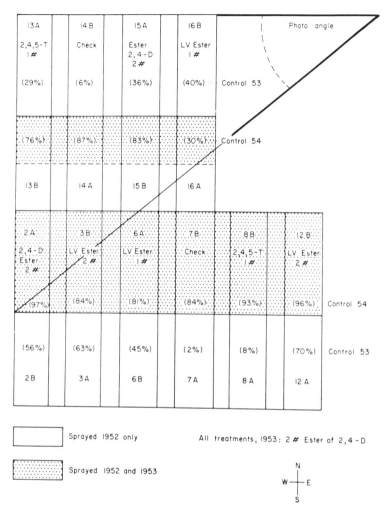

Figure 11-4. A sketch of an airplane applied herbicide experiment on sagebrush in Wyoming which was reduced in number of treatments and size due to boundary fences on the west and south sides and a mountain on the northeast corner. A split plot design was used. The main plots (2, 3, . . . to 16) were 238 m by 60 m with 30 m unsprayed buffer strips. All main plots (both A and B) except checks were sprayed the first year with different treatments as indicated while part of each main plot (A or B) including checks and buffer strips was sprayed across all plots the second using the ester of 2,4-D at 2.2 kg/ha. The percentage control observed in the second year after only one herbicide application (non on the check) and the percentage control observed during the third year (first on check plots) are shown enclosed in parentheses.

be located, and (2) the size of the machinery or equipment used.

Hand Spraying

The compressed air or CO_2 sprayer is commonly used in weed control research (Bohmont 1952, Hurd 1955, Cable 1957, Vallentine 1980). The size of the plots treated should be relatively small and usually conveniently measured as square meters. For screening of materials it is suggested that 2 by

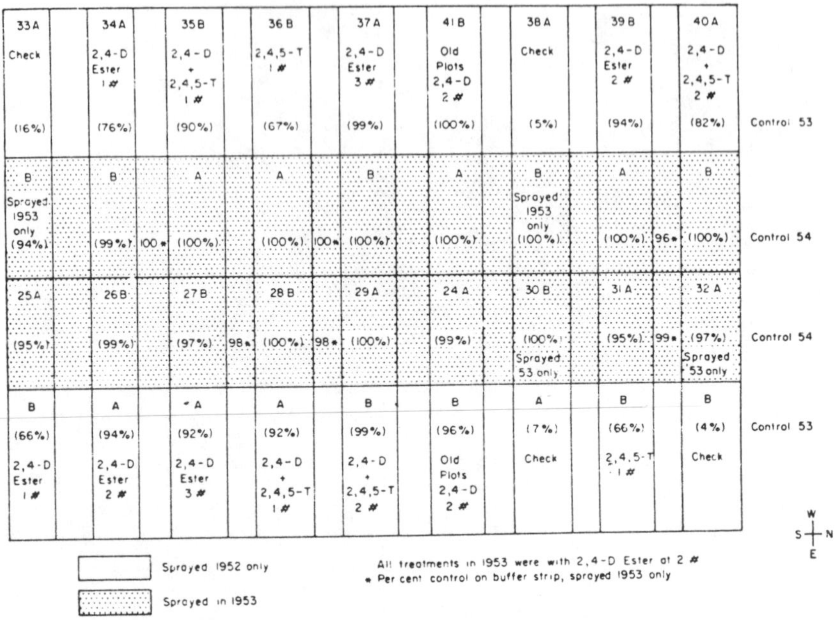

33A	34A	35B	36B	37A	41B	38A	39B	40A	
Check	2,4-D Ester 1#	2,4-D + 2,4,5-T 1#	2,4,5-T 1#	2,4-D Ester 3#	Old Plots 2,4-D 2#	Check	2,4-D Ester 2#	2,4-D + 2,4,5-T 2#	
(16%)	(76%)	(90%)	(67%)	(99%)	(100%)	(5%)	(94%)	(82%)	Control 53
B	B	A	A	B	A	B	A	B	
Sprayed 1953 only (94%)	(99%)	100• (100%)	(100%)	100• (100%)	(100%)	Sprayed 1953 only (100%)	(100%)	96• (100%)	Control 54
25A	26B	27B	28B	29A	24A	30B	31A	32A	
(95%)	(99%)	(97%)	98• (100%)	98• (100%)	(99%)	(100%) Sprayed 53 only	(95%)	99• (97%) Sprayed 53 only	Control 54
B	A	•A	A	B	B	A	B	B	
(66%)	(94%)	(92%)	(92%)	(99%)	(96%)	(7%)	(66%)	(4%)	Control 53
2,4-D Ester 1#	2,4-D Ester 2#	2,4-D Ester 3#	2,4-D + 2,4,5-T 1#	2,4-D + 2,4,5-T 2#	Old Plots 2,4-D 2#	Check	2,4,5-T 1#	Check	

Sprayed 1952 only

Sprayed in 1953

All treatments in 1953 were with 2,4-D Ester at 2 #
• Per cent control on buffer strip, sprayed 1953 only

Figure 11-5. A sketch of an experiment on aerial applications of herbicides on sagebrush showing a split plot design. The main plots (Nos. 25, 26, ... 40) were 235 m by 60 m with 30 m buffer strips between plots. All main plots (both parts A and B) except the checks and old plots were sprayed with different treatments the first year as indicated while the subplot of each main plot (A or B) including checks and buffer strips, was sprayed across all plots during the second year using the 2,4-D ester at 2.2 kg/ha. No observations of results were made closer than 30 m from the ends of the main plots in order to avoid the areas where spray applications have lacked uniformity.

4 m be a minimum size for a trial involving a rather uniform stand of weeds. Plot width will be directly related to the width of the spray boom. If the stand is sparse, a 15 m square plot, or multiple thereof, may be used for preliminary trials.

Motorized Ground-rig Spraying

In extending the evaluation trials and other treatments to a more practical field basis, sprayers mounted on four-wheel drive vehicles, tractors, or trucks are used (Fig. 11-6). Under such conditions, it is suggested that a convenient plot size would be 4 m wide by 40 m long. The inherent difficulty of beginning at the starting point and stopping immediately at the termination point should be recognized. Therefore, measurements of treatment effects should exclude a portion on both ends of the treated plot. The plots should be long enough to permit excluding 2 to 3 m on each end and still provide sufficient area for measuring results.

Aerial Spraying

The airplane or helicopter is especially suitable for applying herbicides for

Figure 11-6. A tractor-mounted ground sprayer that is suitable for large-scale experiments on annual, perennial, and low-growing bush species. (U.S. Forest Service photo.)

Figure 11-7. An experimental aerial application of an herbicide in early morning when there was no wind. Note the uniform spray pattern and absence of spray drift. Both are essential in experimental applications. (U.S. Forest Service photo.)

the control of brush (Fig. 11-7). For experiments using aerial spraying, the area should be readily accessible by air with no serious obstructions for the pilot in maneuvering over the experimental area. Level terrain is best. The width of the treatment plot will depend upon the equipment and the kind of plant (Fig. 11-8). Most planes used for experimental applications have a swath of 8 to 15 m.

Air currents and height of flight will affect the distribution of spray; therefore, an untreated buffer strip 15 to 30 m wide should be included on both sides of each plot (Kissinger et al. 1952, Alley 1956, Robocker et al. 1958). The wider strip should be used when spray drift is expected to be greater due to greater height of spraying or to higher velocity crosswinds. Increasing the width of sprayed plots does not correct for lack of uniformity

Figure 11-8. A portion of the experiment shown in Figure 11-5. The strips of living sagebrush in the area sprayed are due to lack of complete spray coverage. The spray swath width of 15 m should have been reduced to about 10 m for the small airplane used. (Wyoming Agricultual Experiment Station photo.)

of application due to spray drift. Air spraying on experiments should be avoided when wind velocity exceeds 8 km per hour.

The length of the plot should be sufficient to allow the pilot to apply the material under field conditions the same as for nonexperimental spraying. A minimum length should be 250 m. The maximum should not be over 500 m. Longer plots make flagging difficult and increase the expense. The best width of plot is from two to five swaths wide as a minimum for herbaceous weeds and low brush and 45 meters wide for tall brush and trees.

In applying the chemical, two flagmen should be employed for each replicate block one at the beginning of the plot and the other at the end. Each should carry a bamboo pole with three colored (yellow, white, and red) flags on the end. This combination will allow the pilot good visibility in lining up, regardless of the background.

Methods of Sampling to Measure Results

Methods of studying vegetation discussed in Chapter 3 may be applied in a general way to measuring the results of brush and weed control experiments. Choice of sampling techniques will depend upon (1) nature of weeds involved, (2) number of species being studied in one experiment, (3) density of stand, (4) size of plot, and (5) degree of refinement in the experiment and the necessity for reducing sampling error within each plot.

Counts of living plants and estimation of percentage defoliation and percentage topkill before and after treatment give an accurate method of evaluating the effect of herbicide application (Hyder 1953, Alley 1956, Cable 1957, Vallentine 1980). Usually it is desirable to make plant counts in untreated plots each time that they are made in treated plots, in order to measure the effect of factors other than treatments. Sample areas may consist of quadrats or belt transects located permanently or selected at random within each plot each time the results are evaluated. The size of quadrats may vary from 0.25 m^2 for small plants with dense stands such as halogeton *(Halogeton glomeratus)*, 1 m^2 for somewhat larger plants with less dense stands such as tall larkspur *(Delphinium occidentale)*, to 5 m^2 or larger for brush species such as sagebrush (*Artemisia* spp.) with sparse stands in larger treated plots (Bohmont 1952, Kissinger et al. 1952, Klingman and McCarty 1958). For spotted stands of medium to sparse density, belt transects 5 to 30 cm wide and 8 m long or more may give more efficient measurement of plant survival than square quadrats. The number of quadrat or belt transect samples within each plot should be three to five or more, depending upon the density and uniformity of stand, the size of plot, and the accuracy desired.

A variation of the plant-count technique is to count as dead or alive individual plants nearest the right foot every so many steps (5 for example) in a straight line or zigzag course across the treated plot until 100 plants or other desired number have been counted (Kissinger et al. 1952). Care must be used to avoid personal bias in selecting the course. Another variation which is suitable for large brush or tree species is to select and mark a certain number (50 for example) within each plot before the treatments and use these trees for determining defoliation, plant kill, and resprouting. The individual trees should be selected at random and should be representative of sizes and ages of plants as well as locations. Procedures used must enable statistical analysis (see Chapters 1, 9, and 10).

Time of Sampling

Estimates of percentage defoliation should be delayed until the treatments have had the maximum visible effect, but should be made before regrowth or defoliation has developed enough to mask the top kill. Depending upon the type of herbicide, usually the best time for such meaurements is toward the end of the growing season in which the treatments are made or during the early growth stage during the following year.

Estimates of percentage kill or counts of dead or living perennials should be delayed until about one year after the treatments (Bohmont 1952, Hurd 1955). With certain woody species, final readings on kill and resprouting should be delayed until the second growing season following the treatments, or later (Cable 1957, Leonard 1957). Estimates of kill or regrowth of perennial species should be made only when soil moisture, temperature, and other growth factors favor growth from living plants.

Experimental Grazing

Experimental grazing involves the use of animals under control, either through herding or in fenced enclosures. The experiments are made to ascertain animal and vegetation response to selected methods of grazing. They may additionally correlate these measurements with timber production, water yield or other natural values. Many techniques exist for measuring both plant and animal responses (see Chapters 3 and 6). Standardization in experimental grazing studies is undesirable (Amer. Soc. Agron. et. al. 1952), since vegetation, climate, soil, and practices worthy of test vary from one locality to another. The best available procedures and facilities, however, should be adopted and used to meet the objective of each experimental study.

The objectives of grazing experiments include one or more of the following: determination of effects of various stocking rates, best period of use, comparisons of different systems of grazing, and isolation of factors that affect both vegetation and animals. Criteria frequently studied in management of the range are: range condition and trend; forage utilization; plant succession along with interacting factors such as weather, competition from game animals, and rodent infestations; plant life histories; growth and reproduction of important plants; grazing utilization of reseeded ranges; and the general relation of grazing and climate to range maintenance and improvement.

The results of grazing experiments can be measured for animals in such terms as weight gains, condition, reproductive rates, longevity, wool yields, and market values. These factors, in turn, can be related to nutritive quality, yield, seasonal abundance, and other characteristics of forage. Methods of measuring vegetation and selection of animals have been discussed in detail in preceding chapters.

The use of pastures in experimental grazing has advantages over empirical studies because animal and seasonal control are possible. Desired intensities and qualities of treatments can be limitied to specific areas, vegetation or edaphic types, or to watersheds. Permanent installations can permit ecosystem studies of long duration. Statistical control is required.

Disadvantages of pasture experiments include lack of representativeness of ranch units and animal handling practices in the surrounding community. Paddock vegetation may not be typical of overall conditions in the area of application. Cattle distribution and plant utilization may present a pattern different from that on open range, and sheep habits may not be comparable to those in herded bands. Many of the disadvantages can be overcome by coordinating research with practice and by careful selection of representative experimental areas.

Selection of the Experimental Area

The experimental area should be viewed as an outdoor laboratory where range research is the primary objective. Suitability for secondary studies, including timber and watershed management and game management, will, of course, enhance the study value of the area. General considerations in the choice of a suitable area include: representativeness of soil and vegetation; adequate size for experiments contemplated; accessibility from towns and roads; livability for working personnel; usability for demonstration and inspection visits; and adaptability to cooperation with livestock owners and research agencies.

Additional criteria to consider are: suitability of the vegetation, whether normal or deteriorated; uniformity of area for comparative studies; erosion or other factors that could mask treatment effects; and capability of supporting a variety of studies related to the major problems of the locality. Adaptability to experimental designs and intensive plot systems is important. Additional important items include: feasibility of administration with regard to included and adjacent land ownerships, water and mineral rights; community attitudes; and possibility of support from federal, state, and local agencies. A final question: Will range research on the area adequately serve the stockmen, the community, and the region?

Physical Layout of Experimental Area

Unfenced Range Studies

Where control of animals can be planned and executed through herding, successful grazing experiments can be made on unfenced areas. A study of sheep grazing on orange sneezeweed *(Helenium hoopesii)* infested range by Doran and Cassady (1944) furnishes a good example. Observations of two bands of sheep using adjacent allotments were made during three summer seaons. Herders cooperated in directing the band movements so that good and poor management was alternated between allotments in the first two years, and improved for both bands in the third year. Utilization of forage plants was determined by clipping and weighing ahead of each band before grazing and behind each band soon after grazing (Cassady 1941). Records were maintained for each band, including routes of travel, methods of herding, use of bedgrounds, use of sneezeweed, symptoms of poisoning, death losses, average weights, and gross income from sale of lambs after the animals were marketed each fall. The principal physical layout of the area consisted of a series of flags and markers which enabled the observers to determine at all times the band locations and the spots where the various observations were made or to be made. Labor costs will be high and must be taken into consideration before designing this type of experiment. Today, replications of the treatments would be a necessity.

Fenced Paddocks for Range Studies

The size, shape, number and arrangement of paddocks into replicates for statistical comparison should be considered when the area is being selected. Adequate acreage should be available to permit installation of all the paddocks necessary to the experimental grazing contemplated at the time and visualized for the foreseeable future. Due to the high cost of grazing studies, it is extremely improtant for the researcher to work with a statistician to develop an efficient experimental design. Requirements for physical facilities—fences, corrals, water developments, reserve or holding areas, roads within paddocks— should be mapped for tentative study of cost, feasibility in the experimental design, and practicability with regard to routes of animal travel and handling of livestock.

Size. Paddock sizes in grazing experiments have varied from 0.5 ha to several hundred hectares. Ideally, paddock areas approximating those used in grazing by ranch operators should produce the least bias in applying results but may limit replication. Cost, area limitations, and sampling considerations usually dictate a choice different from the community average. The selected research procedure may even require different sized paddocks.

On the San Joaquin Experimental Range in California, duplicate pad-docks of 64, 96, and 128 ha for three intensities of grazing were used (Camp-bell 1940). At the U.S. Range Livestock Experiment Station in Montana, summer and winter areas were each divided into three pairs of pastures radiating from central wells and handling facilities (Hurtt 1951). Paddocks varying in size from 7 to 21 ha were used at the Panhandle Experimental Range in western Nebraska (Stubbendieck 1977). At the Desert Experimental Range in Utah and the Central Plains Experimental Range in Colorado, pastures of 128 ha each were used. In the latter case, 7.2 million ha of surveyed range in the Great Plains indicated that the average pasture used by ranchers in the area was approximately 128 ha.

Controversy exists over the practice of varying the size of paddocks for different intensities of grazing with the same number of animals in each pasture as compared with pastures of the same size and different numbers of animals. In considering these alternatives, bear in mind that pastures are seldom comparable in the first place. Different sizes and shapes result in different animal habits. Also, grazing capacity varies with seasons and years, and the impact of different degrees of grazing becomes cumulative with use. Thus, to achieve uniformity in utilization of forage, numbers of animals usually have to be varied on perhaps small, uniform areas.

Shape. Rectangular paddocks, approximately twice as long as wide, generally are preferred in gentle topography because they are most efficient from a sampling standpoint, and cause the least divergence from normal animal distribution habits. In mountainous areas, rectangular paddocks seldom are feasible. Depending upon the grazing treatment, wagon-wheel and other unusual layouts may influence animal movements and result in areas in which animals are concentrated. Paddocks built on watersheds for comparisons of water yield, erosion, soil stabilization, and other studies must necessarily be of different shapes.

Number of paddocks in the experimental design. Cost, man-power, and facilities for making vegetation records have usually limited the paddocks to less than the number that proper statistical procedure would suggest. Numerous studies report the use of only two paddocks, with no replications. These studies can only be considered to be demonstrations because statistical inferences can not be made from the data. A few extensive experimental designs have reported the use of 12 or more paddocks in a single study.

On the Central Plains Experimental Range, Colorado, 12 paddocks were grouped into four blocks, with three intensities of grazing each. Cattle numbers were varied each year to approximate 20, 40, and 60% utilization of the major short grass species. On the Desert Experimental Range, Utah, 18 paddocks were grazed with sheep at three intensities in three seasons in a factorial experiment (Fig. 11-9).

Randomized blocks, Latin squares, and other statistical arrangements are

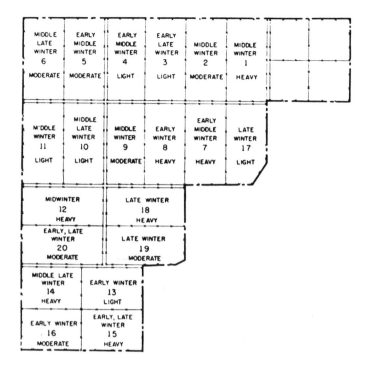

Figure 11-9. Fenced range paddocks at the Desert Experimental Range, Utah, used to study effects of time of grazing winter sheep ranges. All combinations of early, middle, and late winter grazing were each grazed to three intensities of use. (From Hutchings and Stewart 1953).

desirable in the design of range experiments, but true replication of vegetation, animal characteristics, or treatment effects can only be approached, not actually attained. On the Central Plains Experimental Range, for example, more than ten years of trials achieved not three rates of grazing replicated four times, but 12 rates of grazing that could be ranked in order from marked overgrazing down to definite undergrazing. The randomized block design, however, was still valid for analytical purposes.

Experimental Animals

The kind and class of animals used in range grazing experiments are important considerations and are usually determined by the purpose of the experiment and the availability of the animals. Discussion of this phase is covered in Chapter 6.

Paddock Management in the Experimental Program

The management program involves several choices which should be made before the experiment begins. Period of grazing, for example, can be set to correspond with prevailing practices in the locality, to relate to vegetation cycles, or to test animal and plant responses for periods that previously have not been tried. The system of grazing usually is established for comparison of seasonal, alternate, rotation, deferred, or some combination of these methods such as short duration or high intensity-low frequency, depending on the objectives of the study (Fig. 11-10). Establishment of the basic rate of grazing sometimes must be deferred until a calibration has been made over a period of

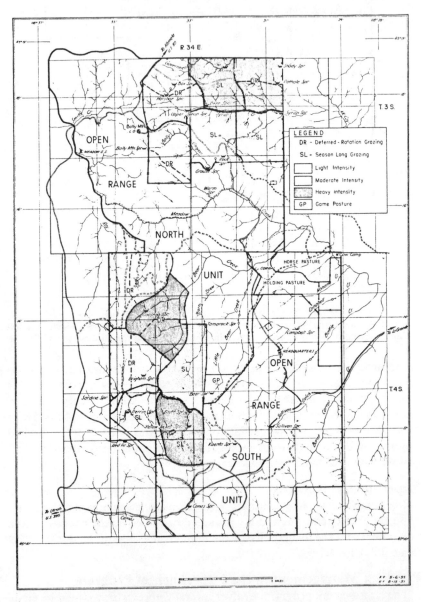

Figure 11-10. Arrangement of treatments in a range grazing experiment on the Starkey Experimental Forest and Range, Wallowa-Whitman National Forest in Oregon. Grazing Methods such as deferred-rotation vs. season (summer and fall) long grazing are being tested. Because effects of grazing by deer and elk cannot be eliminated from the paddocks, special measurements of it are necessary.

years by comparing forage yield, utilization, and stocking. If the initial stocking rates are in error, an experiment involving intensity of use, for example, may result in three degrees of overgrazing and three degrees of undergrazing. In like manner, it could result in different degrees of grazing all of which are overgrazing or all of which are undergrazing.

Basic Rate of Grazing

The desired intensity of grazing is best established by actual trial in the experimental paddocks. A three-year calibration period is usually the minimum, if weather is near average. Constant adjustment of animal numbers or of period of grazing usually is necessary even to approximate a given degree of plant utilization.

Past stocking records are an aid to establishment of basic grazing rates (Pechanec and Stewart 1949) and are most useful when combined with a close examination of range condition and trend. Range surveys also may furnish an index for grazing rates, but subsequent adjustments are almost invariably necessary. Hurtt (1951) used the survey method to determine forage acres available before the experiment started and then adjusted pasture sizes to obtain different rates of grazing with equal numbers of animals in the different paddocks. How this worked out in the face of differential cumulative plant response and in drought cycles is not clear. Hutchings and Stewart (1953) varied the number of sheep grazed in each paddock. The desired percentages of use were not attained in actual practice, but they were closely approximated. Variation in animal numbers allows for adjustments for type of growing season, drought and wet cycles, and animal death losses.

Systems of Grazing

Numerous systems of grazing have been tested and no general conclusion has been reached as to which is most desirable, even under rather local conditions. Yearlong and seasonal grazing are common practices, dictated in part by climate and ranching facilities. In experimental trials, alternate, rotation, deferred, deferred-rotation, high intensity-low frequency, and short duration grazing have been studied in many localities (Sarvis 1923, Hodgson et al. 1934, Black et al. 1937, Black and Clark 1942, Biswell and Foster 1947, Leithead 1974, Mathis et al. 1974, Stubbendieck 1977, Heitschmidt and Walker 1983). The systems used, and their advantages and disadvantages have been discussed by Sampson (1951), Shiflet and Heady (1971), Wambolt (1973), Herbel (1974), Stoddart et al. (1975), and Holechek (1983).

In the development of grazing experiments, consideration of seasonal weather patterns and of plant growth cycles is essential. Animals should not be rotated or grazed by calendar dates. Great emphasis should be placed on obtaining the desired animal months of impact on the paddocks being grazed. In a system where grazing may occur only once in four years, for example, it must be remembered that the grazing impact may coincide with a period of poor growth, or with a period of especially good growth, thus adding to the difficulty of interpreting the results of the study. If an area is deferred during the entire season, an entirely different response from both animals and plants will be obtained, compared to only partial deferment. In the application of rotation grazing systems on the range, the expense of fencing, watering, and handling of the animals should be balanced against possible increased favorable animal responses and benefits to the soil and vegetation.

Study of Fire on Rangeland

Fire is used as a tool on certain kinds of rangeland to remove unwanted vegetation and to promote growth of desirable plants. Special problems of field experimentation result from difficulties in (1) obtaining replications of treatments; (2) classifying fire intensity; (3) determining or classifying factors which determine fire intensity; (4) duplicating topographic features; and (5) repeating phenological growth stage from year to year.

Purpose

Fire may be used to remove existing vegetation to prepare an area for seeding. Such a study can be a simple one of determining the best time to obtain a clean burn and prevent reproduction of unwanted plants. Fire also may be used to remove one species or class of plants and to preserve others. For example, undesirable shrubs may have a good understory of grasses and forbs that can be released by burning the shrubs. Under these conditions, burning should be at a time and under conditions that will kill the shrubs, but do the least damage to desirable plants. The problem is more complex when determining how to make a selective burn. Both the heat intensity and the resistance of various plant species to heat at different seasons are variables that are difficult to evaluate.

In various parts of the United States, the purpose of burning might be to thin the underbrush under a forest to make livestock management easier, or to reduce the accumulation of coarse herbaceous material without controlling any plants. To study burning for such purposes, the effects of season of burning, frequency of burning, and the fire intensities on each growth form are important (Kozlowski and Ahlgren 1974, Wright 1974, Wright and Bailey 1982).

Obtaining Replication of Treatments

To obtain comparable replications of treatment, the researcher should consider site, vegetation, and weather, as well as the application of the burning treatments on the plots themselves.

Variations in Site, Vegetation, and Weather

It is desirable to include all treatments within a replication on relatively homogeneous areas. However, different treatments often must be widely separated so that one treatment will not affect another. This need to place different plots on rather widely separated areas makes necessary rather detailed classifications of site and vegetation to make certain that all plots within a replication are representative of a single condition. Weather conditions should also be as near constant as possible.

Site. When classifying and defining climatic zones and soil productivity classes, there may be a tendency not to give soil uniformity within an experimental area adequate consideration because of the desire to balance other factors that influence use of fire. This should be avoided because all treatment plots should be on a single soil productivity class so that followup measurements of herbage will reflect treatments rather than soil variations.

Slope and exposure must be comparable on all plots because they influence response of vegetation and because differences in terrain greatly affect the spread and intensity of fire. Uniformity in minor relief on all plots is essential, but difficult to achieve.

Vegetation. Standard classification of vegetation types based on size, canopy density, species composition, and growth stage are useful in study of the impact of burning. Further detailed classification by fuel types is essential for selecting experimental areas and treatment plots and for extension of the results from the experiments.

Fuel classes are defined according to size and volume of woody and herbaceous material, continuity of fuels both horizontally and vertically, and proportion of dry and green fuels in the cover. This usually requires a breakdown by species, density, and age of stand for woody plants and seasonal development for herbaceous plants. A single experiment should include only one fuel type, or the different fuel types should be stratified and equally represented in each treatment block. Effects of fire should be measured separately within each fuel type. Each vegetation-fuel type should contain a characteristic proportion of certain key species so that comparable measurements can be made of removal and/or brush or weed kill on the various plots.

Weather. Weather can be classified by season of burning and by fire-weather conditions during burning. Season is classified according to the prevailing weather conditions at certain times of year. For example, in California brushlands an early spring season corresponds to a period of dry weather before initiation of new twig growth on woody vegetation, when fine fuels are dry, and heavy fuels are still moist and cool. The summer season corresponds with a period of dry, hot weather when heavy dead fuels have dried and all fuels are warm.

Ideally, all plots within a replication should be burned at the same time because this is the best way comparable weather conditions can be assured. Because this often cannot be attained, current weather must be classified exactly according to air temperature, relative humidity, wind velocity, wind direction, and gustiness of wind. Each phase of burning must be conducted within a narrow range of these factors so that treatments are comparable within each replication.

Application of Burning Treatments

Size, shape, orientation, and location of treatment plots within a single experiment usually are dictated by the nature of planned preburning treatments and by the anticipated behavior of fire during the burning treatments. Preburning treatments usually are aimed at drying or compacting woody fuels or otherwise making green or discontinuous fuels easier to burn. A common objective of experimentation is to compare different methods of pretreatment. For example, complete smashing or compressing of brush may be compared with smashing brush on only one-quarter of an area (Fig. 11-11

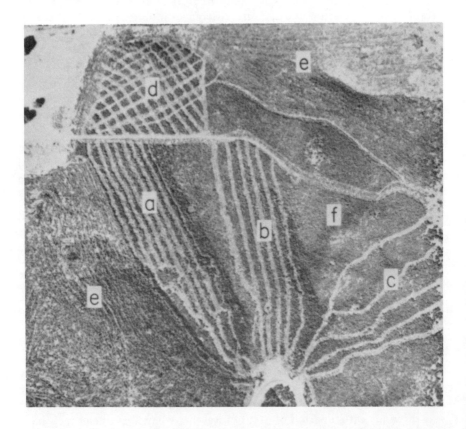

Figure 11-11. Brush smashed or compressed with bulldozer for area ignition tests. A, 50% of area smashed; B, 33% of the area smashed; C, 25% of the area smashed; D, 50% of the area smashed in gridiron pattern; E, 100% of area smashed; and F, untreated brush. (From Fenner et al. 1955.)

and 11-12). If heavy equipment is used, plots must be one to several hectares in size to obtain typical effects and to allow maneuverability of the equipment. Where desiccation of fuels with herbicides is used, plots must be large and must be separated by rather wide buffer strips to prevent drift of chemicals onto adjacent plots.

One problem in experimental design is the fact that fire in ground vegetation tends to follow local air movement caused by wind direction or by

Figure 11-12. Area ignition in the foreground after smashing 40% of the brush. Unmasked brush in background did not burn wth conventional line firing. (From Fenner et al. 1955).

upslope drafts. An objective of study may be comparing different techniques for spreading fire. Plots must be oriented so that fire can be spread by prevailing wind or upslope drafts, or carried into the wind or downslope, or spread in other ways. In light fuels on nearly level terrain, spread of fire may not seriously affect the experimental design. In heavy fuels on uneven terrain, the characteristic spread of fire may determine plot shape and orientation, and it will greatly limit experimental design. Sometimes, one treatment plot cannot be placed below another on a slope because fire may spread from the lower to upper plot. In some cases, however, a design can be used that will allow burning all of the upper plots before the lower plots are burned.

Another characteristic of fire that greatly influences plot shape, size, and orientation is the transfer of heat by radiation or convection columns from the burn to vegetation outside of the plot. Plots must be separated by buffer strips of sufficient width so that vegetation on one will not be influenced by the burning treatment on adjacent plots. This may raise no particular problem in slow burning of light fuels on flat terrain. But, a wide cleared line is needed when burning heavier, taller growing fuels. A wide buffer strip also is needed to prevent predrying of vegetation on adjoining plots which are not to be burned or are to be burned by a different treatment. It may be possible to design the experiment so that the plots burned first will serve as control lines for plots burned later. If two or more plots are to be burned separately but at the same time, they must be quite widely spaced so that one fire does not affect the other.

In studies of broadcast burning of woody vegetation, it is difficult to duplicate on small plots the energy situation which exists on large burns. On small plots, the surrounding vegetation and air have an influence on the release and dissipation of heat so that thermal conditions occurring on the plots are not typical of those inside large burns. This is the common condition where conventional line firing and spread of fire by wind are used to burn unprepared brush. For this treatment, areas of 8 to 50 ha, or more, can be used and measurements made on small plots well within the poorly burned borders of the larger area. Frequently if the brush is prepared by smashing or compressing and drying ahead of burning, ignition is easier and faster so that sufficient heat can be generated on smaller acres with only narrow border effects. Development of the area-ignition technique (Fenner et al. 1955) made possible the use of hot brush fires on small plots under moderate weather conditions (Fig. 11-13).

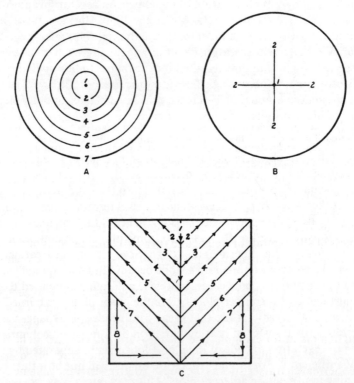

Figure 11-13. Examples of methods of firing for area ignition burns. A, (concentric method) and B, (radius method) are applicable to flat terrain or aeas with a central high point, and C, is adapted for steeper even slopes. Numbers indicate the order of firing. In C, number one torch continues straight through the center of the area downhill, with a two-man firing team working away from the center after they pass each firing course.

The fact that fire is dangerous raises problems in conduct of experiments. An objective of experimentation is to develop methods of using fire effectively and at times when danger of escape is at a minimum. Sometimes studies must be conducted at a time when there is danger of fire escaping to adjoining land. This means that adequate crews must be on hand to guard against escape.

Considerable expense in preparation of adequate fire control lines is necessary, unless studies can be tied into other burning operations so that there is no danger of fire escaping.

Classifying Fire Intensity

Classifying fire intensity is difficult so procedures must be well planned. Intensity must be defined for every study. It usually embodies four components: (1) heat energy, (2) mass, (3) time, and (4) location. The definition must specifically cover all components. For example, intensity in one study might be the maximum instantaneous temperature reached at the center of a pine needle 2 m above ground. But in another it might be the total number of heat units released at the surface of the ground during passage of the fire.

Intensity is classified by several procedures, chiefly: (1) observation of the fire while burning, (2) observation of the effects on vegetation and soil after the fire has burned (Nelson 1935, McCulley 1950, Herman 1954), and (3) measurement with devices (Lindenmuth and Byram 1948, Silen 1956, Wright and Bailey 1982). In classification by observing the fire, such criteria as flame height, flame angle, and time required for the flames to burn past a point are usually estimated. In observing effects after the fire, criteria are: (1) height of scorch line and/or amount of live crown consumed of trees or other plants, (2) amount of fuel consumed, and (3) other evidence of heating, such as discoloration of soil.

Among measuring devices that can be used are thermocouples, thermometers, and alloys or lacquers with specific individual melting or fusing temperatures. Mass is an important consideration in using any of these. Two thermocouples side by side, one large and one small, may give different readings. Likewise, the size of the reservoir in a thermometer affects temperature readings, as does the mass of the shield, if the thermometer is shielded. Thickness of alloy spirals or weight and thermal characteristics of the base on which lacquers are painted affect the amount of heat required to melt or fuse them.

Methods of heat transfer are also important considerations in using measuring devices. A satisfactory device must be sensitive to both radiation and ambient heat. If the objective is to measure intensity in terms of the heat rise in the bud of a plant, for example, and the measuring device cannot be inserted inside the bud, the measuring device must have the same or consistently similar thermal characteristics as the bud—same reflectiveness, same conductance, and so on. Because of the complexities of measuring fire intensity, observational procedures for classifying intensity are often chosen, and intensity commonly is expressed qualitatively rather than quantitatively.

Problems in Experimental Design

Complex experimental designs may have some use in study of grass burning on level terrain where all treatments within a block can be applied on a single, relatively homogeneous area. A somewhat different approach seems to be necessary, however, in study of brush burning on rough, broken terrain where a single replication of all treatments cannot be put on a single area.

Each study must be kept simple so that a minimum number of areas and conditions of burning will be involved. The possibilities are limited for increased efficiency through use of complex designs.

Sites, vegetation types, fuel types, and weather conditions must be well classified and described in order that the different treatments within a block will be comparable and treatments can be replicated. In each dominant vegetation-fuel class at each critical season of the year, a series of simple studies can be obtained to determine effects of different methods of fuel preparation or of different ignition methods for initial removal of brush. After information is accumulated for each site-vegetation-fuel class condition, comparisons can be made of the effects of season of burning for any or all combinations of fuel preparation and ignition. Obtaining all of this information from one experiment does not appear feasible.

Studies using split-plot design are sometimes possible where plots involved in the initial brush-removal treatments can be split into subplots for comparison of different followup treatments. These followup treatments such as reburning or the application of an herbicide to control regrowth, can be applied to smaller individual areas than the initial treatments. A statistician should be consulted to obtain the best experimental design.

Literature Cited

Alley, H.P. 1956. Chemical control of big sagebrush and its effect upon production and utilization of native grass species. Weeds 4:164-173.

Alley, H.P., D.W. Bohmont, and L.W. Weldon. 1956. Chemical sagebrush control: Summary of four years' data. Cir. 67. Wyoming Agr. Exp. Sta.

American Society of Agronomy, American Dairy Science Association, American Society of Animal Production, and American Society of Range Management. Joint Committee. 1952. Pasture and range research techniques. Agron. J. 44:39-50.

Barker, R.E., J.J. Bond, and L.C. Zachmeier. 1976. Equipment for seeding experimental plots of small grains, grasses, and legumes. Agron. J. 68:141-142.

Biswell, H.H., and J.E. Foster. 1947. Is rotational grazing on native range practical? Bull. 360. North Carolina Agr. Exp. Sta.

Black, W.H., and V.I. Clark. 1942. Yearlong grazing of steers in the northern Great Plains. Cir. 642. USDA, Washington, D.C.

Black, W.H., A.L. Baker, V.I. Clark, and O.R. Mathews. 1937. Effect of different methods of grazing on native vegetation and gain of steers in northern Great Plains. Tech. Bull. 547. USDA, Washington, D.C.

Bohmont, D.W. 1952. The chemical control of poisonous range plants. Bull. 313. Wyoming Agr. Exp. Sta.

Branson, F.A., R.F. Miller, and I.S. McQueen. 1966. Contour furrowing, pitting and ripping on rangelands of the western United States. J. Range Manage 19:182-190.

Cable, D.R. 1957. Chemical control of chaparral shrubs in central Arizona. J. Forest. 55:899-903.

Campbell, R.S. 1940. Range management research methods in the western United States. Herb. Rev. 8:121-138.

Cassady, J.T. 1941. A method of determining range forage utilization by sheep. J. Forest. 39:667-671.

Cornelius, D.R., and M.W. Talbot. 1955. Rangeland improvement through seeding and weed control on eastern slope Sierra Nevada and on southern Cascade Mountains. Handbook 88. USDA, Washington, D.C.

Doran, C.W., and J.T. Cassady. 1944. Management of sheep on range infested with orange sneezeweed. Cir. 691. USDA, Washington, D.C.

Fenner, R.L., R.K. Arnold, and C.C. Buck. 1955. Area ignition for brush burning. Tech. Paper 10. U.S. Forest Service, California Forest and Range Exp. Sta.

Frischknecht, N.C. 1959. Effects of presowing vernalization on survival and development of several grasses. J. Range Manage. 12:280-286.

Heitschmidt, R., and J. Walker. 1983. Short duration grazing and the Savory grazing method in perspective. Rangelands 4:147-150.

Herbel, C.H. 1974. A review of research related to development of grazing systems on native ranges of the western United States. Misc. Pub. 1271. USDA, Washingon, D.C.

Herman, F.R. 1954. A guide for marking fire damaged ponderosa pine in the Southwest. Res. Note 13. U.S. Forest Service, Rocky Mountain Forest and Range Exp. Sta.

Hodgson, R.E., M.S. Grunder, J.C. Knott, and E.V. Ellington. 1934. A comparison of rotational and continuous grazing of pastures in western Washington. Bull. 294. Washington Agr. Exp. Sta.

Holechek, J.L. 1983. Considerations concerning grazing systems. Rangelands 5:208-211.

Hull, A.C., Jr. 1954. Rating seeded stands on experimental range plots. J. Range Manage. 7:122-124.

Hull, A.C., Jr., and W.M. Johnson. 1955. Range seeding in the ponderosa pine zone in Colorado. Cir. 953. USDA, Washington, D.C.

Hurd, R.M. 1955. Effect of 2,4-D on some herbaceous range plants J. Range Manage. 8:126-128.

Hurtt, L.C. 1951. Managing northern Great Plains cattle ranges to minimize effects of drought. Cir. 865. USDA, Washington, D.C.

Hutchings, S.S., and G. Stewart. 1953. Increasing forage yields and sheep production on Intermountain winter ranges. Cir. 925. USDA, Washington, D.C.

Hyder, D.N. 1953. Controlling big sagebrush with growth regulators J. Range Manage. 6:109-116.

Hyder, D.N., and F.A. Sneva. 1955. Effect of form and rate of active ingredient, spraying season, solution volume, and type of solvent on mortality of big sagebrush *(Artemisia tridentata)*. Tech. Bull. 35. Oregon Agr. Exp. Sta.

Hyder, D.N., W.R. Furtick, and F.A. Sneva. 1958. Differences among butyl, ethyl and isopropyl ester formulations of 2,4-D., 2,4,5-T and MCPA in the control of big sagebrush. Weeds 6:194-197.

Kissinger, N.A., Jr., A.C. Hull, Jr., and W.T. Vaugh. 1952. Chemical control of big sagebrush in central Wyoming. Paper 9. U.S. Forest Serv., Rocky Mountain Forest and Range Exp. Sta.

Klingman, D.L., and M.K. McCarty. 1958. Interrelations of methods of weed control and pasture management at Lincoln, Nebraska. 1949-55. Tech. Bull. 1180. USDA, Washington, D.C.

Kozlowski, T.T., and C.E. Ahlgren. 1974. Fire and ecosystems. Academic Press, New York, New York.

Lavin, F., and H.W. Springfield. 1955. Seeding in the southwestern pine zone for forage improvement and soil protection. Agr. Handbook 89. USDA, Washington, D.C.

Leithead, H.L. 1974. High intensity-low frequency grazing system increase livestock production. Intern. Grassland Cong. Proc. Sect. Papers: Grassland Utilization 12:355-361.

Leonard, O.A. 1957. Effect of phenoxy herbicide concentrates applied to cuts of sprouting tree species. Weeds 5:291-303.

Lindenmuth, A.W., Jr, and G.M. Byram. 1948. Headfires are cooler near the ground than backfires. U.S. Forest Service Fire Control Notes 9:8-9.

McCulley, R.D. 1950. Management of natural slash pine stands in the flatwoods of south Georgia and north Florida. Cir. 845. USDA, Washington, D.C.

Major, J. 1951. A functional, factorial approach to plant ecology. Ecology 32:392-412.

Martin, A.R., R.S. Moomaw, and K.P. Vogel. 1982. Warm-season grass establishment with atrazine. Agron. J. 74:916-920.

Mathis, G.W., M.M. Kothmann, and G.K. Burton. 1974. Cow-calf response to high-intensity, low-frequency grazing. Prog. Rep. 3236. Texas Agr. Exp. Sta.

Mayer, A.M., and A. Poljakoff-Mayber. 1975. The germination of seeds. Pergamon Press, Oxford, England.

Miller, R.K. 1956. Control of halogeton in Nevada by range seedings and herbicides. J. Range Manage. 9:227-229.

Nelson, R.M. 1935. A method for rating forest fire intensity. Tech. Note. 8. U.S. Forest Service, Appalachian Forest Exp. Sta.

Pechanec, J.F. 1950. Converting standard seed rates for grasses to actual seeding rates. Res. Note 67. Pacific Northwest Forest and Range Exp. Sta.

Pechanec, J.F., and G. Stewart. 1949. Grazing spring-fall sheep ranges of southern Idaho. Cir. 808. USDA, Washington, D.C.

Pechanec, J.F., G. Stewart, A.P. Plummer, J.H. Robertson, and A.C. Hull, Jr. 1954. Controlling sagebrush on rangelands. Farmers' Bull. 2072. USDA, Washington, D.C.

Plummer, A.P., A.C. Hull, Jr., G. Stewart, and J.H. Robertson. 1955. Seeding rangelands in Utah, Nevada, southern Idaho and western Wyoming. Agr. Handbook 71. USDA, Washington, D.C.

Rauzi, F. 1968. Pitting and interseeding native shortgrass rangelands. Res. J. 17. Wyoming Agr. Exp. Sta.

Rauzi, F., and R.L. Lang. 1956. Improving shortgrass range by pitting. Bull. 344. Wyoming Agr. Exp. Sta.

Rehm, G.W. 1984. Yield and quality of a warm-season grass mixture treated with N, P, and atrazine. Agron. J. 76:731-734.

Robocker, W.C., R. Holland, R.H. Haas, and K.R. Messenger. 1958. The aerial application of 2,4-D on halogeton. Weeds 6:198-202.

Rogler, G.A., and R.J. Lorenz. 1974. Fertilization of mid-continent range grasses, p. 237-254. *In;* D.A. Mayes (ed.), Forage fertilization. Amer. Soc. Agron. Crop. Soc. Amer., and Soil Sci. Soc. Amer., Madison, Wisconsin.

Samson, J.F., and L.E. Moser. 1982. Sod seeding perennial grasses into eastern Nebraska pastures. Agron. J. 74:1055-1060.

Sampson, A.W. 1951. A symposium on rotation grazing in North America. J. Range Manage. 4:19-24.

Sarvis, J.T. 1923. Effects of different systems and intensities of grazing upon the native vegetation at the Northern Great Plains Field Station. Bull. 1170. USDA, Washington, D.C.

Schultz, R.D., and J. Stubbendieck. 1982. Herbage yield of fertilized cool-season grass-legume mixtures in western Nebraska. J. Range Manage. 35:473-476.

Schultz, R.D., and J. Stubbendieck. 1983. Herbage quality of fertilized cool-season grass-legume mixtures in western Nebraska. J. Range Manage. 36:571-575.

Scifres, C.J. 1980. Brush management. Texas A&M Univ. Press, College Station, Texas.

Shiflet, T.N., and H.F. Heady. 1971. Specialized grazing systems—their place in range management. TP-152. USDA, SCS, Washington, D.C.

Silen, R.R. 1956. Use of temperature pellets in regeneration research. J. Forest. 54:311-312.

Snedecor, G.W., and W.G. Cochran. 1967. Statistical methods. Iowa State Univ. Press. Ames. Iowa.

Stevenson, E.W. 1950. Reseeding tarweed infested ranges. Res. Note 68. U.S. Forest Service, Pacific Northwest Forest and Range Exp. Sta.

Stoddart, L.A., A.D. Smith, and T.W. Box. 1975. Range management. McGraw-Hill Book Co., Inc., New York, New York.

Stroup, W., and J. Stubbendieck. 1983. Multivariate statistical methods to determine changes in botanical composition. J. Range Manage. 36:208-212.

Stubbendieck, J. 1977. Grazing systems and range fertilization. Ext. Cir. 77-218. Beef cattle Rep. Nebraska Coop. Ext. Service.

Stubbendieck, J., and W.G. McCully. 1972. Factors affecting grmination, emergence and establishment of sand bluestem. J. Range Manage. 25:383-385.

Stubbendieck, J., P.T. Kochi, and W.G. McCully. 1973. Establishment and growth of selected grasses. J. Range Manage. 26:39-41.

Tschirley, F.H. 1956. The effect of concentration and season on basal spraying of velvet mesquite with fortified diesel oil, p. 35-36. *In:* West. Weed Control Conf. Res. Prog. Rep.

U.S. Forest Service. 1957. Handbook of range reseeding equipment. Washington, D.C.

U.S. Forest Service. 1948. Woody plant seed manual. Misc. Pub. 654. USDA, Washington, D.C.

U.S. Production and Marketing Administration. 1952. Testing agricultural and vegetable seed. Agr. Handbook 30. USDA, Washington, D.C.

Vallentine, J.F. 1980. Range development and improvements. Brigham Young Univ. Press, Provo, Utah.

Vogel, K.P. 1978. A simple method of converting rangeland drills to experimental plot seeder. J. Range Manage. 31:235-237.

Wambolt, C.L. 1973. Range grazing systems for resource conservation and greater production. Bull. 340. Montana Agr. Ext. Service.

Wilson, R.G., and J. Stubbendieck. 1981. Fringed sagebrush (*Artemisia frigida* Willd.) control in western Nebraska. Weed Sci. 29:525-530.

Wright, H.A. 1974. Range burning. J. Range Manage. 27:5-11.

Wright, H.A., and A.W. Bailey. 1982. Fire ecology. John Wiley and Sons. New York, New York.

Index

Bob Patton